**INTERSCIENCE LIBRARY**
**OF CHEMICAL ENGINEERING AND PROCESSING**

Editors:

HERBERT M. SCHOEN
*Quantum, Incorporated*
*Wallingford, Connecticut*

JOHN J. McKETTA, JR.
*Department of Chemical Engineering*
*The University of Texas*
*Austin, Texas*

**INTERSCIENCE LIBRARY**
**OF CHEMICAL ENGINEERING AND PROCESSING**

# NEW
# CHEMICAL
# ENGINEERING
# SEPARATION
# TECHNIQUES

Edited by
## HERBERT M. SCHOEN

*Quantum, Incorporated*
*Wallingford, Connecticut*

1962
INTERSCIENCE PUBLISHERS
a division of JOHN WILEY & SONS
New York · London

# INTRODUCTION

The editors and publisher have long felt that there is a need for a chemical engineering library directed primarily toward chemical engineers, but also intended for use by other engineers and scientists in some way involved in the broad field of the "engineering of chemistry."

The volumes to be included in the series will all be of a moderately advanced level and will not be designed as texts, although they are expected to find some outlets in graduate and senior courses.

The series will not be limited to volumes which are considered chemical engineering subjects as such, but will also include the support subjects frequently a part of the chemical engineer's areas of endeavor. These will range from the theoretical topics, general business, unit operations and specific processing areas. In addition, titles will be chosen so as to present specialized sub-areas to those not specifically engaged in them. The library will expand as the need for additional topics is created.

The editors hope that the readers will let them have their criticisms, comments and suggestions so that improvements can be made in future volumes.

HERBERT M. SCHOEN
JOHN J. McKETTA, JR.

# PREFACE

The separation of substances from one another constitutes a major segment of the chemical engineering field. The classical techniques such as distillation, extraction, crystallization, drying, etc., are treated in numerous texts and reference works. In addition to these techniques, however, there are many others which are less a part of the chemical engineer's repertory. In this volume some of the newer techniques not so familiar to the chemical engineer are discussed.

Some of the techniques treated in this book have found wide application on a laboratory scale but await scale-up before they can find their place in the plant. Others have been successfully applied on an industrial scale *but* only in relatively restricted areas. All of them have one thing in common; namely, they offer a significant potential to play an increasingly important role in the field of separations technology.

It is hoped that this volume will in some measure stimulate the chemical engineer into considering the application of separation techniques with which he is less familiar. This volume cannot hope to answer all the questions an engineer might have regarding the various techniques covered, but should serve as a useful guide in determining whether a given technique is applicable to the problem at hand. The underlying principles upon which the various techniques are based are treated in some detail so that the reader will have a sound base from which he may extrapolate to his own needs. Discussion of the laboratory methods should serve to generate many ideas as to how the separation might be conducted on a large scale.

Many persons have assisted in some way in the preparation of this book. The following, in particular, deserve mention: E. Von Halle, M. Bier, P. Bruins, W. G. Pfann, H. Mel, D. Pindzola, J. E. Huff and B. L. Harris.

HERBERT M. SCHOEN

*Stamford, Connecticut*
*August 10, 1962*

# AUTHORS

**D. O. Edwards**  *Film Department, E. I. du Pont de Nemours and Company, Circleville, Ohio (formerly Chemical Engineering Department, The University of Wisconsin, Madison, Wisconsin)*

**R. A. Findlay**  *Research & Development Department, Phillips Petroleum Company, Bartlesville, Oklahoma*

**R. K. Finn**  *School of Chemical Engineering, Cornell University, Ithaca, New York*

**Elmer L. Gaden, Jr.**  *Department of Chemical Engineering, Columbia University, New York, New York*

**W. D. Lawson**  *Royal Radar Establishment, Malvern, Worcestershire, England*

**E. N. Lightfoot**  *Chemical Engineering Department, The University of Wisconsin, Madison, Wisconsin*

**S. Nielsen**  *Royal Radar Establishment, Malvern, Worcestershire, England*

**John E. Powers**  *Department of Chemical and Metallurgical Engineering, The University of Michigan, Ann Arbor, Michigan (formerly School of Chemical Engineering, The University of Oklahoma, Norman, Oklahoma)*

**Eliezer Rubin**  *Radiation Applications, Inc., Long Island City, New York*

**R. Sanchez-Palma**  *IBM de Mexico, S.A., Mexico, D.F. (formerly Chemical Engineering Department, The University of Wisconsin, Madison, Wisconsin)*

ix

# CONTENTS

# 1 THERMAL DIFFUSION

## John E. Powers

**Contents**

1

# I. Introduction

The thermal diffusion effect was first noted in the literature by Ludwig (1) in 1856. He reported that when a sodium sulfate solution, saturated at 0 °C, was placed in an inverted U-tube of which one leg was maintained at 0 °C and the other immersed in boiling water, crystals of sodium sulfate formed in the cold leg in several days' time. This simple experiment demonstrated that there had been a net transfer of the salt from the hot to the cold leg. Later Soret (2), apparently unaware of Ludwig's report, carried out a series of experiments in which it was noted that, if a temperature gradient was imposed on a homogeneous salt solution, a concentration gradient would generally be established in the solution. The name *Ludwig-Soret effect* or *Soret effect* has been given to this phenomenon as it occurs in the liquid state. The name *thermal diffusion* (or *thermodiffusion*) is applied in the general case.

The equipment used by Soret represented a considerable improvement over the crude apparatus described by Ludwig. Soret mounted a warm bath directly over a cold one and installed a cylinder containing the solution between the two baths in a vertical position. With such an apparatus it is difficult to eliminate convection currents in the solution, and the time required to attain steady-state conditions is excessive. Tanner (3) proposed the use of horizontal flat plates with the hot plate on the top (Fig. 1). Decreasing the distance between the two plates served to inhibit convective remixing and to decrease the time required to attain steady-state conditions. Close positioning of the plates presented problems in connection with sampling and analysis which were very cleverly

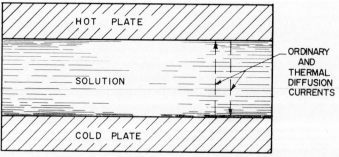

Fig. 1. Flat-plate static thermal diffusion cell.

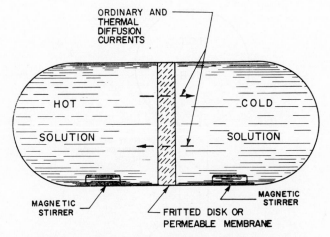

Fig. 2. Agitated thermal diffusion cell with barrier.

solved by use of optical techniques. The reader is referred to the original article by Tanner (3) and a later one by Thomaes (4) for details of this technique.

Other investigators have attempted to minimize the effects of convective remixing by localizing the temperature gradient and the resulting separation. Riehl (5) suggested the use of a permeable membrane, and Huse, Trevoy, and Drickamer (6) applied a fritted glass disk. Mixing is usually provided in both the hot and cold compartments by means of magnetic stirrers. The localization of the temperature and concentration gradients in a membrane of fritted glass disk permits operation of the cell with a horizontal temperature gradient.

Many theoretical attempts have been made to explain the Soret effect. Early attempts include the kinetic treatment of Nernst (7), a development based on consideration of osmotic pressure proposed by van't Hoff (8), and the treatment of Wereide (9), all of which were unsuccessful. More recent attempts based on modern theories of the liquid state (10–12) have met with limited success and will be discussed in a subsequent section. Continued frustration of attempts to explain thermal diffusion phenomena in the liquid phase serves to emphasize the lack of an adequate model of the liquid state.

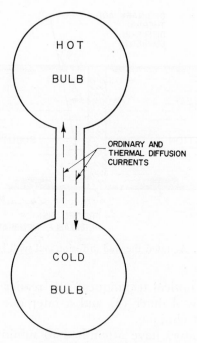

Fig. 3. Two-bulb static cell.

On the other hand, the kinetic theory has been remarkably effective in describing gas phase behavior, and as a result Ensog (13) in 1911 and Chapman (14) independently in 1916 predicted thermal diffusion phenomena in gas mixtures prior to the first experimental investigation of this effect reported by Chapman and Dootsen (15) in 1917. The prediction of the thermal diffusion effect in gases results from refinement of the kinetic theory and therefore had been overlooked for many years by previous investigators working with the kinetic theory of gases. Some of the results of these theoretical analyses will be presented in Section II-B-1.

In making measurements of the thermal diffusion effect in gases, Chapman and Dootsen introduced a modification of the static cell. A schematic drawing of their two-bulb apparatus is shown in Figure 3.

In all of the experimental investigations on both gas and liquid systems described above, attempts have been made to eliminate

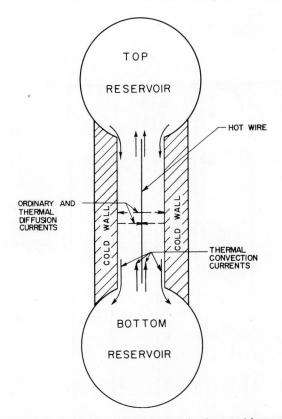

Fig. 4. Hot-wire batch thermogravitational column with reservoirs.

convection currents which might otherwise diminish the separation. Separations obtained in this manner are small and the energy requirements excessive. As a result thermal diffusion did not seem to be a practical means of separating materials, as was pointed out by Mulliken (16). Measurements made with gas mixtures were used primarily to investigate the nature of intermolecular forces based on the theoretical analyses of Enskog and Chapman. The effect in liquids remained primarily a laboratory curiosity.

In 1938, Clusius and Dickel (17) reported the development of a device which utilized convective flow induced by thermal gradients to produce a cascading effect. The cascading resulted in a tremendous increase in the separation obtainable in a single piece of

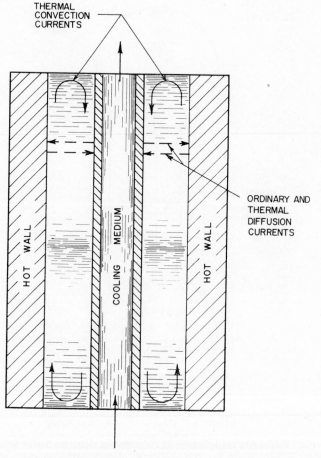

THERMAL
CONVECTION
CURRENTS

ORDINARY AND
THERMAL
DIFFUSION
CURRENTS

HOT WALL

COOLING MEDIUM

HOT WALL

Fig. 5. Concentric-cylinder batch thermogravitational column without reservoirs.

equipment. The apparatus developed by Clusius and Dickel is simple in operation and very effective. A hot wire is located along the axis of a vertical tube which is cooled (Fig. 4). The ends of the tube are connected to reservoirs. The presence of the hot wire has two effects: (a) A temperature gradient is established between the hot wire and the cold tube resulting in a net transport of one component in the radial direction. (b) Density differences resulting from the temperature gradient cause convective flow to be estab-

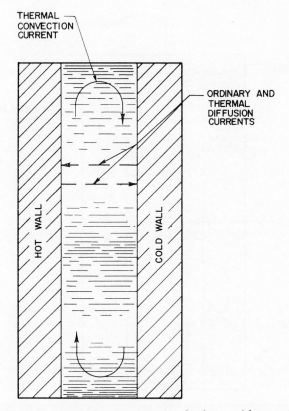

THERMAL
CONVECTION
CURRENT

ORDINARY AND
THERMAL
DIFFUSION
CURRENTS

HOT WALL

COLD WALL

Fig. 6. Flat-plate batch thermogravitational column without reservoirs.

lished in a direction normal to the transport of material by thermal diffusion. As a result material which moves toward the hot region because of thermal diffusion is carried upward by the convective flow in the vicinity of the hot wire and concentrated in the top reservoir. Clusius and Dickel demonstrated the utility of their *thermogravitational* column by obtaining the isotopes of chlorine in high purity (18) and a great deal of interest in the method resulted.

Numerous modifications of the original hot-wire thermogravitational column were proposed soon after its introduction. A central calrod heater is sometimes used in place of the hot wire. Much laboratory equipment in use today is made of concentric tubes with external electrical heating (Fig. 5). Some equipment has been

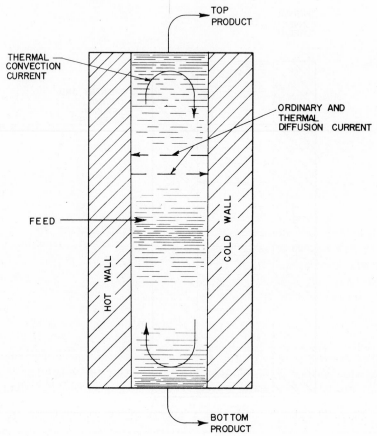

Fig. 7. Continuous-flow thermogravitational column.

fabricated of flat plates (Fig. 6). Any of the above-mentioned types of equipment can be operated with continuous feed and product removal (Fig. 7) as well as in the batch manner shown in Figures 4–6.

In addition to the thermogravitational method, reflux can also be provided by external pumping as suggested by Jury and Von Halle (19). In such an apparatus the hot and cold fluids are physically separated by a permeable membrane and mixing within each portion is provided by placing the hot plate on the bottom in addition to operating the reflux flow in forced convection (Fig. 8).

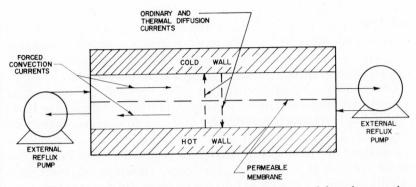

Fig. 8. Horizontal thermal diffusion column with barrier and forced-convection reflux.

Many other attempts have been made to modify the basic Clusius-Dickel column to improve its operation. The convective flow pattern has been changed both by tilting flat plate columns (20,21) and rotating columns of special construction (22–24). Insertion of packing (24,25) and systems of baffles (26–28) in the columns have been tried with limited success. Another unsuccessful attempt to improve column operation involves pulsing the column (29).

The development of the thermogravitational column and its early use to separate isotopes initiated a number of experimental and theoretical investigations. Several phenomenological theories were developed which successfully predicted the effect of changes in the dimensions and operating conditions of thermogravitational columns on the separation obtained. One of the more successful of the theories was proposed by Furry, Jones, and Onsager (30). Their development was originally directed to the separation of gas mixtures, but later Jones and Furry (31) demonstrated that the general method of analysis was equally valid for liquid mixtures. Krasney-Ergen (32) used the results of these analyses to develop optimum design equations which appear to have general utility when dealing with gas mixtures. Use of these equations will be demonstrated by several examples in Section IV-B-2.

In spite of the fact that the development of the thermogravitational column tremendously increased the potential of thermal diffusion as a means of separation and results of theoretical analyses permitted reasonable selection of optimum operating conditions, thermal diffusion has not been used widely as a method of separation. Benedict (33) in 1947, compared the thermogravitational method with other well-known separation processes and concluded that the method is relatively expensive and that possible application is limited to processes with very special requirements.

On a laboratory or preparative scale, thermal diffusion offers several advantages as a method of separation and analysis. The basic equipment is relatively inexpensive and easy to operate. Trace material can be concentrated for recovery or removal. Significant separations in "pure grade" materials placed in a thermogravitational column is a common experience. Complex mixtures such as lube oil can be separated into ten or more distinct fractions with widely differing properties.

Intelligent application of thermal diffusion as a method of analysis or as a method of separation requires some understanding of the factors which influence the separation not only in thermogravitational columns but in static cells as well. The next section is devoted to a brief development of the theoretical analysis of both static cells and thermogravitational columns.

## II. Theory

Thermal diffusion in both gaseous and liquid phases has been the subject of extensive experimental and theoretical investigations during the past century, as indicated in Section I. The introduction of the thermogravitational method in 1938 stimulated both experimental and theoretical studies. As a result, an extensive literature exists which deals with the theoretical aspects of thermal diffusion. This material is reviewed briefly in this section in order to introduce the reader to some of the more important developments.

### A. THE BASIC RATE LAW

Several rate laws have been proposed in the literature in attempting to relate the flux of a component in a nonisothermal solution, $J_{x-TD}$, to the temperature gradient, $dT/dx$. The relatively simple relation

$$J_{x-TD} = (\rho D_T/T)(dT/dx) \tag{1}$$

serves to define $D_T$ where $\rho$ is density. Another expression commonly used as the basic rate law incorporates the concentration dependence of the coefficient but not the temperature dependence

$$J_{x-TD} = \rho D' C_1 C_2 \, (dT/dx) \tag{2}$$

where $C_1$ and $C_2$ are the fractions of components 1 and 2 in a binary solution and, by convention, the subscript 1 refers to the component of lesser molecular weight. Much of the data for liquid systems in the literature is in terms of the *Soret coefficient*, $D'/D$, in which $D$ is the coefficient of ordinary diffusion. Both $D_T$ and $D'$ are referred to as the coefficient of thermal diffusion in the literature.

The theoretical analyses of thermal diffusion based on kinetic theory (13,14) yield perhaps the most basic rate law for thermal diffusion.

$$J_{x-TD} = + \rho(\alpha D/T) \, C_1 C_2 \, (dT/dx) \tag{3}$$

The choice of sign is arbitrary and is taken as positive in order to be consistent with the notation of Jones and Furry (31). Equation 3 was developed to represent the behavior of isotopic gas mixtures. In this case, $\alpha$ is essentially independent of temperature, pressure, and composition. Although nonisotopic liquid solutions bear little or no resemblance to isotopic mixtures of gases, equation 3 can be used to define the *thermal diffusion "constant,"* $\alpha$, for liquids.

For gases, $C_1$ and $C_2$ are volume fraction. In liquids, various values of $\alpha$ are reported based on the use of $C_1$ and $C_2$ as volume, mole, or weight fraction. There is some indication that volume fraction should be used in treating liquids as well as gases.

Theoretical developments in the general field of thermal diffusion have progressed along two different paths. Application of various models of the gaseous and liquid states in attempting to explain the basic thermal diffusion phenomenon and predict the thermal diffusion constant $\alpha$ has been of interest to many investigators. Others have been primarily interested in applying rate expressions such as equations 1 and 3 in conjunction with basic principles of heat, mass, and momentum transfer to predict the phenomenological behavior of thermal diffusion equipment. Both such considerations are of interest in the application of thermal diffusion to the analysis and separation of mixtures and will be discussed briefly.

## B. FUNDAMENTAL THEORY OF THE THERMAL DIFFUSION PHENOMENON

As was pointed out in Section I, the thermal diffusion effect was first noted experimentally in liquids and theoretical attempts to explain this phenomenon in liquids have met with limited success. The reverse is true in the case of gases. The theoretical prediction of the thermal diffusion effect in gases preceded experimental verification. Chapman (34) has pointed out that the thermal diffusion phenomenon results from complex interactions of molecules and as a result complete understanding of the phenomenon will be obtained only by application of advanced methods of analysis. In spite of this fact, it is instructive to review the results of several simplified analyses of the thermal diffusion effect in order to obtain some appreciation of the factors which influence the effect and then to present some results of the more advanced analyses.

### 1. Gas Mixtures

The following qualitative discussion is based on an analysis by Frankel (35). For a careful and detailed discussion and a more rigorous treatment, the reader is referred to a book by Chapman and Cowling (36).

Consider a nonisothermal gaseous mixture in which a steady-state concentration gradient is established. A partial pressure gradient therefore exists, and it is reasoned that there must be a constant force on the particles which restrains them from diffusing toward the region of lower concentration. This force results from the steady transfer of momentum from particles of one species of those of another. The transfer of momentum from species 2 to species 1 is proportional to

$$(M_2 V_2 - M_1 V_1) V \sigma \tag{4}$$

where $M_1$ and $M_2$ are the masses of the two molecules, $V_1$ and $V_2$ are their velocities before collision, $V$ is their relative velocity, and $\sigma$ is the cross section for momentum transfer between molecules of the two species. The total momentum transfer is calculated by averaging equation 4 over the velocity distributions of the two species of molecules. Frankel considered the case in which the molecules repel each other according to a law of the type $F = Kr^{-\nu}$ where

K and $\nu$ are constants and $r$ is the distance between the centers of the molecules. On the basis of dimensional considerations, it was reasoned that the cross section for momentum transfer, $\sigma$, is proportional to $V^{-4/(\nu-1)}$ and therefore the momentum transfer is proportional to

$$(M_2V_2 - M_1V_1)V^{(\nu-5)/(\nu-1)} \tag{5}$$

For a gas pair with $\nu = 5$ (Maxwellian gas) equation 5 reduces to $M_2V_2 - M_1V_1$. The case of steady-state separation is being considered and therefore there is no net transport of either species. As a result, the average value of both $V_1$ and $V_2$ are zero and no force and therefore no separation will exist.

In cases where $\nu \neq 5$ the averages will be taken with respect to the products $V_2V^\gamma$ and $V_1V^\gamma$ where $\gamma \equiv (\nu - 5)/(\nu - 1)$ is a positive or negative number depending on the value of $\nu$. From basic kinetic theory, molecules at the same temperature have equal kinetic energies, and the kinetic energies increase with an increase in temperature. Therefore, at equal temperatures the lighter molecules will have a greater velocity than the heavier species, and in general molecules moving into the region from the high temperature side will have relatively high velocities. As a result, $V$ will be large when a light molecule from the hot region collides with a heavy molecule from the cold region and such collisions will contribute a great deal to the average.

For the case in which $\gamma$ is positive ($\nu > 5$) the average momentum transfer from species 2 to species 1 as calculated from equation 5 is therefore directed toward the warmer part of the gas causing the lighter species to concentrate in the hot region and therefore $\alpha$ is positive. If $\gamma$ is negative ($\nu < 5$) the average momentum transfer is in the opposite direction and $\alpha$ is negative. In general $\nu > 5$ and $\alpha$ is indeed positive.

The above development yields a qualitative picture of the factors influencing thermal diffusion but yields no quantitative results other than the fact that Maxwellian gases do not separate in a temperature gradient and that $\alpha$ will be positive if $\nu > 5$. The analyses of Enskog and Chapman yield quantitative expressions for the thermal diffusion constant in terms of ratios of infinite determinants, the elements of which are integrals over the velocity spaces of the two types of particles. Evaluation of these expressions is extremely complicated and therefore several simplifications have been developed. The results presented below are essentially those discussed by Jones and Furry (31) and Grew and Ibbs (37).

Grew and Ibbs present the following general expression for a first approximation of the thermal diffusion constant $\alpha$

$$\alpha = 5(C' - 1) \ [(S_2 n_2 - S_1 n_1)/(Q_1 n_1{}^2 + Q_{12} n_1 n_2 + Q_2 n_2{}^2)] \qquad (6)$$

where $n_1$ and $n_2$ are the volume fractions of the light and heavy components, respectively, and $S_1$, $S_2$, $Q_1$, $Q_2$, and $Q_{12}$ are expressed in terms of ratios $(A', B', C', E_1, \text{ and } E_2)$ of collision integrals:

$$S_1 = [E_1 M_1 (M_1 + M_2) - 4A' M_1 M_2$$
$$- 3M_2 (M_2 - M_1)]/(M_1 + M_2)^2 \qquad (7)$$

$$Q_1 = E_1 [6M_2{}^2 + 8A' M_1 M_2 + (5 - 4B') M_1{}^2]/(M_1 + M_2)^2 \qquad (8)$$

$$Q_{12} = 2E_1 E_2 + [3(5 - 4B')(M_2 - M_1)^2$$
$$+ 4A'(11 - 4B') M_1 M_2]/(M_1 + M_2)^2 \qquad (9)$$

where $M_1$ and $M_2$ are the molecular weights of species 1 and 2.

(Expressions for $S_2$ and $Q_2$ are obtained from equations 7 and 8 by interchange of subscripts.)

The collision integrals and their ratios $(A', B', C', E_1, \text{ and } E_2)$ have been evaluated only for a few relatively simple cases involving molecules with similar force fields. For such mixtures the expressions for $E_1$ and $E_2$ are related to $A'$ and the molecular diameters ($d_1$ and $d_2$) and masses ($M_1$ and $M_2$) as follows:

$$E_1 = 8A'[d_1/(d_1 + d_2)]^2[(M_1 + M_2)/2M_2]^{1/2} \qquad (10)$$

$$E_2 = 8A'[d_2/(d_1 + d_2)]^2[(M_1 + M_2)/2M_1]^{1/2} \qquad (11)$$

Values of $A'$, $B'$, and $C'$ have been evaluated for several specific cases.

**Hard Spheres.** For gases which interact as rigid elastic spheres the ratios of collision integrals reduce to

$$A' = 2/5 \qquad B' = 3/5 \qquad C' = 6/5 \qquad (12)$$

For molecules of the same diameter and nearly the same mass the following approximate expression is obtained

$$\alpha = (105/118)[(M_2 - M_1)/(M_1 + M_2)] \qquad (13)$$

**Inverse Power Repulsion.** In many cases interaction between isotopic gas pairs can be expressed in terms of the simple force law considered by Frankel

$$F = Kr^{-\nu} \tag{14}$$

Values of $A'$, $B'$, $C'$, $E_1$, and $E_2$ have been calculated for this case (37) and are presented in Table I.

TABLE I

Values of the Quantities $A'$, $B'$, $C'$, $E_1$, and $E_2$ for Various Values of the Force Index, $\nu$

| $\nu$ | $A'$ | $B'$ | $C'$ | $E_1[2M_2/(M_1 + M_2)]^{1/2} =$ $E_2[2M_1/(M_1 + M_2)]^{1/2}$ |
|---|---|---|---|---|
| 3 | 0.531 | 0.800 | 0.800 | 1.062 |
| 5 | 0.517 | 0.750 | 1.00 | 1.034 |
| 7 | 0.493 | 0.711 | 1.967 | 0.986 |
| 9 | 0.477 | 0.687 | 1.100 | 0.954 |
| 11 | 0.465 | 0.672 | 1.120 | 0.930 |
| 15 | 0.450 | 0.653 | 1.143 | 0.900 |
| ∞ | 0.400 | 0.600 | 1.200 | 0.800 |

Some simplification results when the collision diameters of the molecules are identical and their difference in mass is small. For such systems

$$\alpha = (105/118)[(M_2 - M_1)/(M_1 + M_2)][(\nu - 5)/(\nu - 1)]C(\nu) \tag{15}$$

The function $C(\nu)$ has been evaluated numerically by Chapman (38,39) and presented by Jones and Furry (31). These values are reproduced in Table II.

TABLE II

Values of $C(\nu)$ for Various Values of the Force Index, $\nu$

| $\nu$ | $C(\nu)$ | $\nu$ | $C(\nu)$ |
|---|---|---|---|
| 3 | 0.807 | 11 | 0.882 |
| 5 | 0.816 | 15 | 0.906 |
| 7 | 0.843 | ∞ | 1.000 |
| 9 | 0.865 | — | — |

Values of $\nu$ can be estimated from the equation of state of a gas or from the temperature variation of viscosity. If viscosity data of the form $\mu = kT^m$ are available, $\nu$ can be estimated from the relation

$$\nu = (2m + 3)/(2m - 1) \tag{16}$$

and used in equation 15.

In some cases the temperature variation of viscosity is represented in terms of the Sutherland equation

$$\mu = kT^{1/2}/(1 - c/T) \tag{17}$$

If such data are available, the following equation is applicable:

$$\alpha = \frac{105}{118} \frac{M_2 - M_1}{M_2 + M_1} \left[ \frac{1 - 0.9679\,c/T}{1 + c/T} \right] \left[ \frac{1 + 0.9771\,c/T}{1 + 0.9110\,c/T} \right] \tag{18}$$

**The Lennard-Jones Model.** In many cases it has been found necessary to consider not only forces of repulsion between molecules but also forces of attraction. The intermolecular force for the Lennard-Jones model is expressed as

$$F = kr^{-\nu} - k'r^{-\nu'} \tag{19}$$

TABLE III
Values of $A'$, $B'$, and $C'$ for the (13,7) Model

| $kT/\epsilon$ | $A'$ | $B'$ | $C'$ |
|---|---|---|---|
| 0.3 | 0.4185 | 0.7739 | 1.017 |
| 0.5 | 0.4370 | 0.7698 | 0.9901 |
| 0.65 | 0.4409 | 0.752 | 0.9868 |
| 0.80 | 0.4418 | 0.734 | 0.9918 |
| 1.0 | 0.4410 | 0.715 | 1.004 |
| 1.25 | 0.4396 | 0.696 | 1.021 |
| 1.60 | 0.4382 | 0.683 | 1.042 |
| 2.0 | 0.4374 | 0.671 | 1.061 |
| 2.5 | 0.4374 | 0.664 | 1.079 |
| 4.0 | 0.4391 | 0.657 | 1.109 |
| 6.0 | 0.4413 | 0.656 | 1.125 |
| 10 | 0.4441 | 0.657 | 1.134 |
| 20 | 0.4477 | 0.6569 | 1.137 |
| 30 | 0.4496 | 0.6569 | 1.138 |
| 40 | 0.4508 | 0.6574 | 1.138 |
| 60 | 0.4528 | 0.6569 | 1.138 |
| 100 | 0.4551 | 0.6569 | 1.138 |
| 200 | 0.4582 | 0.6568 | 1.138 |
| 400 | 0.4615 | 0.6571 | 1.138 |

The case in which $\nu = 13$ and $\nu' = 7$ (the 13,7 model) has been used extensively to account for properties of gases. The collision integrals have been evaluated by Hirschfelder, Bird, and Spotz (40) and values of $A'$, $B'$ and $C'$ for use in equations 6–11 have been presented by Grew and Ibbs (37). These values are reproduced in Table III. Collision integrals based on the 12,6 model are also available (91).

The application of these various results to estimate $\alpha$ for isotopes is illustrated by an example. The system hydrogen–deuterium is chosen because of the availability of basic data.

*Hard spheres.* For $H_2$–$D_2$, $d_1 = d_2$, $M_1 = 1.00$ and $M_2 = 2.00$. Equation 13 was developed for cases in which the isotopes have nearly the same mass but is applied to obtain a first approximation.

$$\alpha = (105/118) \, [(2 - 1)/(2 + 1)] = 0.297$$

A better answer should be obtained by using equations 6–12. The following values are obtained:

$$E_1 = 0.694 \qquad E_2 = 0.981$$

$$S_1 = -0.791 \qquad S_2 = 0.632$$

$$Q_1 = 2.54 \qquad Q_2 = 2.48 \qquad Q_{12} = 5.28$$

For an equimolar mixture ($n_1 = n_2 = 0.5$) substitution into equation 6 yields

$$\alpha = 0.276$$

*Inverse power repulsion.* Viscosity data for hydrogen in the temperature range from 100 to 500°K (41,42) are well represented by the equation

$$\mu = 1.68 \times 10^{-6} T^{0.700} \text{ g/cm-sec}$$

Therefore the repulsive force index, $\nu$, can be calculated for hydrogen from equation 16

$$\nu = 4.40/0.40 = 11.0$$

The force index for $H_2$ and $D_2$ should be nearly the same and therefore $\nu = 11.0$ can be used to approximate $\alpha$ for a $H_2$–$D_2$ mixture. Values are read from Table I as follows:

$$A' = 0.465 \qquad B' = 0.672 \qquad C' = 1.120$$

$$[2M_1/(M_1 + M_2)]^{1/2} E_2 = [2M_2/(M_1 + M_2)]^{1/2} E_1 = 0.930$$

Using these values in equations 7–11 yields

$$S_1 = -0.813 \qquad S_2 = 0.681$$

$$Q_1 = 3.02 \qquad Q_2 = 2.87 \qquad Q_{12} = 6.05$$

Therefore, from equation 6

$$\alpha = 0.150$$

A similar result is obtained by application of equation (15). From Table II, $C(\nu) = 0.882$ and from equation 15

$$\alpha = 0.157$$

*The Lennard-Jones model.* Hirschfelder, Bird, and Spotz (40) have determined $\epsilon/k$ for hydrogen to be $33.3\,°K$ from viscosity data. Grew and Ibbs (37) report a value of $\alpha = 0.173$ for $H_2$–$D_2$ with a cold bulb temperature of $288\,°K$ and a hot bulb temperature of $373\,°K$. Assuming $\alpha$ to vary linearly with the inverse of the absolute temperature, the mean value of temperature corresponds to

$$\bar{T} = [T_c T_H/(T_H - T_c)] \ln (T_H/T_c) = 321\,°K \qquad (20)$$

where $\bar{T}$ refers to the mean temperature and the subscripts $H$ and $C$ identify temperatures of the hot and cold bulbs.

Using this temperature for purposes of comparison and the value of $\epsilon/k$ for $H_2$ as determined from viscosity measurements yields $kT/\epsilon = 9.63$. Values of $A'$, $B'$, and $C'$ read from Table III by linear interpolation are

$$A' = 0.4438 \qquad B' = 0.657 \qquad C' = 1.133$$

Application of equations 7–11 yields

$$S_1 = -0.804 \qquad S_2 = 0.662$$

$$Q_1 = 2.86 \qquad Q_2 = 2.73 \qquad Q_{12} = 4.23$$

and therefore, from equation 6

$$\alpha = 1.98$$

The results of the above computations are summarized in Table IV.

TABLE IV
Values of $\alpha$ for an Equimolar Mixture of $H_2$–$D_2$ at 321 °K

|  | $\alpha$ |
|---|---|
| Experimental value (37, p. 128) | 0.173 |
| Hard sphere | |
| Equation 13 | 0.297 |
| Equations 6–12 | 0.276 |
| Inverse power repulsion | |
| Equation 15 and Table II | 0.157 |
| Equations 6–11 and Table I | 0.150 |
| Lennard-Jones model | |
| Equations 6–11 and Table III | 0.198 |

The theory does not apply nearly so well for gas pairs whose collisions are not at all like those of elastic spheres. Recent experiments with butane and pentane isomers (43) indicate that the theoretical values for $\alpha$ calculated on the basis of the Lennard-Jones model are a factor of 20 or 30 smaller than the values observed experimentally.

## 2. Liquid Mixtures

The kinetic theory has provided a remarkably accurate description of the gaseous state. In cases where molecular interactions are relatively uncomplicated, such as isotopic gas mixtures and gases which are composed of simple molecules, application of the analyses of Chapman and Enskog to estimate $\alpha$ has been remarkably successful. The fact that the analysis fails for pairs of gas molecules whose structures suggest the possibility of complicated collisions might indicate that the analysis of the thermal diffusion effect in the liquid state might not be expected to yield satisfactory results. Chapman (34) made note of this fact in 1929 as follows:

"The prospect of arriving at an even approximately correct theory seems rather remote. This is not only because of the additional difficulties present in every branch of the kinetic theory of liquids, as compared with the corresponding theory of gases, but because the theory of thermal diffusion even in gases is unusually complex."

In spite of the complexities involved, a qualitative picture of thermal diffusion in liquids (similar in some respects to that given by

Frankel in the case of gases) is provided by the cage model of liquids. The cage model considers that each molecule in the liquid is retained temporarily in an equilibrium position by the potential field of the surrounding molecules. At the same temperature all molecules have the same kinetic energy and therefore the heavier molecules have a higher momentum. When a heavier molecule jumps to a colder region, it penetrates farther than a lighter molecule and therefore the heavier molecules tend to concentrate in the cold region. In liquids the steric effect is of primary importance in that a large molecule moving from a region of relatively high temperature is able to force its way into a small hole and is thus trapped (concentrated) in the cold region.

Several attempts have been made to extend the kinetic theory to the analysis of thermal diffusion in the liquid state (7,44,45) but more recently the trend has been to base such analyses on the thermodynamics of irreversible processes as originally suggested by de Groot (46). It is interesting to note that both analyses yield similar relations for $\alpha$ in terms of quantities noted as $Q_1^*$ and $Q_2^*$ and identified as the "net heat of transport" or alternately as the energy in excess of the partial molal enthalpy transported into a region as a result of isothermal diffusion. For both ideal and nonideal systems, the most suitable form of expression relating $\alpha$ to $Q_1^*$ and $Q_2^*$ appears to be

$$\alpha = [\bar{V}_1\bar{V}_2/(\underline{V}_m x_1(\partial\bar{G}_1/\partial x_1)_{T,P})][(Q_2^*/\bar{V}_2) - (Q_1^*/\bar{V}_1)] \quad (21)$$

where $\bar{V}$ is the partial molal volume and $\underline{V}_m$ is the molar volume of the mixture,

$$\underline{V}_m = x_1\bar{V}_1 + x_2\bar{V}_2 \quad (22)$$

$x$ is mole fraction and $\bar{G}_1$ is the partial molar Gibbs free energy (chemical potential) of component 1.

The several methods of evaluating $Q_2^*$ and $Q_1^*$ suggested in the literature have been fairly successful in predicting both the sign and magnitude of $\alpha$ for ideal solutions, but none have enjoyed more than very moderate success when the solution behavior is nonideal.

The availability of accurate viscosity data for binary mixtures at several temperature levels suggested application of the development of Glasstone, Laidler, and Eyring (47) as a method of estimating activation energies. According to this development the total activation energy associated with movement of a molecule from one equilibrium position to another, $\Delta H^{\ddagger}$, is given by

$$\Delta H^{\ddagger} = R[\partial \ln (\mu \underline{V}_m)/\partial(1/T)]_P \tag{23}$$

where $\mu$ is the viscosity and $R$ is the gas constant.

The total activation energy is further related to two other terms $\Delta H^{\ddagger}_j$ and $\Delta H^{\ddagger}_h$ by the expression

$$\Delta H^{\ddagger} = \Delta H^{\ddagger}_j + \Delta H^{\ddagger}_h \tag{24}$$

where

$$\Delta H^{\ddagger}_j = R\ [\partial \ln (\mu \underline{V}_m)/\partial(1/T)]_V \tag{25}$$

$\Delta H^{\ddagger}_j$ is usually associated with the activation energy required to detach a molecule from its equilibrium environment and $\Delta H^{\ddagger}_h$ is similarly regarded as the energy associated with the formation of a hole to accept the moving molecule.

Drickamer *et al.* (10) noted that the term $\Delta H^{\ddagger}_j$ is usually suggested as the measure of thermal diffusion separation but obtained the best correspondence with experimental data by using the relation

$$Q_i^* = \overline{\Delta H^{\ddagger}_{hi}} \cong \overline{\Delta H^{\ddagger}_i}(\Delta H^{\ddagger}_{ho}/\Delta H^{\ddagger}_o) \tag{26}$$

where the subscript $o$ refers to pure component $i$ and the superscript bar designates a partial molar quantity. The approximation for $\overline{\Delta H^{\ddagger}_{hi}}$ suggested in equation 26 was made because insufficient data were available to permit direct estimation of this term. For ideal mixtures reasonable agreement between predicted and experimental values of $\alpha$ were obtained. For nonideal mixtures the relation was successful only to the extent that the sign and concentration dependence of $\alpha$ were approximated. For such systems the predicted values, in general, were between 10 and 20 times larger than experimental values.

In an attempt to improve upon the approximation for $Q_i^*$ suggested by Drickamer *et al.*, Whitaker and Pigford (11) suggested that

$$Q_i^* = C\,\overline{\Delta H^{\ddagger}_{ji}} - \overline{\Delta H^{\ddagger}_{hi}} \tag{27}$$

where

$$0 \le C \le 1$$

For all ideal mixtures it was found that the pure component activation energies $\Delta H^{\ddagger}_{ji}$ and $\Delta H^{\ddagger}_{hi}$ could be used for the partial molar quantities $\overline{\Delta H^{\ddagger}_{ji}}$ and $\overline{\Delta H^{\ddagger}_{hi}}$. For nonideal mixtures it was assumed that $\Delta H^{\ddagger}_{hi} = \overline{\Delta H^{\ddagger}_{hi}}$ and that $\overline{\Delta H^{\ddagger}_{ji}}$ could be obtained by making use of equation 28.

$$\Delta H^{\ddagger}_{j} = x_1 \Delta H^{\ddagger}_{j1} + x_2 \Delta H^{\ddagger}_{j2} + \Delta H^{\ddagger E} \tag{28}$$

where $\Delta H^{\ddagger E}$, the excess total enthalpy of activation, is defined by

$$\Delta H^{\ddagger E} = \Delta H^{\ddagger} - (x_1 \Delta H^{\ddagger}_1 + x_2 \Delta H^{\ddagger}_2) \tag{29}$$

In attempting to fit the data, Whitaker and Pigford treated the parameter $C$ in equation 27 as a constant for each individual system although they reasoned that $C$ might vary with composition. Incorporation of this additional parameter as a constant yielded a better fit of the data for nonideal systems than that obtained by Drickamer et al. However, the fit was quite poor for ideal systems, in one case differing in sign. In general, Whitaker and Pigford used small values of $C$ to obtain the best fit of the data, lending some support to the empirical observation of Drickamer et al. that $\Delta H^{\ddagger}_h$ is the important correlating group.

The approximations for $Q_i^*$ proposed by the above investigators were made in attempting to predict the sign and magnitude of $\alpha$ and also the concentration dependence from viscosity measurements alone. Finn (12) has applied the methods of thermodynamics of irreversible processes to develop equation 30 which is useful in predicting the effect of concentration on the thermal diffusion constant making use of one measured value.

$$\alpha = -\{[(\bar{H}_2 - \underline{H}_2) + q_1^* \text{ at } x_1 = 0]/[x_1(\partial\mu_1/\partial x_1)_{T,P}]\} \tag{30}$$

where $\bar{H}_2 - \underline{H}_2$ is the difference between the partial molar enthalpy of component 2 and its enthalpy in the pure state and $q_1^*$ at $x_1 = 0$ is related to the net heat of transport used by the other investigators, evaluated at $x_1 = 0$. Finn chose to evaluate this term from a measured value of $\alpha$ and for the systems investigated it is found that this relation predicts the concentration effect fairly well.

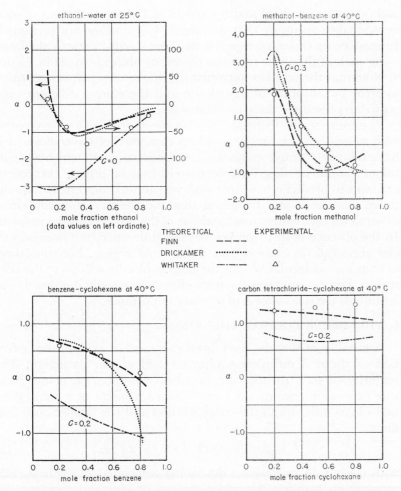

Fig. 9. Comparison of experimental and calculated values of the thermal diffusion constant $\alpha$ for several liquid systems.

The development of equation 30 from a relation very similar to equation 21 is based, in part, on the observation that $\alpha$ is essentially constant for ideal solutions. For very nonideal solutions use was made of the observation that the concentration at which $\alpha$ changes sign corresponds to the maximum on the heat of mixing curve.

The calculations required for application of Equations 26, 27, and 30 are so involved and the results of these calculations of such questionable accuracy that no sample calculations are presented. Instead comparison of experimental data with values calculated using each of the three relations presented above is made in Figure 9. Note that the relation suggested by Drickamer *et al.* is sometimes in error by an order of magnitude and therefore a different scale is used in presenting these calculated results.

In summary, the thermal diffusion constant, $\alpha$, can be estimated with some accuracy for gas mixtures composed of molecules which have relatively simple collisions, but for mixtures in which the collisions cannot be described accurately (gas or liquid) theoretical attempts to predict $\alpha$ have met with very limited success. In a qualitative manner it can be stated that the thermal diffusion effect depends on the relative mass and size of the species being separated. In the absence of any appreciable size difference, the heavier species almost always concentrate in the cold region. For substances of identical molecular weight the large molecule will go to the cold region. For gas mixtures the mass effect is generally dominant, but for liquids the size factor is of primary importance.

## C. PHENOMENOLOGICAL THEORIES

A number of theories have been proposed to explain the operation of thermal diffusion equipment and aid in its design. The majority of such theories are based on combination of the basic rate expression relating the flux of one component in a nonisothermal binary mixture to the concentration and the temperature gradient,

$$J_{x-TD} = + \rho(\alpha D/T)\, C_1 C_2\, (dT/dx) \qquad (3)$$

with other rate expressions describing associated mass, heat, and momentum transfer. The development of several important differential equations will be reviewed in this section and various solutions of these equations will be presented. The use of these solutions in connection with design of thermal diffusion equipment for laboratory use will be discussed in Section III.

### 1. Approximate Thermal Diffusion Rate Expressions

In general, combination of equation 3 with other basic rate expressions yields a differential equation relating the concentration of

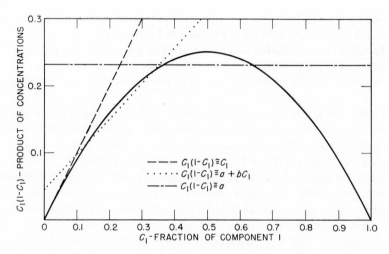

Fig. 10. The function $C(1-C) = f(C)$ and various approximations.

component 1 to position in a static cell or a thermogravitational column. The product form of the concentration dependence of the thermal diffusion effect incorporated in equation 3 introduces a nonlinearity into the differential equation which usually makes the solution difficult to obtain. If an analytical solution is obtained, the form is generally so complicated that meaningful interpretation of the results is difficult. Therefore approximate solutions have been obtained by replacing the product, $C_1 C_2 = C(1 - C)$ with a linear approximation. (The developments that follow are restricted to consideration of binary solutions and henceforth $C$ will be used as $C_1$, the fraction of component of lesser molecular weight.) The three approximations that are commonly used will be referred to frequently in this and the subsequent section and are explained before proceeding with the mathematical analysis of the equipment.

The function $C(1 - C) = f(C)$ is zero at $C = 0$ and 1.0 and passes through a maximum at $C = 0.5$. The function is represented by means of a solid line on Figure 10.

**Dilute Solutions.** The approximation

$$C(1 - C) \cong C \tag{31}$$

is valid when $C \ll 1$ and represents the curve reasonably well for $C \leq 0.1$ as shown by the dashed line on Figure 10.

**Equifraction Solutions.** The portion of the curve near the maximum can be approximated by a constant value.

$$C(1 - C) \cong a \tag{32}$$

Often the value at the maximum ($a = 1/4$) is used, but a somewhat lower value applies over a more extended region. The value $a = 0.23$ represents the curve over the interval $0.3 < C < 0.7$ with a maximum error of 8% (center line on Figure 10).

**The General Linear Approximation.** In the concentration range for which neither of the above approximations apply, the curve can be approximated by a straight line over a considerable range of concentration (dotted line on Figure 10).

$$C(1 - C) \cong a + bC \tag{33}$$

Equations 31 and 32 are easily recognized as special cases of the general linear approximation, equation 33.

### 2. The Static Case

Until the introduction of the thermogravitational column by Clusius and Dickel in 1938 (17), thermal diffusion apparatus were operated so as to eliminate convection currents as much as possible. The static cell consisting of two horizontal flat plates with the hot plate on top (Fig. 1) and the two bulb apparatus (Fig. 3) are typical of such equipment, and both types are amenable to mathematical analysis. In static cells a temperature gradient is applied to a portion of the solution, and this temperature gradient gives rise to a flux of component 1 as described by the general thermal diffusion rate expression, equation 3. The resulting concentration gradient establishes a diffusion flux, $J_{x-OD}$, as represented approximately by Fick's law.

$$J_{x-OD} = -\rho D \ (\partial C/\partial x) \tag{34}$$

Convective flow is inhibited in static cells and, in the ideal case, is eliminated altogether. As a result there is no mass transfer by bulk flow, and the net flux of component 1 in the $x$ direction, $J_x$, is obtained by combination of equations 3 and 34.

$$J_x = \rho D \ [(\alpha/T) \ C(1-C)(\partial T/\partial x) - (\partial C/\partial x)] \tag{35}$$

The method of application of this general flux expression depends on the specific type of equipment and the method of operation.

**Steady-State Separation.** Historically, it has been found to be a very difficult experimental task to obtain consistent data in static cells, and therefore interpretation of such data has usually been limited to analyses made at steady-state conditions. At steady-state the net flux of either component is zero and equation 35 reduces to

$$0 = (\alpha/T)\, C(1 - C)\, (dT/dx) - (dC/dx) \qquad (36)$$

*Concentration as a function of temperature.* The solution of this differential equation describing the conditions at steady-state is readily obtained without incorporation of approximations regarding the concentration product, $C(1 - C)$ or the temperature. Assuming that $\alpha$ is constant, integration of equation 36 yields

$$[C_H(1 - C_c)]/[C_c(1 - C_H)] = (T_H/T_c)^\alpha \qquad (37)$$

Application of the linear approximation which is valid for dilute solutions, equation 31, yields another form of the steady-state concentration difference which can also be obtained directly from equation 37 ($C << 1$)

$$C_H/C_c = (T_H/T_c)^\alpha \qquad (38)$$

If the concentration product $C(1 - C)$ is approximated as a constant (equation 32) the solution is

$$C_H - C_c = a \ln\, [(T_H/T_c)^\alpha] \qquad (39)$$

The general linear approximation, equation 33, yields the result

$$(a + bC_H)/(a + bC_c) = (T_H/T_c)^{ab} \qquad (40)$$

A simple expression is obtained in terms of the *Soret coefficient*, $D'/D$. Incorporating equation 2 in place of equation 3 in the basic flux expression, equation 35, yields an expression describing the steady-state separation as

$$D'C(1 - C)(dT/dx) = D(dC/dx) \qquad (41)$$

Considering $D'/D$ to be constant over the temperature and concentration range encountered in the experiment, the solution of equation 41 is

$$\ln\, \{[C_H/(1 - C_H)][(1 - C_c)/C_c]\} = (D'/D)(T_H - T_c) \qquad (42)$$

A large proportion of the experimental data on liquid systems obtained in static cells is reported in terms of the Soret coefficient. (Von Halle (48) lists more than 690 values of $D'/D$.)

*The mean value of temperature.*   In many cases, especially those involving gas mixtures, $\alpha$ is quite small (0.1 or less), and it is necessary to apply a large temperature difference in order to obtain a measurable separation. The value of $\alpha$ thus determined by application of any of the above equations represents a mean value associated with some temperature, $\bar{T}$. Brown (49) assumed that $\alpha$ varied linearly with the inverse absolute temperature and developed the following expression for $\bar{T}$ in terms of the hot temperature, $T_H$ and the cold one, $T_C$.

$$\bar{T} = [T_H T_C/(T_H - T_C)] \ln (T_H/T_C) \tag{43}$$

This equation was used in Section II-B-1 to estimate $\bar{T}$ corresponding to an experimental value of $\alpha$.

*Concentration as a function of position.*   In some cases it is necessary to obtain an expression for the concentration as a function of position in the static cell. For this purpose, equation 36 is modified slightly by assuming that the temperature gradient is constant and replacing $dT/dx$ in the equation by $\Delta T/l$ where $\Delta T \equiv T_H - T_C$ and $l$ is the linear distance between the points identified by $T_H$ to $T_C$. In addition $\bar{T}$ is used as a constant replacing $T$ in the differential equation

$$dC/dx = (\alpha/\bar{T}) (\Delta T/l) C(1 - C) \tag{44}$$

The function obtained by solving equation (44) will depend on the type of equipment used as well as the approximation made for the concentration product, $C(1 - C)$.

*The flat-plate cell.*   In this type of cell (Fig. 1) all of the solution is subject to the temperature gradient and therefore by material balance

$$C_0 = (1/l)\int_0^l C \, dx \tag{45}$$

where $C_0$ is the fraction of component 1 in the solution of uniform composition which initially filled the cell and $l$ here refers to the distance between plates.

A solution to equations 44 and 45 can be obtained without linearizing the concentration dependence.

$$C(x) = [1 + \psi_0 \exp(-2A\phi)]^{-1} \qquad (46)$$

where

$$A \equiv \alpha \Delta T / 2\bar{T} \qquad (47a)$$

$$\phi \equiv x/l \qquad (47b)$$

$$\psi_0 \equiv [e^{2A(1-C_0)} - 1]/(1 - e^{-2AC_0}) \qquad (48)$$

Somewhat simpler expressions are obtained by applying the linear approximations:

$$C(1 - C) \cong C$$

$$C(x) = [2AC_0/(e^{2A} - 1)]e^{2A\phi} \qquad (49)$$

$$C(1 - C) \cong a$$

$$C(x) = C_0 - aA(1.0 - 2\phi) \qquad (50)$$

$$C(1 - C) \cong a + bC$$

$$C(x) = [2bA(C_0 + a/b)/(e^{2bA} - 1)]e^{2bA\phi} - (a/b) \qquad (51)$$

The two-bulb apparatus.    It is desirable to be able to predict the composition in each bulb at equilibrium. The analysis of this problem is simplified by assuming that the volume of the bulbs is much greater than that of the connecting tube. By material balance

$$C_0(V_H + V_c) = C_H V_H + C_c V_c \qquad (52)$$

where the subscripts $H$ and $C$ indicate the hot and cold bulbs at equilibrium and $C_0$ is the fraction of component 1 in the initial charge to the apparatus.

For the general case, solution for $C_H$ in terms of the initial concentration, $C_0$, the volume ratio $V_R \equiv V_C/V_H$, and the temperature ratio $T_R \equiv [T_H/T_C]^\alpha$ yields a solution in the form of the quadratic equation:

$$C_H = \{-b' + [(b')^2 - 4a'c']^{1/2}\}/2a' \qquad (53)$$

where

$$a' = T_R - 1 \qquad (54a)$$

$$b' = -[V_R + T_R + (T_R - 1)(V_R + 1)C_0] \qquad (54b)$$

$$c' = T_R C_0(V_R + 1) \qquad (54c)$$

Somewhat simpler equations are obtained by application of the approximate rate expressions.

$$C(1 - C) \cong C$$

$$C_H = [(1 + V_R)/(1 + V_R/T_R)]C_0 \qquad (55)$$

$$C(1 - C) \cong a$$

$$C_H = C_0 + (aV_R \ln T_R)/(1 + V_R) \qquad (56)$$

**Approach to Equilibrium.** In the design of static thermal diffusion equipment it is desirable to be able to estimate the time required for the cell to approach steady-state conditions. In this particular case the theoretical analysis of such equipment is far ahead of experimental developments.

Although the basic approach to the analysis differs markedly for the various types of static cells it is found that the *final* approach to steady-state is exponential in all types of thermal diffusion equipment, i.e., for $t \gg t_r$

$$f \equiv [C(l,t) - C(0,t)]/[C(l, \infty) - C(0, \infty)] = (1 - ce^{-t/t_r}) \qquad (57)$$

where $f$ is the fractional approach to equilibrium separation, $l$ is a characteristic length of the apparatus, $c$ is a constant, and $t_r$ is the *relaxation time* (or *characteristic time*) of the apparatus, i.e., the time required to attain $(1 - c/e)$ of the equilibrium separation.

*Flat-plate cell.* Equation 35 describes the flux of component 1 under transient conditions and when combined with the conditions of continuity

$$\partial(\rho C)/\partial t = - \partial J_x/\partial x \qquad (58)$$

yields an expression relating $C$ to both time, $t$, and distance, $x$. As mentioned before, convective flow is inhibited in static cells and, in the ideal case, is eliminated altogether. Under such conditions heat is transferred through the mixture by conduction and a linear temperature gradient may be assumed. The time required for this gradient to be established is so small, compared to the time required to transfer mass by thermal diffusion, that little accuracy of analysis is sacrificed by assuming that a linear gradient is established immediately and therefore $\partial T/\partial x$ can be reasonably replaced with $\Delta T/l$ in the basic flux expression and treated as a constant. Additional simplification is achieved by assuming $\rho$, $\alpha$, and $D$ to be constant and replacing the absolute temperature, $T$, with its average value, $\bar{T}$.

$$\partial C/\partial t = D\ (\partial^2 C/\partial x^2) - (\alpha D/\bar{T})\ (\Delta T/l)\ \{\partial[C(1 - C)]/\partial x\} \quad (59)$$

The necessary boundary conditions are obtained by analysis of the physical situation in the flat plate cell.

Initially the cell is filled with material of fraction, $C_0$, of component 1.

At $t = 0$, all $x$

$$C = C_0 \tag{60}$$

The hot and cold plates are impervious to mass transfer and therefore the net flux of component 1 is equal to zero at these plates.

At $x = 0, l$, all $t$

$$\partial C/\partial x = (\alpha/\bar{T})\ (\Delta T/l)\ C(1 - C) \tag{60a}$$

Von Halle (48) has made a rather thorough investigation of the solution of equation 59 subject to the boundary conditions expressed in equations 60 and 60a. His work supplements the earlier analysis of de Groot (50) for the dilute case. These results are summarized here in terms of $t_r$ and $c$ to be used in equation 57 for predicting experimental times, $t$, for $t \gg t_r$.

The general solution

$$t_r = l^2/[D(\pi^2 + A^2)] \tag{61}$$

$c =$

$$\frac{4\pi^2 C_0(1 - C_0)\ (e^{-2AC_0} + e^{-A})(e^{2A} - 1)(e^A + e^{2AC_0})}{A(A^2 + \pi^2)[1 + (\pi^2/A^2) - 4C_0(1 - C_0)](1 - e^{-2AC_0})(e^{2A} - e^{2AC_0})} \tag{62}$$

$C(1 - C) \cong C$

$$t_r = l^2/[D(A^2 + \pi^2)] \tag{63}$$

$$c = 4\pi^2(1 + \cosh A)/(A^2 + \pi^2)^2 \tag{64}$$

$C(1 - C) \cong a$

$$t_r = l^2/D\pi^2 \tag{65}$$

$$c = 8/\pi^2 \tag{66}$$

$$C(1 - C) \cong a + bC$$

$$t_r = l^2/[D(b^2A^2 + \pi^2)] \tag{67}$$

$$c = [4\pi^2/(b^2A^2 + \pi^2)^2][1 + \cosh (bA)] \tag{68}$$

Note that equations 67 and 68 reduce to equations 65 and 66 for $b = 0$ $[C(1 - C) \cong a]$ and for $b = 1$ $[C(1 - C) \cong C]$ equations 67 and 68 reduce to 63 and 64.

*Two-bulb apparatus.* The analysis of the approach to equilibrium in the two-bulb apparatus is simplified by application of the "quasi-stationary" assumption originally proposed by Jones and Furry (31) and adapted to the analysis of the two-bulb static cell for $C(1 - C) \cong a$ by Grew and Ibbs (37). As in the case of the analysis of steady state separation in such a cell (Section II-C-2) it is assumed that the volume of the bulbs is much larger than that of the connecting tubes and, as a result, the net flux of component 1 anywhere within the tube is adequately described by the general flux expression, equation 35.

$$J_x = \rho D[(\alpha/T) (\Delta T/l) C(1 - C) - (\partial C/\partial x)] \tag{35a}$$

As a consequence of this assumption, the net flux of component 1 is essentially constant along the tube connecting the bulbs $(J_x \neq f(x))$ and therefore equation 35a can be solved to yield $J_x$ as a function of $t$. The resulting expression for $J_x$ is then used in conjunction with mass balances made on the bulbs to obtain equations relating the concentration in the bulbs to time. For the hot bulb:

$$V_H[d(\rho C_H)/dt] = A_c J_x \tag{69}$$

where $A_c$ is the cross sectional area of the connecting tube. Similarly for the cold bulb:

$$V_C[d(\rho C_C)/dt] = -A_c J_x \tag{70}$$

Application of this method of analysis is demonstrated for the approximate case $C(1 - C) \cong a$. If this expression is substituted into equation 35a and the additional simplifications of constant $\rho$, $\alpha$, and $D$ are made, the resulting equations can be integrated to yield $J_x$ as a function of the concentrations in the two bulbs at any instant.

$$J_x = \rho D\{(a\alpha/T) (\Delta T/l) - [(C_H - C_C)/l]\} \tag{71}$$

It is also assumed that an average value of $T$ can be used (see Section II-C-2). Again incorporating the assumption of constant $\rho$, a separable differential equation is obtained by combination of equations 69 through 71.

$$d(C_H - C_C)/dt = (DA_c/l) (1/V_H + 1/V_c)$$
$$\times [a (\alpha/T)\Delta T - (C_H - C_C)] \quad (72)$$

The solution of this equation is in the form of equation 57.

$$C(1 - C) \cong a$$

$$t_r = (l/DA_c) [V_H V_C/(V_H + V_C)] \quad (73a)$$

and

$$c = 1.0 \quad (73b)$$

In the treatment presented by Grew and Ibbs (37), the ideal gas law is applied and the diffusion coefficient is assumed to be proportional to $T^2$. The resulting expression for the relaxation time is

$$t_r = (l/DA_c) \{V_H V_C/[(V_H/T_H) + (V_C/T_C)]\}$$
$$\times (\bar{T}^2/T_H T_C \Delta T) \ln (T_H/T_C) \quad (73c)$$

The value of $D$ to be used in this expression is to be evaluated at $\bar{T}$. Other analogous cases have been treated by Jones and Furry (31) and the results are presented below.

$$C(1 - C) \cong a + bC$$
$$t_r = [(e^{2bA} - 1)/2bADA_c][V_H V_C/(V_H e^{2bA} + V_c)] \quad (74a)$$
$$c = 1.0 \quad (74b)$$

$$C(1 - C) \cong C.$$

In such a case, it is usual to concentrate the dilute component in a bulb whose volume is very much smaller than the other (feed) bulb. For concentration of the light component in such an apparatus equation 57 applies with

$$t_r = [(e^{2A} - 1)/2A] (l/DA_c) V_H \quad (75a)$$

For this particular case the fractional approach to equilibrium, $f$, is given by

$$f = [(C_H/C_0) - 1]/(e^{2A} - 1) \quad (75b)$$

Note that equations 74a and 75a reduce, in form, to equation 73a when $2bA \ll 1$, and use of equation 73a introduces little error for $2bA \leq 0.2$.

Von Halle (48) has analyzed the approach to equilibrium of thermogravitational columns with reservoirs without making the quasi-stationary assumption. He presents analytical solutions for the linear approximations $C(1 - C) \cong a$ and $C(1 - C) \cong a + bC$ and notes that Burton (52) has presented the solution for the dilute case, $C(1 - C) \cong C$. These solutions are directly applicable to the analysis of the approach to equilibrium in two-bulb static cells and the above reference should be consulted in making detailed consideration of the design of two-bulb apparatus in which the volume of the connecting tube is significant compared to the volume of either bulb. Jones and Furry (31) state that equations 73–75 will hold quite well in the cases in which the harmonic mean of the volumes of the reservoirs is only several times the volume of the separating tube.

*Agitated thermal diffusion cell.*    Von Halle (48) has also made an analysis of the approach to steady-state in an agitated thermal diffusion cell equipped with a fritted disk or permeable membrane. Von Halle considered that there were film resistances on each side of the disk or membrane, and obtained the results

$$t_r = [(l + 2dF)/(DA_cF)][V_H V_C/(V_H + V_C)] \tag{76a}$$

$$c = 1.0 \tag{76b}$$

where $l$ refers to the thickness of the membrane or frit, $A_c$ to its area and $F$ the fraction of the area open to diffusion, and $d$ is the thickness of one of the laminar films at the surface of the frit or membrane.

## 3. Thermogravitational Column

The mathematical analysis of the thermogravitational thermal diffusion column is somewhat more complicated than the corresponding analysis of the static cell. The temperature gradient applied between the plates of a thermogravitational column has two effects: (a) a flux of one component of the solution relative to the other is brought about by thermal diffusion as in the static cell and (b) convection currents are produced parallel to the plates owing to density differences. The combined result of these two effects is to produce a concentration difference between the two ends of the column which is generally much greater than that obtainable by the static method.

**Graphic Description of the Separation.** A very graphic illus- tration of the manner in which the thermal diffusion column in- creases the separation over that obtained in the static cell has been presented by Grew and Ibbs (37) and their presentation is worthy of repetition. Consider a thermal diffusion column consisting of a pair of vertical flat plates, initially filled with an equimolar mixture of a gas pair. (An exactly analogous description applies to liquid mixtures.) This situation is illustrated in Figure 11a in which, for simplification, it is considered that the gas mixture is composed of 16 portions individually uniform in composition. The separation is ini- tiated by heating one wall and cooling the other. A relatively short time is required to establish a linear temperature gradient between the plates. Separation by thermal diffusion in the direction normal to the plates and convective flow of solution parallel to the plates occur simultaneously but are considered to take place al- ternately. First, thermal diffusion occurs and an equilibrium separation of 4% is attained between each pair of the 16 portions, Figure 11b. (The composition is expressed in terms of the heavier component.) Next, the solution is transported upward a distance equal to the length of one portion at the hot wall and down a like distance at the cold wall as shown in Figure 11c. The continuation of the sequence of figures makes clear how the heavy molecules are transported toward the bottom of the column with each convection resulting in a concentration difference between the ends of the column which is greater than the 4% separation obtainable by application of the same temperature difference to a static cell. Note that in Figure 11h relatively concentrated material is being carried upward from the bottom of the column and, conversely, relatively dilute material enters the downward flowing stream at the top. Thus it is the convection itself that limits the degree of separation although in some cases diffusion in the vertical direction can be a contirbuting factor.

**Mathematical Description of the Column.** In formulating a mathematical description of the column behavior, an infinitesimal volume element is considered rather than the gross elements em-

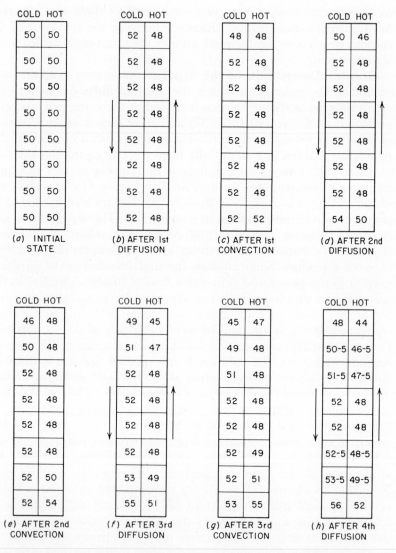

Fig. 11. Illustrating the beginning of the course of concentration changes in a thermogravitational column in which convection and thermal diffusion are supposed to occur alternately (Grew and Ibbs (37)).

ployed in Figure 11, the velocity distribution is treated as a continuous function and the effects of thermal diffusion, ordinary diffusion, and convective flow are considered simultaneously. The flux
of material in the direction of the temperature difference (normal to
the walls, $x$) is adequately described by the general flux expression
developed for the static cells, equation 35. Diffusion in the direction parallel to the plates ($y$) is approximated by Fick's law, equation 34. The hydrodynamic edge and end effects are ignored in
assuming that the convective velocity in the $y$ direction is a unique
function of $x$, $v(x)$. Figure 12 illustrates the flows and fluxes as
they exist in a thermal diffusion column and the coordinate system
used in the analysis.

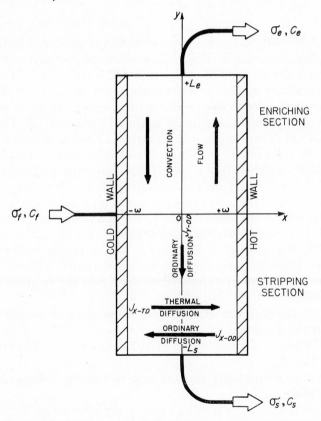

Fig. 12. Flows and fluxes in a thermogravitational thermal diffusion column.

The nonlinear partial differential equation resulting from consideration of all these factors is descriptive of the relation between the fraction of component 1, $C$, time, $t$, and the two space coordinates, $x$ and $y$, in a column constructed of two parallel plates.

$$\frac{\partial C}{\partial t} = D \left[ \frac{\partial^2 C}{\partial x^2} + \frac{\partial^2 C}{\partial y^2} \right] - \frac{\alpha D}{T} \frac{dT}{dx} \frac{\partial [C(1 - C)]}{\partial x} - v(x) \frac{\partial C}{\partial y} \quad (77)$$

The velocity distribution, $v(x)$, is determined by applying the Navier-Stokes relations for laminar flow. For the enriching section of a column with continuous feed and product removal:

$$v(x) = (\beta_T g \cos\theta \, \Delta T/12 \, \omega\mu) \, (\omega^2 x - x^3) \\ + (^3/_4) \, (\sigma_e/B_e\rho\omega^3) \, (\omega^2 - x^2) \quad (78)$$

where $\beta_T = -\partial\rho/\partial T$, $g$ is the acceleration of gravity, $\theta$ is the angle of the plates from the vertical, $\omega$ is one-half the distance between the plates, $\mu$ is the viscosity of the mixture, $B_e$ is the width of the plates in the enriching section, $\sigma_e$ is the mass flow rate of material exiting from the enriching section, and $\rho$ is the average density of the mixture. A similar equation applies to the stripping section. The velocity distribution function is seen to consist of two independent parts; a cubic in $x$ describing the natural convective flow and a parabolic term which represents the forced flow through the column. For a batch column $\sigma = 0$ and $v(x)$ contains only the first term.

In addition to the assumptions regarding the hydrodynamic edge and end effects mentioned above, the following assumptions are implicit in the development of equations 77 and 78.

1. The temperature varies only in the direction normal to the plates ($x$ direction), and the temperature variation is linear in $x$.

2. Any variation in the direction normal to the $xy$ plane may be neglected.

3. The temperature and concentration dependence of $D$, $\alpha$, $\mu$, and $\beta_T$ can be ignored.

4. The effect of composition on density, $\rho$, can be ignored; i.e., $\rho = f(T)$ only.

5. A mean value of $\rho$ can be used to convert volumetric flows to mass flows.

6. The temperature level, $T$, can be replaced by its mean value, $\bar{T}$.

7. The column width, $B$, is constant in any one section.

8. Laminar flow conditions exist between the plates.

Several investigators have attempted to eliminate the necessity for several of these basic assumptions, and their efforts will be considered later.

A solution of equation 77 must be found subject to boundary conditions descriptive of the physical situation in the column. The walls are assumed to be impervious to mass flow except at specific injection and withdrawal points and therefore the net flow caused by thermal diffusion and ordinary diffusion must be zero at both walls.

At $x = \pm\omega$

$$-D\,(\partial C/\partial x) + (\alpha D/\bar{T})C(1 - C)\,(\Delta T/2\omega) = 0 \qquad (79)$$

**The Transport Equation.** Equations 77–79 provide the basis for an adequate description of a thermal diffusion column subject to the assumptions listed above, but the nonlinear form of the basic partial differential (eq. 77), the nonconstant coefficients involved in $v(x)$ (eq. 78), and the associated boundary conditions (eq. 79) make it difficult to obtain a rigorous mathematical solution. Furry, Jones, and Onsager (30) have considered the operation of a batch thermal diffusion column in detail and have obtained a suitable approximate expression to describe column behavior. The result of their reduction of equations 77–79 is known as the *transport equation*.

The method used by Furry, Jones, and Onsager (30) and later modified by Bardeen (54) will not be discussed in detail here as adequate discussions are available elsewhere (30,51,53). Jones and Furry (31) present a simplified derivation of the transport equation which is repeated in Grew and Ibbs (37). It will be sufficient for our purposes to note that the transport equation was developed by considering the net transport of one component of a binary system passing through a plane perpendicular to the walls of a batch thermal diffusion column. This transport is the net result of convective flow and diffusion and is given by

$$\tau = \int_{-\omega}^{+\omega} B\rho\, C\, v(x)\, dx - \int_{-\omega}^{+\omega} B\rho D\, (\partial C/\partial y)dx \qquad (80)$$

Integration of this expression and incorporation of the boundary condition at the walls (eq. 79) together with several approximations yield equation 81.

$$\tau = HC\ (1 - C) - K(dC/dy) \tag{81}$$

where:

$$H = \alpha\beta_T\rho g\ \cos\theta\ (2\omega)^3 B(\Delta T)^2/(6!\bar{T}\mu) \tag{82a}$$

$$K = K_c + K_d \tag{82b}$$

$$K_c = \beta_T^2\ \rho g^2\ \cos^2\theta\ (2\omega)^7 B(\Delta T)^2/(9!\ D\mu^2) \tag{82c}$$

$$K_d = 2\omega DB\rho \tag{82d}$$

in which $\Delta T$ is the temperature difference between the plates.

This is the *transport equation* as presented by Furry, Jones, and Onsager. Application of this relation to the analysis of the behavior of thermal diffusion columns will be considered in detail.

Development of equation 81 together with equations 82a–d incorporates the following assumptions in addition to those listed on pages 38 and 39.

1. The vertical diffusion term $D(\partial^2C/\partial y^2)$ in equation 77 is small compared with the velocity term, $v(x)(\partial C/\partial y)$. (The effect of vertical diffusion is incorporated as $K_d$ in the final expression.)

2. $(\partial C/\partial y)$ does not depend on $x$.

3. Mean values of $C_1$ and $C_2$ with respect to $x$ can be used after their $x$ dependence has been described by $H$ and $K$.

The similarity between equation 81 which describes the transport of the light component in a thermogravitational column and equation 35a which represents the flux of the light component in a static cell is worthy of note.

$$J_x = \rho[(\alpha D/\bar{T})(\Delta T/l)C(1 - C) - D(\partial C/\partial x)] \tag{35a}$$

$$\tau = HC(1 - C) - K(\partial C/\partial y) \tag{81}$$

In the developments that follow, frequent use will be made of this similaritiy of form. It should be noted, however, that $\tau$ as given in equation 81 is *not* a flux as it represents the net transport of mass of component 1 through the *total cross* section of the column and is not based on a unit cross-sectional area.

**The Batch Column.** Batch thermogravitational columns may be operated to obtain small quantities of material for analysis or preparatory purposes, and have been operated both with and without reservoirs attached to the ends of the separation tube. Such columns may be designed to obtain a specified separation either at steady-state or at some time during the transient period. Both the steady-state and transient behavior of batch thermal diffusion columns as well as their optimum method of operation will be considered in the paragraphs that follow.

*Steady-state.* At steady-state the net transport of material, $\tau$, in the batch column is zero and the transport equation, equation 81, reduces to

$$0 = HC(1 - C) - K(dC/dy) \tag{83}$$

Of particular importance is the following relation which results directly from integration of equation 83 and therefore applies to any batch column, either with or without reservoirs:

$$\ln q \equiv \ln \left\{ [C/(1 - C)]_e / [C/(1 - C)]_s \right\} = 2A = HL/K \tag{84}$$

As was the case for the static cells, other solutions of equation 83 depend on the type of column and the approximation made for the product $C_1 C_2 = C(1 - C)$.

Columns without reservoirs. All of the solution is contained between the walls of the column and equations 45, 46, and 47a–51 apply directly to such columns with the substitution of $y$ for $x$, $L$ for $l$, and use of the definition

$$A \equiv HL/2K \tag{85}$$

where $L$ refers to the total length of the thermal diffusion column.

Columns with reservoirs. As in the case of the batch thermal diffusion column without reservoirs, the equations describing the steady-state separation in columns with reservoirs have already been presented for the analogous case of the two-bulb static cell. Thus, equations 52–56 are applicable to thermal diffusion columns with reservoirs wherein the subscript $H$ is replaced with $e$ denoting the enriching (top) reservoir, $s$ replaces $C$ in referring to the bottom or stripping reservoir and $T_R$ is replaced by $e^{2A}$. For example consider application of equation 55 to the case of a batch thermogravitational column with reservoirs.

$$C(1 - C) \cong C$$

$$C_e = [(1 + V_R)/(1 + V_R e^{-2A})]C_0 \tag{86}$$

where

$$V_R = V_s/V_e \tag{86a}$$

Similar substitutions apply to the other cases.

*Approach to steady-state.* In consideration of the transient operation of static cells it was sufficient to treat only the final approach to equilibrium, i.e., $t \gg t_r$. For thermogravitational thermal diffusion columns, it is often practical to limit separations to a fractional approach to equilibrium, and therefore a more detailed analysis of the transient separation is desired.

The transport equation,

$$\tau = HC(1 - C) - K(\partial C/\partial y) \tag{83}$$

serves as the basic rate expression for the analysis of the approach to equilibrium in a thermogravitational column. The analyses of columns without and with reservoirs closely parallel those of the flat-plate cell and the two-bulb apparatus, respectively.

Columns without reservoirs. Combination of equation 81 with the conditions of continuity yields

$$m(\partial C/\partial t) = K(\partial^2 C/\partial y^2) - H\{\partial[C(1 - C)]/\partial y\} \tag{87}$$

where $m$ is the mass of solution per unit column length.

Initially, the cell is filled with material of fraction, $C_0$, of component 1.

At $t = 0$, all $y$ $\hspace{6cm}$ (88)
$$C = C_0$$

For a batch column, the transport as represented by equation 83 must be zero at both ends of the column.

At $y = 0, L$, all $t$ $\hspace{6cm}$ (89)
$$\partial C/\partial y = (H/K)C(1 - C)$$

Von Halle (48) has presented the general solution to equation 87 and the associated boundary conditions, equations 88 and 89. The solution applicable for $t \gg t_r$ was given in a previous section as equations 57, 61, and 62 which apply to columns without reservoirs when $A$ is given by equation 85 and $D$ in equation 61 is replaced by $K/m$. The general solution relating $C$ to time, $t$, and position in the column, $v$, is presented as equation 90.

$$C(\phi,t) =$$

$$(1-e^{-2AC_0})e^{2A\phi}+(1/2)(e^{2A}-1)e^{A\phi}\sum_{n=1}^{\infty}K_n(\sin n\pi\phi+(n\pi/A)\cos n\pi\phi)e^{-t/t_n}$$

$$(1-e^{-2AC_0})e^{2A\phi} + (e^{2A(1-C_0)}-1) + (e^{2A}-1)e^{A\phi}\sum_{n=1}^{\infty}K_n(\sin n\pi\phi)\,e^{-t/t_n}$$

$$(90)$$

where

$$\phi = y/L \tag{91}$$

$$K_n = \frac{8n\pi\ C_0(1-C_0)[e^{-2AC_0}+(-1)^{n+1}e^{-A}]}{[A^2+(n\pi)^2][1+(n\pi/A)^2-4C_0(1-C_0)]} \tag{92}$$

$$t_n = mL^2/[K(A^2+n^2\pi^2)] \tag{93}$$

Powers (55) has presented the results of numerical solution of equation 87 subject to equations 88 and 89 for the case $C_0 = 0.5$ in the form of graphs. Two of these graphs are presented here as Figures 13 and 14. In both of these graphs, the parameter $A$ is given by equation 85. The abscissa is dimensionless time, $\xi$, where

$$\xi \equiv (\pi^2 K/mL^2)t \tag{94}$$

and the ordinate is the fractional approach to equilibrium at specified points in the column. For $X = 1.0$ (Fig. 13) $\Delta = C_e - C_s$, i.e., the difference in concentration measured at the extremities of the column, whereas for $X = 0.6$ (Fig. 14) the concentration difference, $\Delta$, is between two points, each displaced one-fifth of the total length from each end. Similar graphs corresponding to $X = 0.8, 0.4$, and $0.2$ have been presented by Powers (55).

Use of the various approximations for $C(1 - C)$ yields somewhat simpler analytical expressions for the approach to steady-state in batch thermogravitational cells.

$C(1 - C) \cong C$.

Jones and Furry (31) present the results of analyses by Bardeen (56) and Debye (57) for this case.

$$C(\phi,t) = ke^{2\phi A} + e^{\phi A}\sum_{n=0}^{\infty}K_n[\cos(n\pi\phi) + (A/n\pi)\sin(n\pi\phi)]e^{-t/t_n} \tag{95}$$

$$k = 2AC_0/(e^{2A} - 1) \tag{96}$$

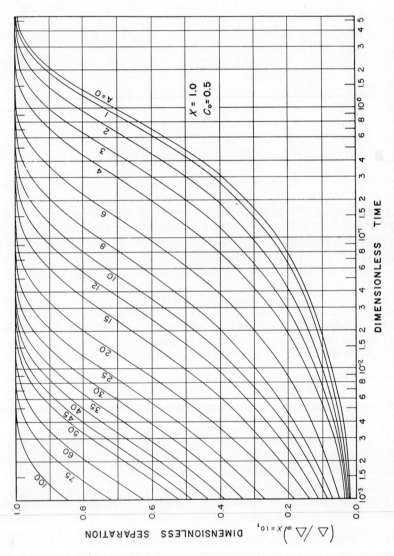

Fig. 13. Concentration change with time at the ends of a batch thermal diffusion column without reservoirs ($C_0 = 0.5$).

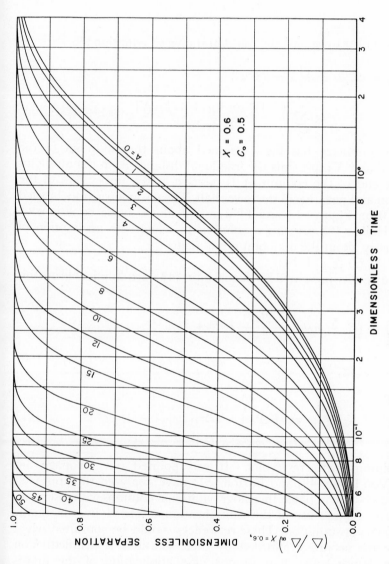

Fig. 14. Concentration change with time at points displaced $1/5$ of the total length from each end of a batch thermal diffusion column without reservoirs ($C_0 = 0.5$).

$$K_n = 4C_0(n^2\pi^2/A^3)[1 - (-1)^n e^{-A}]/(1 + n^2\pi^2/A^2)^2 \qquad (97)$$

$$t_n = mL^2/[K(A^2+n^2\pi^2)] \qquad (98)$$

$C(1 - C) \cong a$.

Powers (58) presents the solution shown in equation 99,

$$C(X,t) = C_0 + 2aA\Bigg\{X - (8/\pi^2)$$

$$\times \sum_{n=0}^{\infty} \frac{(-1)^n \sin [(n + 1/2)\pi X]}{(2n + 1)^2} e^{-(n+1/2)^2\xi}\Bigg\} \qquad (99)$$

where symmetry has been assumed about the midpoint of the column and $X$ represents the fractional distance from the midpoint to the end of the column. $X$ is positive in the upper half of the column and negative in the lower half. The parametric lines labeled $A = 0$ on Figures 13 and 14 were calculated using equation 99. Von Halle (48) presents a solution in which the assumption of symmetry about the midpoint is not made.

$C(1 - C) \cong a + bC$.

The results presented by Von Halle (48) are applicable to this case.

$$C(\phi,t) = (C_0 + a/b)\Bigg[\frac{2bA}{(e^{2bA}-1)}e^{2bA\phi} + 4bAe^{bA\phi}$$

$$\times \sum_{n=1}^{\infty} K_n [\cos n\pi\phi+(bA/n\pi) \sin n\pi\phi]e^{-t/t_n}\Bigg] - (a/b) \qquad (100)$$

where

$$K_n = [n^2\pi^2/(b^2A^2 + n^2\pi^2)^2][1 + (-1)^{n+1}e^{-bA}] \qquad (101)$$

$$t_n = mL^2/[K(b^2A^2 + n^2\pi^2)] \qquad (102)$$

Columns with reservoirs. It was pointed out on page 34, that Von Halle (48) and Burton (51) have analyzed the approach to steady-state in batch thermogravitational columns with reservoirs without making use of the simplification afforded by the quasi-stationary assumption. These references should be consulted when the extra accuracy afforded by their solutions is justified. Von Halle demonstrates that in one case application of the quasi-stationary assumption gives a very good approximation to the approach to steady-state of the column and since the form of the results of such analyses is much less complicated, these results are presented here.

In applying the quasi-stationary assumption to the analysis of batch thermogravitational columns with reservoirs, it is assumed that the volume of solution contained in the separation tube is small compared with the volume of either reservoir. (See last sentence of the second paragraph following equation 75b, page 34) Therefore, the net transport of component 1 into the enriching reservoir and out of the stripping reservoir is described by the transport equation (eq. 81) in which it is assumed that the net mass transfer of component 1, $\tau$, is independent of $y$. The analysis of thermal diffusion columns with reservoirs proceeds in a manner exactly analogous to the analysis of the transient behavior of two-bulb static cells. As a result, equation 57 and equations 72–78 apply to such columns as follows ($c = 1.0$ for all cases).

$$C(1 - C) \cong a$$

$$t_r = (L/K) \left[ M_e M_s / (M_e + M_s) \right] \qquad (103)$$

$$C(1 - C) \cong a + bC$$

$$t_r = \left[ (e^{2bA} - 1)/2bA \right] (L/K) \left[ M_e M_s / (M_e + M_s) \right] \quad (104)$$

$$C(1 - C) \cong C; \ (M_e \ll M_s)$$

$$t_r = \left[ (e^{2A} - 1)/2A \right] (L/K) M_e \qquad (105)$$

For this last case the fractional approach to equilibrium, $f$, is given by

$$f = \left[ (C_e/C_0) - 1 \right]/(e^{2A} - 1) \qquad (106)$$

*Optimum operation of batch columns.*   In preparing samples using batch thermogravitational columns, it is desirable to operate the column in such a manner as to yield product at minimum unit cost. It has been shown by Krasney-Ergen (32) that optimum design considerations can be separated into two independent categories, one involving the column length and mode of column operation and the other considering the parameters included in $H$ and $K$ (eqs. 82a–d).

Optimum column length.   For a column in which $H$ and $K$ are fixed, both the equipment and operating costs are proportional to the column length, $L$. For a specified separation, the rate of production is proportional to the mass of material in the reservoir

$M$, and inversely proportional to the time, $t$, required to attain the desired separation. Thus, the group $(M/tL)$ should be made as large as possible. Jones and Furry chose to maximize the dimensionless quantity

$$O_m \equiv (K/H^2)(M/tL) \tag{107}$$

as $H$ and $K$ are constants as previously discussed. Two solutions are presented corresponding to the case in which $M_e \ll M_s$.

$C(1 - C) \cong a$

$$L_b = 1.398 \ K \ \Delta/aH \tag{108a}$$

$$t_b = 1.76 \ M_e \ \Delta/aH \tag{108b}$$

where $L_b$ and $t_b$ are the column length and time of operation corresponding to minimum unit cost.

$C(1 - C) \cong C.$

The optimum column length, $L_b$, is determined by maximizing $(K/H^2)(M/tL)$ as given in the following expression.

$$1/O_m = 2A(e^{2A} - 1) \ln \{1 - [((C_e/C_s) -1)/(e^{2A} -1)]\} \tag{109}$$

where $C_s = C_0$ because $M_e \ll M_s$.

Results of graphical solution of this expression for the two cases $C_e/C_0 = 10$ and $C_e/C_0 = 50$ are presented.

$C_e/C_0 = 10$

$$L_b = 3.1 \ K/H \tag{110a}$$

$$t_b = 11.7 \ M_e/H \tag{110b}$$

$C_e/C_0 = 50$

$$L_b = 5.1 \ K/H \tag{110c}$$

$$t_b = 58.4 \ M_e/H \tag{110d}$$

Other optimum column dimensions. In the above analysis, the optimum column length was determined by optimizing the group $(K/H^2)(M/tL) = O_m$. This was done by considering both the operating costs and depreciation charges to be proportional to the length. For a maximum value of $O_m$ as determined above the inverse unit cost of product is given by

$$M/tLQ = O_m H^2/KQ \tag{111}$$

where $Q$ is the combined operating costs and depreciation charges per unit column length per unit time. Clearly it is desirable to maximize the ratio of $(H^2/K)$ to $Q$ because $O_m$ is itself individually maximized. Consider the optimum value of plate spacing, $\omega$, first. From equations 82a–d

$$H^2/KQ = a'/(Q\omega[1 + u/\omega^6]) \tag{112}$$

where $u/\omega^6$ equals $K_d/K_c$ and $a'$ is a grouping of column parameters other than $\omega$.

In general, the costs are principally those for heat transfer required to maintain the temperature gradient. Consideration by Jones and Furry (31) of the case in which heat transfer is by conduction led to the conclusion that for gas mixtures the plate spacing, $\omega$, should be as large as possible without causing turbulence. This consideration places an upper limit of 25 on $K_c/K_d = \omega^6/u$ and thus limits $\omega$. (This upper limit corresponding to the onset of turbulence is based on measurements by Onsager and Watson (59) and, as far as the author knows, has never been checked for liquids.) If radiation is the primary mode of heat transfer $H^2/KQ$ is maximized when $K_c/K_d$ is equal to 5. In the general case, Jones and Furry recommended a value of $K_c/K_d = 10$ as the basis of specification of the plate spacing $\omega$.

The optimum temperature ratio was also considered by Jones and Furry. For $K_c/K_d \cong 10$, $K_d$ can be neglected in relation to $K_c$ and considering the properties of the mixture as those of a Maxwellian gas ($\nu = 5$), equations 82a–d indicate that $H^2/KQ$ is proportional to $\Delta T/\bar{T}^2$ for the case in which heat transfer is by conduction. If one of the temperatures is fixed, $\Delta T/\bar{T}^2$ and therefore $H^2/KQ$ is maximized for $T_H/T_C = 3$. If $T_C$ is approximately room temperature, this relation yields high hot wall temperatures and radient heat transfer must be taken into account. Under these conditions, the maximization equations are cumbersome and the best value of $T_H/T_C$ must be determined for each case.

*Entropy efficiency.* Consideration of the entropy efficiency of separations using thermal diffusion is based on an inequality developed by Onsager (60) for gas mixtures

$$-\dot{S}_m/\dot{S}_c \leq (1/4)\alpha^2 C(1 - C)(PD/kT) \tag{113}$$

where $\dot{S}_m$ is the rate of entropy production associated with mixing of two components, $\dot{S}_c$ is similarly associated with the irreversible heat transfer, and $k$ is the thermal conductivity of the mixture. The equality in equation 113 applies if and only if the diffusive flux described by Fick's law (eq. 34) is opposite in sign and numerically equal to one half of the flux caused by thermal diffusion (eq. 3). Consideration of the separation of a gas mixture with the properties of a Maxwellian gas (other than $\alpha$) in a batch column under conditions such that equations 57 and 103 apply leads to the conclusion that the separation efficiency of the column attains a maximum of 70% of the fundamental efficiency (eq. 113) at only one time during the separation. The greatest time average efficiency that can theoretically be obtained in such a batch column is limited to about 50% of the value given by the equality in equation 113.

**Continuous-Flow Thermal Diffusion Columns.** Figure 12 illustrates the external feed and product take off streams in a single continuous-flow thermal diffusion column. A cascade arrangement can be made by interconnecting a number of such columns. The theoretical analyses of both single and multicolumn apparatus is based on a relatively simple modification of the transport equation.

*Modification of the transport equation.* As noted previously, development of the transport equation (eq. 81) by Furry, Jones, and Onsager (30) is based on consideration of flow conditions inside a batch column. These authors have made a very useful approximate extension of the transport equation to include consideration of continuous-flow operation of a thermal diffusion column. These authors add a term to the transport equation to account for the presence of bulk flow through the column in addition to the convective flow within the column.

$$\tau = HC\,(1 \,-\, C) + \sigma C - K\,(\partial C/\partial v) \qquad (114)$$

In the development of Furry, Jones, and Onsager, incorporation of the bulk flow term into the transport equation as represented by equation 114 was the only correction made for the presence of a net flow through the column, and the parameters $H$ and $K$ to be used in equation 114 are those developed for the batch case (eqs. 82a–d). Powers and Wilke (21) demonstrated that incorporation of the term describing the bulk flow contribution in the velocity distribution, $v(x)$, (eq. 78) was incompatible with the basic assumption made by Furry, Jones, and Onsager that $\partial C/\partial y$ is independent of $x$. Corrections introduced by Powers and Wilke can be incorporated as modifications to $H$ and $K$ which do not change the form of the resulting equations. These corrections will be discussed later.

In most cases, continuous-flow columns will be operated as batch columns without reservoirs until the desired separation is reached and then flow will be initiated. (Operation designed to maintain a constant composition at one end of the column by continuous flushing with fresh feed would be one exception.) Under nonflow conditions, the equations presented in a previous section for the approach to equilibrium of batch columns will apply. Vichare and Powers (61) have considered the approach to steady-state in a column with flow in connection with an investigation of the effect of sampling rate on the approach to equilibrium in columns without reservoirs. This theoretical analysis and experimental investigation were restricted to the case $C(1 - C) \cong a$. Only the steady-state operation of single-stage continuous-flow columns will be treated in this section. Some consideration will be given to the transient behavior of cascade (multicolumn) apparatus.

*Steady-state operation of a single continuous flow column.* For purposes of analysis and some preparatory work, single-stage apparatus as shown in Figure 12 will sometimes be used. Under steady-state conditions a material balance made at any cross section of the enriching section and enveloping the total product stream leaving that section, $\sigma_e$ yields the general relation

$$\tau_e = \sigma_e \, C_e \qquad (115)$$

where $C_e$ refers to the composition of the product stream exiting from the enriching section.

Incorporation of the modified transport equation (eq. 114) and rearrangement yields:

$$H_e \, [C(1 - C) - n_e \, (C_e - C)] = K_e(dC/dy) \qquad (116)$$

where

$$n_e \equiv \sigma_e/H_e \qquad (117)$$

The subscript $e$ serves to identify the enriching section.

In general apparatus with but one enriching and one stripping section will be constructed as one column and therefore will have identical dimensions in each section. The flow rate through each section as well as the section lengths may differ, and therefore it is convenient to present the results of the analysis for the enriching section only. In order to modify the equations to apply to the stripping section it is only necessary to substitute $(1 - C)$ for $C$ and change the subscript $e$ to $s$ in the equations. This results in interchanging the roles of the two components, and it is often convenient to look at it in that light.

Separation as a function of product flow rate $\sigma$. In all of the equations presented below it is assumed that feed of fraction $C_f$ is entered at the point in the column at which the fraction of component 1 is equal to $C_f$. Column operation should be designed with this objective in mind. Several investigators (62, 63) have reported that the exact location of the feed port is not critical. Jones and Furry (31) present solutions of equation 116 incorporating the above assumptions and subject to the boundary conditions for the enriching section:

At $y = 0$ $\hspace{8cm}$ (118)
$$C = C_f$$

At $y = L_e$ $\hspace{7.5cm}$ (119)
$$C = C_e$$

Integration of equation 116 yields the relation

$$\tanh b'A_e = b'(C_e - C_f)/[C_e + C_f - n_e(C_e - C_f) - 2C_eC_f] \quad (120)$$

where

$$b' \equiv [(1 + n_e)^2 - 4n_eC_e]^{1/2} \quad (121)$$

Somewhat less complicated forms are obtained by considering the various approximations for the concentration product $C(1 - C)$.

$C(1 - C) \cong a$
$$C_e - C_f = (aH_e/\sigma_e)(1 - e^{-\sigma_eL_e/K_e}) \quad (122)$$

$C(1 - C) \cong C$
$$C_e/C_f = (1 + n_e)/[n_e + \exp(-2(1 + n_e)A_e)] \quad (123)$$

$C(1 - C) \cong a + bC$
$$C_e = [(b + n_e)C_f + a(1 - e^{-2(b + n_e)A_e})]/[n_e + be^{-2(b + n_e)A_e}] \quad (124)$$

As in previous cases, equations 122 and 123 are reduced forms of the general linear approximation, equation 124.

As an example of the modification of the above equations for application to the stripping section and combination of the two for analysis of the total column behavior, consider substitution of $(1 - C)$ for $C$ and the subscript $s$ for $e$ in equation 122.

$$C_f - C_s = (aH_s/\sigma_s)(1 - e^{-\sigma_s L_s/K_s}) \qquad (125)$$

Addition of equations 122 and 125 eliminates $C_f$ and yields

$$\Delta \equiv C_e - C_s = a[(H_e/\sigma_e)(1 - e^{-\sigma_e L_e/K_e}) + (H_s/\sigma_s)(1 - e^{-\sigma_s L_s/K_s})] \qquad (126)$$

For the special case in which $\sigma_e = \sigma_s = \sigma_f/2$ and $L_e = L_s = L_T/2$, equation 126 reduces to

$$\Delta \equiv C_e - C_s = (4aH/\sigma_f)\,[1 - \exp\,(-\,\sigma_f L_T/4K)] \qquad (127)$$

From equations 50 and 85 the separation between ends of the column at zero flow rate, $\Delta_0$, i.e., in a batch column is

$$\Delta_0 = 2aA = a(HL_T/K) \qquad (128)$$

This relation can be used in combination with equation 127 to express the effect of flow rate on separation conveniently in dimensionless form for this special case.

$$\Delta/\Delta_0 = (1 - e^{-Z})/Z \qquad (129)$$

where

$$Z \equiv \sigma_f L_T/4K \qquad (130)$$

A plot of $\Delta/\Delta_0$ versus $Z$ is given in Figure 15 to illustrate the manner in which the flow rate influences the separation in a continuous-flow thermal diffusion column.

Optimum column operation.  Krasney-Ergen (32) considered minimization of the costs of operating a continuous-flow thermal diffusion column and developed the following equations for optimum column dimensions to produce a given separation $C_e/C_f$ at a desired rate, $\sigma_e$, in a single-stage column.
$C(1 - C) \cong C$.

For optimum plate spacing $(2{*}\omega)$

$$(2{*}\omega)^7 - 5(b'/a')\,(2{*}\omega) - 6\,(b'/a')(p_c/S) = 0 \qquad (131)$$

where

$$(b'/a') \equiv 9!\,[D\mu/\beta_T g \cos\theta\,\Delta T]^2 \qquad (132)$$

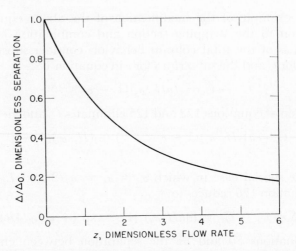

Fig. 15. The effect of flow rate through a continuous-flow thermal diffusion column on separation achieved in the column $[C(1-C) = a;\ \sigma_e = \sigma_s$ and $L_e = L_s]$.

and $p_c/2\omega$ is the power cost per unit area per unit time and $S$ is the amount of fixed charges per unit area per unit time.

For optimum column width $(B^*)$

$$B^* = \sigma/[n^*a''(2\omega)^3] \tag{133}$$

where

$$a'' \equiv \alpha\beta_T\rho g\ \cos\theta\ (\Delta T)^2/(6!\mu\bar{T}) \tag{134}$$

and $n^*$ is the root of the equation.

$$[(C_f/C_e) - 1]n^*(1 + n^*) = (1 + 2n^*)[(1 + n^*)(C_f/C_e) - n^*]$$
$$\times \ln\ [(1 + n^*)(C_f/C_e) - n^*] \tag{135}$$

For optimum column length $(L_T^*)$

$$L_T^* = (2K/H)\{1 + [b'/(a'2\omega)^6]\}X' \tag{136}$$

where

$$X' = -\{\ln[(1 + n^*)(C_f/C_e) - n^*]\}/[2(1 + n^*)] \tag{137}$$

The terms $n^*$ and $X'$ are both listed in Table V as functions of $C_e/C_f$, the desired separation.

TABLE V

Values of $n^*$ and $X'$ to be Used to Determine Optimum Column Dimensions for
$$C(1 - C) \cong C$$

| $C_e/C_f$ | $n^*$ | $X'$ | $C_e/C_f$ | $n^*$ | $X'$ |
|---|---|---|---|---|---|
| 2 | 0.745 | 0.59 | 9 | 0.101 | 1.74 |
| 3 | 0.381 | 0.91 | 10 | 0.090 | 1.80 |
| 4 | 0.259 | 1.14 | 11 | 0.081 | 1.86 |
| 5 | 0.197 | 1.37 | 12 | 0.074 | 1.92 |
| 6 | 0.159 | 1.46 | 13 | 0.068 | 1.97 |
| 7 | 0.133 | 1.56 | 14 | 0.063 | 2.06 |
| 8 | 0.115 | 1.67 | 15 | 0.060 | 2.16 |

Powers and Wilke (21) treated the case for $C(1 - C) \cong a$, for which it is also reasonable to assume that $\sigma_e = \sigma_e \equiv \sigma$, $L_e = L_s$ and $B_e = B_s$ (see eq. 127). Their expression for the optimum plate spacing $(2^*\omega)$ is identical to that presented by Krasney-Ergen (eqs. 131 and 132) but the corresponding relations for $B^*$ and $L_T^*$ are somewhat simpler.

$C(1 - C) \cong a$.

For optimum plate spacing $(2^*\omega)$, the relations are identical to equations 131 and 132.

For optimum column width $(B^*)$

$$B^* = 0.6985\sigma\Delta/[aa''(2^*\omega)^3] \tag{138}$$

where $a''$ is given by equation 134.

For optimum column length $(L_T^*)$

$$L_T^* = [2.54(2^*\omega)DB^*\rho/\sigma] \, [(a'/b')(2^*\omega)^6 + 1] \tag{139}$$

Application of these relations will be illustrated by a design example in Section IV-B-1.

Entropy efficiency. The entropy efficiency of continuous flow thermal diffusion columns has been considered by White and Fellows (64). For their treatment, equation 113 was rewritten in terms of the energy efficiency, $\eta_t$,

$$\eta_t \leq \alpha^2 DC(1 - C)R\rho\Delta T/(4\bar{M}k\bar{T}) \tag{140}$$

where $\bar{M}$ is the average molecular weight and the equality represents the limiting thermodynamic efficiency as in equation 113. The actual energy efficiency of a continuous flow apparatus operating with a flow rate $\sigma$ and a separation $\Delta$ under conditions such that $C(1 - C) \cong a$ was calculated according to

$$\eta_a = \sigma\Delta^2 R\omega\bar{T}/(4a\bar{M}kLB\Delta T) \qquad (141)$$

White and Fellows obtained separations of hydrocarbon systems in single-stage continuous-flow thermal diffusion columns and demonstrated that the limiting thermodynamic efficiency is approached in actual column operation. These authors also considered the operation of an ideal cascade and concluded that under certain conditions, the thermal efficiency of a single unit in a stage and that of the cascade are identical.

*Cascading.* Application of thermal diffusion for almost any commercial application and for many small scale (gram per day) separations will require the use of cascading of thermal diffusion columns both to increase efficiency of the separation and decrease the time required to begin production at the desired separation. Jones and Furry (31) have considered cascading in detail and this reference should be consulted if a multicolumn plant design is contemplated. Several important results taken from the article by Jones and Furry are presented below. A design illustrating the use of these equations will be presented in a subsequent section.

It was noted in Section II-C-3, that Krasney-Ergen (32) had demonstrated that optimum design considerations could be separated into two independent categories, one involving the column length and mode of column operation and the other considering the parameters included in $H$ and $K$. On this basis, Jones and Furry considered that the plate spacing, $2\omega$, would in general be established by the relation $K_c/K_d = 10$ and went on to consider optimum separation schemes that could be obtained by paralleling similar columns. The multicolumn scheme considered by Jones and Furry is shown diagrammatically in Figure 16.

Other methods of combining thermal diffusion columns to improve separation have been proposed in the literature (33,64,65) but the analysis of Jones and Furry is the only one that will be presented here.

*Separation as a function of product flow rate.* Jones and Furry choose to write a material balance cutting across all columns in any one stage and enveloping the stream leaving the final or $N$th

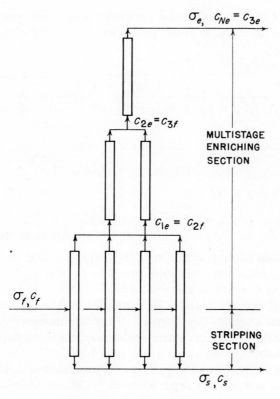

Fig. 16. Cascade of continuous-flow thermal diffusion columns as proposed by Jones and Furry (31).

stage with concentration, $C_{Ne}$. The transport equation for a cascade apparatus is then very similar to that used for a single stage (eq. 116).

$$H_j \left[ C(1 - C) - n_j(C_{Ne} - C) \right] = K_j \, dC/dy \qquad (142)$$

The flow rate through each total enriching section, $j$, made up of $N_j$ individual columns is equal to $\sigma_e$ at steady state and therefore

$$n_j = \sigma_e/H_j \qquad (143)$$

The meaning of the term $H_j$ as applied to multicolumn cascades will be clarified later. Solutions of equation 142 are presented by

Jones and Furry for any total enriching stage. The equations are very similar in form to those presented earlier for the single enriching stage.

General solution

$$\tanh b_j' A_j = \frac{b_j'(C_{je} - C_{jf})}{[C_{je} + C_{jf} + n_j(C_{je} + C_{jf} - 2C_{Nf}) - 2C_{je} C_{jf}]}$$

(144)

where

$$b_j' = [(1 + n_j)^2 - 4n_j C_{Ne}]^{1/2}$$

(145)

$$C(1 - C) \cong a + bC$$

$$(b_j + n_j)C_{je} = [(b_j + n_j)C_{jf} + a_j - n_j C_{Ne}]e^{2(b_j + n_j)A_j} - a_j + n_j C_{Ne}$$

(146)

The equations corresponding to $C(1 - C) \cong a$ and $C(1 - C) \cong C$ are easily obtained from equation 146 by setting $b = 0$ in the first case and $a = 0$, $b = 1$ in the latter.

The ideal cascade plant. Investigation of the optimum design equations for a single-stage thermal diffusion column (eqs. 131–139) reveals that the optimum column width and length are dependent on the separation to be obtained in the column ($C_f/C_e$ in equation 135 and $\Delta$ in eq. 138). In treating the optimum design of cascade plants not only must the total separation to be obtained be considered but also the separation to be achieved in each stage must be taken into account. Investigation of a number of cases led Jones and Furry (31) to the conclusion that, in each stage of a properly designed cascade, the separation should be approximately one-half of that obtained in a batch column of the same dimensions under steady-state conditions. Therefore from equation 84 proper column design dictates that for each and every one of the $j$ stages

$$\ln q_j = A_j$$

(147)

where

$$A_j = HL_j/2K$$

(148)

and

$$q_j = [C/(1 - C)]_{je}/[C/(1 - C)]_{jf}$$

(149)

The multicolumn plant has the advantage over the single-stage device in that in the former the value of $H$ may be varied along the cascade in such a way that the condition given by equation 147 is satisfied for short sections of the cascade as well as for the plant as a whole. Thus if the $j$th stage of a cascade is composed of $N_j$ identical columns then

$$H_j = N_j H \tag{150}$$

where $H$ refers to the dimensions of the individual columns.

Jones and Furry applied the condition of equation 147 to develop design equations for an ideal apparatus. In such a cascade the number of stages is considered to be infinite and the number of identical tubes in each stage $N_j$, varies in a continuous manner in order to satisfy equation 147 throughout the entire apparatus.

$$N_j = 2\sigma_e (C_{Ne} - C_j)/[HC_j(1 - C_j)] \tag{151}$$

For such a cascade, the following equations apply:

Number of tubes in first enriching stage

$$N_{1,\text{ideal}} = 2\sigma_e (C_{Ne} - C_{1f})/[HC_{1f}(1 - C_{1f})] \tag{152}$$

Total length of enriching section

$$L_{e,\text{ideal}} = \overset{j}{\Sigma} L_j = (2K/H) \ln q_e \tag{153}$$

where

$$q_e = [C/(1 - C)]_{Ne}/[C/(1 - C)]_{1f} \tag{154}$$

and $K$ and $H$ refer to the individual columns which in total comprise each stage.

Total length of tubing in enriching section

$$\Lambda_{e,\text{ideal}} = (4\sigma_e K/H^2) \{ [(1 - 2C_{1f})(C_{Ne} - C_{1f})/(C_{1f}(1 - C_{1f}))] \\ - (1 - 2C_{Ne}) \ln q_e \} \tag{155}$$

Similar expressions can be written for the stripping section. (See remarks included in paragraph following equation 117.) The length of the stripper will be determined from an economic balance between the cost of feed and the cost of operating stripping stages. For enrichment of very dilute solutions such as isotopes only one stripping stage will often be required as shall be illustrated in Section III by means of an example.

Although the calculations of Jones and Furry indicate that some increase in efficiency is afforded by cascading continuous product flow columns, a more important advantage is the reduction of time required before the apparatus attains a condition such that production can be initiated. An estimate of this time is provided by Jones and Furry. The mass of component 1 which must be transported into the enriching section before production can start, $M_1'$, is given by equation 156.

$$M_1' = (4m\sigma_e K/H^2)[(C_{1f} + C_{Ne} - 2C_{1f}C_{Ne})$$
$$\times \ln q_e - 2(C_{Ne} - C_{1f})] \quad (156)$$

and the rate of transport of component 1 into the enriching section at the feed point varies from $N_1 H C_{1f}(1 - C_{1f})$ to one-half that value. Therefore the time required to begin operation, $t_B$, is given by

$$M_1'/[N_1 H C_{1f}(1 - C_{1f})] < t_B < 2M_1'/[N_1 H C_{1f}(1 - C_{1f})] \quad (157)$$

In addition, Jones and Furry show that when $\ln q \gg 1$ the ratio of time required to initiate flow in a single stage apparatus to that for an ideal multicolumn apparatus is approximately equal to $q/(4 \ln q)$. If a separation factor $q = 10^5$ is desired as is sometimes necessary in the concentration of isotopes, the single stage apparatus will require about 2000 times as long to place in production as a cascade.

Practical multicolumn units.   Jones and Furry also considered the design of practical apparatus in which the number of columns in each sequential stage decrease in a constant ratio which they call the stepping ratio,

$$N_{j+1} = N_j/\gamma \quad (158)$$

Figure 16 illustrates a simple case in which $\gamma = 2$. These authors develop the following relations covering practical design.

$$N_1 = [(\gamma + 1)/2\gamma]N_{1,\text{ideal}} \quad (159)$$

$$L_e = \sum^j L_j = L_{e,\text{ideal}} \quad (160)$$

$$\Lambda_e = \sum^j N_j L_j = [(\gamma + 1) \log \gamma/(2(\gamma - 1))] \Lambda_{e,\text{ideal}} \quad (161)$$

In the design of practical multicolumn apparatus, it is desirable to optimize the length of each stage of the cascade. In some cases a compromise will be reached by making all columns in the cascade of one length.

Jones and Furry demonstrate that for maximum efficiency, the composition of material leaving the $j$th stage, $C_{je}$, is given by

$$C_{je} = (1/2) \{1 + [(\gamma + 1)n_j] - (1 + 2(1 - 2C_{Ne})[(\gamma + 1)n_j] + [(\gamma + 1)n_j]^2)^{1/2}\} \quad (162)$$

where from equations 143 and 150

$$n_j = \sigma_e/N_j H \quad (163)$$

The compositions thus calculated are used in conjunction with equations 147 and 148 to determine the optimum lengths of each stage in the cascade.

In estimating the time required to begin production in the practical stepped apparatus, $M_1'$ is calculated according to

$$M_1' = \frac{mK}{2H} \sum^{j} N_j \left\{2A_j(1 - n_j - 2C_{1f})\right.$$
$$\left. - \ln \frac{[C(1 - C)]_{je} - n_j(C_{jf} - C_{Ne})}{[C(1 - C)]_{jf} - n_j(C_{jf} - C_{Ne})}\right\} \quad (164)$$

The authors point out that the use of the value of $M'_1$ calculated from equation 164 together with $N_1$ as calculated from equation 159 in equation 157 will yield a conservative (pessimistic) estimate of the time required to begin production.

The presentation of the above equations was of necessity rather sketchy and their application will be illustrated in Section III by means of a design example. The reader is referred to the original article by Jones and Furry (31) for additional details.

**Attempts to Improve on the Theoretical Analyses of Column Behavior.** The theoretical analyses of thermogravitational thermal diffusion columns presented in Section II-C-3 require a number of simplifying assumptions before solutions of reasonable form are obtained. Numerous investigators have made attempts to improve upon the theory, and the results of several of these modified analyses will be presented here. In most cases, very few details will be given because of lack of space, and the reader is referred to the references cited if more information is desired.

*Corrections for temperature dependence of physical properties.*    Equations 82a–d for $H$, $K_c$, and $K_d$ are strictly valid only for small temperature differences between the plates. Furry, Jones, and Onsager (30) present expressions for $H$, $K_c$, and $K_d$ for the case of a column made of parallel plane walls in terms of general integrals. These authors present the results of integration for a Maxwellian gas ($\nu = 5$, $m = 1$) and for a gas mixture composed of hard spheres ($\nu = \infty$, $m = 1/2$) for each of the following cases: (a) $\alpha$ independent of $T$, (b) $\alpha$ varies as $T^{1/2}$, (c) $\alpha$ proportional to $T$. Additional consideration will be given to the case of a Maxwellian gas when the corrections for cylindrical thermal diffusion columns are presented.

Two investigators have considered the effect of temperature on the physical properties of liquid mixtures in thermal diffusion columns. Niini (66) considered the effect of temperature on viscosity and concluded that the temperature variation of viscosity would only rarely change the steady-state separation in a batch column by more than 30%. Emery (67) considered the temperature dependence of both viscosity and diffusivity. He presents the results of his computations as corrections to be applied to equations 82a–d. These corrections are given graphically as functions of the temperature ratio, $T_H/T_C$ and the exponent $n$ in the expression $\mu = aT^{-n}$.

*The effect of concentration on density.*    The theoretical considerations of Furry, Jones, and Onsager were developed principally for gas mixtures and for such mixtures the assumption that density is not a strong function of concentration is a reasonable one. In working with liquid mixtures, several investigators have found that the influence of concentration on density may be dominant and cause flow *downward* at the hot wall. This result has been called the "forgotten effect" and has been investigated both theoretically and experimentally (68,69,70). The results obtained by these investigators and their explanation of these results is little short of fascinating. Investigators working with liquid systems should be sure to make note of the "forgotten effect."

*Cylindrical columns.*    Jones and Furry (31) present the results of consideration of cylindrical thermal diffusion columns. Their analyses are restricted to gases with properties similar to a Maxwellian gas. They present results for two cases: (a) nearly plane case ($r_1/r_2 \lesssim e = 2.718$) and (b) the extreme cylindrical case ($r_1/r_2$

$\gtrsim 10$). The second case is especially useful in consideration of hot wire columns (Fig. 4) and is adequately treated by Jones and Furry. The results for the nearly plane case are presented in terms of corrected values $H'$, $K_c'$, and $K_d'$ which are obtained from values of $H$, $K_c$, and $K_d$ calculated for the plane case, equations 82a–d. The corrections are expressed in terms of two temperature parameters,

$$u = (T_H - T_C)/(T_H + T_C) \tag{165}$$

and

$$\phi(u) = 15 \sum_{n=0}^{\infty} \{u^{2n}/[(2n+1)(2n+3)(2n+5)]\} \tag{166}$$

and the logarithm of the ratio of radii, $\ln (r_1/r_2)$. The results are

$$H' = H\{\phi(u) + h_1(u) \ln (r_1/r_2) + h_2(u) [\ln (r_1/r_2)]^2 + \ldots\} \tag{167}$$

$$K_c' = K_c\{1 + k_{c1}(u) \ln (r_1/r_2) + k_{c2}(u) [\ln (r_1/r_2)]^2 + \ldots\} \tag{168}$$

$$K_d' = K_d\{1 + (^1/_3)u^2 + k_{d1}(u) \ln (r_1/r_2) + k_{d2}(u) [\ln (r_1/r_2)]^2 + \ldots\} \tag{169}$$

where

$$h_1(u) = 1.010u + 0.165u^3 + 0.059u^5 + \ldots \tag{170}$$

$$h_2(u) = -0.174 + 0.496u^2 + 0.088u^4 + \ldots \tag{171}$$

$$k_{c1}(u) = 1.721u \tag{172}$$

$$k_{c2}(u) = -0.213 + 1.505u^2 \tag{173}$$

$$k_{d1}(u) = -0.333u + 0.067u^3 \tag{174}$$

$$k_{d2}(u) = -0.022u^2 + 0.010u^4 \tag{175}$$

The above relation for $H'$ is based on the assumption that $\alpha$ is independent of $T$. For $\alpha$ proportional to $T$, Jones and Furry report

$$H' = H\{1 + h_1(u) \ln (r_1/r_2) + h_2(u) [\ln (r_1/r_2)]^2 + \ldots\} \tag{176}$$

where

$$h_1(u) = 0.838u \tag{177}$$

$$h_2(u) = -0.174 + 0.363u^2 \tag{178}$$

The above correction factor equations are based on Maxwellian gas behavior and their application will be illustrated by means of a design example in Section IV. More recently shape factors based on the 12,6 potential (92) and the inverse power law (93) have been made available.

*Correction for distortion of the convective velocity in continuous-flow columns.* In Section II-C-3, it was noted that the extension of the basic transport equation to treat continuous-flow columns as proposed by Furry, Jones, and Onsager did not take into account the fact that the velocity distribution within the column is influenced by the superimposed flow. Powers and Wilke (21) have considered this effect and have presented their results as corrections to the terms $H$ and $K_c$ as defined by the relations $H' = h(\lambda)H$ and $K' = k(\lambda)K$ where

$$\lambda = -6!\mu\sigma/[2\beta_T\rho g \cos\theta\ (2\omega)^3 B\Delta T] \qquad (179)$$

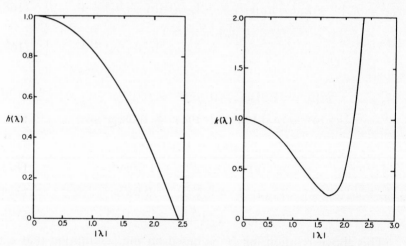

Fig. 17. Correction factors $h(\lambda)$ and $k(\lambda)$ to account for continuous flow through a thermal diffusion column.

The terms $h(\lambda)$ and $k(\lambda)$ have been obtained semiempirically and are presented in Figure 17. The use of these flow dependent correction terms is illustrated by Powers and Wilke (21).

*Turbulent flow conditions.* Several investigators have reported that the existence of some turbulence between the column walls actually increases the separation over that predicted on the basis of the laminar flow assumption. Becker (71) was able to correlate his data obtained with a gas mixture under turbulent conditions by merely applying a correction to the measured plate spacing. Other investigators have found it necessary to modify the theory even when turbulence was not evident in the columns. Two of these empirical modifications are discussed in the next paragraph.

*Empirical modifications.* The empirical modification of the thermal diffusion column theory proposed by Drickamer, Mellow, and Tung (72) has been applied by several other investigators working with gas pairs. These authors proposed the modification of equation 84 shown in equation 180 which applies to batch column operation under steady-state conditions.

$$\ln q = (\phi')^3 HL/[\phi(\phi')^6 K_c + K_d] \tag{180}$$

The data used to develop the correlation were obtained with pressure as the primary variable and Drickamer, Mellow, and Tung utilized the factor $\phi'$ to correlate the data obtained at pressures less than optimum, and similarly the factor $\phi$ was used to bring theory and experiment into agreement at higher pressures. The relations used by Drickamer *et al.*, are listed in equations 181–188.

$$\phi' = 1.00$$
$$\text{Gr} > 1.2 \times 10^5 \tag{181}$$

$$\phi' = 0.576 \ \text{Gr}^{0.0486}$$
$$1.2 \times 10^5 > \text{Gr} > 6 \times 10^3 \tag{182}$$

$$\phi' = 0.866$$
$$\text{Gr} < 6 \times 10^3 \tag{183}$$

$$\phi = 1260 \ (\psi)^{1.2}$$
$$\psi < 1.35 \times 10^{-3} \tag{184}$$

$$\phi = 13.6 \ (\psi)^{0.512}$$
$$6.3 \times 10^{-3} > \psi > 1.35 \times 10^{-3} \tag{185}$$

$$\phi = 1.00$$
$$\psi > 6.3 \times 10^{-3} \tag{186}$$

where

$$Gr = \beta_T \rho g \cos \theta (2\omega)^2 L_T \Delta T / 4\mu^2 \tag{187}$$

$$\psi = (2D/2\omega)/(L_T \Delta T g \beta/\rho)^{1/2} \tag{188}$$

In working with liquid systems in continuous flow thermal diffusion columns Powers (53) had need for empirical correction terms similar to those presented by Drickamer, Mellow, and Tung but was not able to use their correlation. Instead Powers developed another correlation based on correction factors $\phi_H$ and $\phi_{Kc}$ defined by $H' = \phi_H H$ and $K_c' = \phi_{Kc} K_c$ where $H$ and $K_c$ are calculated from equations 82a–d. Powers found that $\phi_H$ and $\phi_K$ were related approximately by the simple expression

$$\phi_{K_c} = \phi_K^{4/3} \tag{189}$$

The correlation that was developed using data for both liquid and gas mixtures is

$$\phi_H^{-1} = 8.3 \times 10^{-5} \text{ cm } (T/\alpha \Delta T) \, [1/(2\omega)] \text{Re}^{0.8} (\text{Sc}/\text{Pr})^{0.8} \tag{190}$$

where

$$\text{Re} = [(2\omega)^3/36\sqrt{3}](\beta_{Tf} g \cos \theta \Delta T/\mu^2) \tag{191}$$

and

$$(\text{Sc}/\text{Pr}) = k/(\rho D C_P) \tag{192}$$

The author cautions that equation 190 applies only when values of $\phi_H$ thus calculated lie in the range from 1.0 to 0.2.

## III. Design of Equipment for Laboratory Use

The design of thermal diffusion equipment is critical if it is to function properly and yield the desired results in a reasonable amount of time. The theory presented in Section II provides an adequate basis for proper design and will be applied throughout Section III. The important factors which influence the operation of laboratory scale thermal diffusion equipment will be considered in detail. Data on equipment performance as reported in the literature will be compared with theoretical predictions whenever possible.

## A. STATIC CELLS

Static cells yield the most basic data on the thermal diffusion effect because they are designed to operate without convection and the resulting hydrodynamic complications. The flat-plate apparatus (Fig. 1) and the agitated cell with fritted-disk (Fig. 2) appear to be best suited for experiments with liquid mixtures whereas the two-bulb apparatus (Fig. 3) finds wide application in studies of gas mixtures.

### 1. Equilibrium Separation

In general, separations obtained in static cells are small and most of the useful measurements have been made under steady state conditions. Some typical data are presented in Table VI which is not meant to be a compilation of data. Grew and Ibbs (37) have included such a compilation for gas mixtures in their book and Von Halle (48) has presented an extensive listing for liquid systems. The data in Table VI were chosen to illustrate the following generalizations concerning measurements made in static cells:

TABLE VI
Typical Data Obtained at Equilibrium in Static Cells

| Investigator and system | Type of equipment | $T_H$, °C | $T_C$, °C | Separation | $\alpha$ Expt. | 13,7 model |
|---|---|---|---|---|---|---|
| Grew (73) (g) He 54%–Ne | Two bulb | 96 | 20 | 1.8% mole | 0.33 | 0.34 |
| Whalley et al. (74) (g) $O^{16}O^{18}$ 2%– $O_2^{16}$ | Two bulb | 255 | 22 | 0.074% mole[a] | 0.0128 | 0.0133 |
| Tanner (3) (l) 6 $N$ KI in $H_2O$ | Flat plate | 40.6 | 26.1 | 0.203 $N$ | — | — |
| Whitaker and Pigford (11) (l) $CH_3OH$ 60%–$C_6H_6$ | Flat plate | 36.2 | 33.7 | 0.1% mole | −0.75 | — |
| Saxton et al. (75) (l) $C_2H_2Cl_4$ 50%–$CCl_4$ | Fritted disk | 30 | 20 | 0.2% mole | 0.24 | |

[a] Obtained in six (6) equilibrium contacts.

68    JOHN E. POWERS

1. Small separations are obtained when working with either gas (g) or liquid (l) mixtures. As a result, special techniques of analysis are usually required. Several methods are discussed by Grew and Ibbs for gases, whereas the optical technique developed by Tanner (3) and Thomaes (4) seems to be particularly well suited for study of liquid mixtures in flat-plate cells.

2. Separation of most isotopes is so small that several equilibrium contacts must be provided before a measurable separation is achieved.

3. For relatively simple molecules, the predicted values of $\alpha$ based on the 13,7 model as described in Section II-B-1, are in very good agreement with experimental results. It appears that little or no data on mixtures of complicated gas molecules have been obtained in static cells.

4. Data are available for electrolytes and nonelectrolytic liquids.

5. For liquid mixtures, reasonably reliable data can be obtained in either flat-plate cells or cells equipped with fritted-glass disks if the cells are carefully constructed. Reproducibility of $\pm 25\%$ is attained in such cells. Experimental data for liquid systems were compared with predicted values in Figure 9.

According to the analysis presented in Section II, the equilibrium separation attained in any type of static cell is a unique function of the hot and cold temperatures.

$$q = [C/(1 - C)]_H/[C/(1 - C)]_C = (T_H/T_C)^\alpha \tag{37}$$

As seen from Table VI, $\alpha$ is generally a rather small number, and therefore it would seem desirable to increase the temperature ratio as much as possible to reduce errors in analysis. In some cases, use of a large temperature difference may be necessary because of extremely small values of $\alpha$, but large temperature differences are to be avoided in general. For one thing, if $\alpha$ is a function of temperature, the difficulty of selecting the proper mean temperature is increased as the temperature difference is increased (see Section II-C-2). For another, it is necessary to eliminate convection in static cells if meaningful data are to be obtained. The Grashof number

$$Gr = \beta_T \rho g \cos\theta d^3 \, \Delta T/\mu^2 \tag{193}$$

($d$ is a length scale of the equipment) is a dimensionless parameter which is often used to correlate data on free convection. Thus as the temperature difference is increased, the probability that natural convection will occur is increased.

From equation 193, it can also be surmised that the size of the equipment ($d^3$) as well as its position in the gravitational field (cos $\theta$) are also important in eliminating convection currents in any given system. The importance of obtaining proper dimensions for static cells is well recognized and will be considered in some detail in the next paragraph. The importance of the position of a flat-plate cell in the gravitational field is not as well known. If a flat-plate cell is inclined from the horizontal ever so slightly, it will function as a thermogravitational cell. By application of equations 84 and 82a–d, it can be demonstrated that if a flat-plate cell with a spacing of 0.33 cm is inclined from the horizontal only one-half of a degree, it will give a steady-state separation as large as that of a vertical thermogravitational column with a plate spacing of 0.1 cm. Such a separation may be very appreciable. Application of the theory of the thermogravitational column which will be discussed in detail later indicates that proper choice of the plate spacing $l$ = $2\omega$, will effectively eliminate any important contribution of the thermogravitational effect arising from a very slight tilting of a flat-plate cell.

## 2. Approach to Steady-State

The theoretical analyses of the approach to steady-state in flat-plate and two-bulb static cells as presented in Section II-C-2, were somewhat different, and the results of the analyses also differed. In particular, different design factors influence the rate of approach to steady-state in these two types of apparatus and therefore their design will be considered separately.

**Flat-Plate Cell.** The results of the theoretical analysis presented in Section II-C-2, indicate that the flat-plate static cells approach equilibrium exponentially according to equation 57 with a relaxation time given approximately by

$$t_r = l^2/(D\pi^2) \tag{65}$$

(These relations hold for all cases previously discussed as $\Delta T$ is decreased because then $A^2 \ll \pi^2$.) It is interesting to note that, except for secondary effects involving the temperature dependence of diffusivity, the time required to approach steady-state is independent of the temperature difference. The time required to attain equilibrium in a flat-plate cell is proportional to $l^2$. Since little or nothing can be done to vary the diffusivity, $D$, of a given liquid mixture, the spacing, $l$, is the only important variable.

In addition to determining the time required to attain equilibrium, the spacing $l$ also influences convective flow a great deal. In most cases $l$ can be directly identified with $d$ in the Grashof number (eq. 193), and its influence is very pronounced. Therefore, modern investigators have generally decreased $l$ as much as possible.

Some data on the rate of approach to equilibrium in flat-plate static cells as reported in the literature are presented in Table VII. Whitaker and Pigford (11) found it necessary to reduce $l$ in their cell from 0.915 cm to 0.217 cm in order to reduce convection to a tolerable amount. The limited data reported on the rate of approach to equilibrium in their smallest cell indicates reasonable agreement with equation 64. Tanner (3) performed experiments with pure water which indicate that convection was probably not severe in his

TABLE VII

Data on the Rate of Approach to Equilibrium in Flat-Plate Static Cells

| Investigator and system | $l$, cm | $\Delta T$, °C | Relaxation Time, $t_r$, min From data | From eq. 64 |
|---|---|---|---|---|
| Tanner (3) | | | | |
| Potassium iodide–copper | 1[a] | 14 | 50–60 | 140 |
| sulfate | 1[a] | 14 | 200–375 | 360 |
| Thomaes (4) | | | | |
| Carbon tetrachloride–chlorobenzene | 1.713 | 13.4 | 23 | 500[b] |
| Whitaker and Pigford (11) | | | | |
| (Several systems) | 0.915 | 2.5 | c | 140[b] |
| | 0.457 | 2.5 | c | 36[b] |
| | 0.217 | 2.5 | d | 8[b] |

[a] Not reported. Taken approximately from scale drawing.
[b] A value of $D = 10^{-5}$ cm²/sec was used.
[c] Not reported. Convection in the cell noted.
[d] Less than 1 hour required to attain steady-state.

cell, and his reported results are in approximate agreement with theory. The very low value of the relaxation time noted by Thomaes (4) seems inconsistent with the large value of $l$ for his cell as compared with the data of Tanner and Whitaker and Pigford. It is interesting to note that values of $\alpha$ calculated for the system methanol–benzene from data obtained by Thomaes are much smaller and do not correlate with those obtained by Whitaker and Pigford in their small cell and by Saxton et al. (75) in a fritted-disk cell. The data of the latter two investigations are in good agreement. It would appear reasonable to assume that convection dominated the performance of Thomaes' cell.

In general, other types of equipment designed for investigation of the thermal diffusion effect in liquids take longer to attain equilibrium than flat-plate cells. Saxton et al. (75) report that the relaxation time for their fritted-glass disk cells varied from an hour or so to a day or more, depending on cell volume and diffusion coefficients in the mixture. Unfortunately, they did not report data with which to check equations 76a and 76b.

On the basis of the above observations, it can be concluded that proper design of flat-plate static cells will make use of spacings between the plates as small as possible and preferably less than 0.25 cm. Every effort should be made to ensure that the cell plates are precisely horizontal and calculations should be made to check as to whether or not the thermogravitational effect will be important if the cell is mislocated as much as one-half degree from the horizontal.

**Two-Bulb Apparatus.** For the two-bulb static cells commonly used for fundamental thermal diffusion measurements with gas mixtures, developments discussed in Section II-C-2 led to the result that the approach to equilibrium in such cells should be exponential (eq. 57) with the relaxation time, $t_r$, given by the simplified relation

$$t_r = [l/(DA_c)] [V_H V_C/(V_H + V_C)] \tag{73a}$$

(As in the case of the flat-plate cell, this relation holds when $A$ is small as is usually the case.)

Consideration of equation 73a indicates that, as the volume of one bulb is decreased relative to that of the other, the time required to attain equilibrium becomes directly proportional to the smaller volume only. Thus, most cells of this type are constructed with one large and one small bulb. In such two-bulb apparatus it is usually desirable to obtain an analysis of the material in the smaller bulb and thus the size of such equipment is limited by analytical techniques. Ibbs (37) made use of a thermal conductivity cell as his small bulb and thereby reduced the volume of that bulb to 1.5 cm³. The apparatus attained equilibrium in less than 1 minute.

As discussed in Section II-C-2, the theoretical analysis of the approach to equilibrium in the two bulb apparatus is based on the assumption that the volume of the connecting tube is small compared with that of the bulbs. The harmonic mean of the volumes of the bulbs should be at least several times the volume of the connecting tube. The diameter of the connecting tube and the ratio $l/A_c$ must be given careful consideration in the design of two-bulb cells if convection in the tubes is to be avoided.

An extensive investigation of the approach to steady-state in a two-bulb apparatus has been reported by Nettley (76). Mixtures of $H_2$ and $N_2$ over the entire composition range were separated in a cell with a hot-bulb volume of 82.5 cm³ and a cold-bulb volume of 7.6 cm³ connected by means of a tube 5.0 cm in length and 0.315 cm in diameter. The average relaxation time for this apparatus at

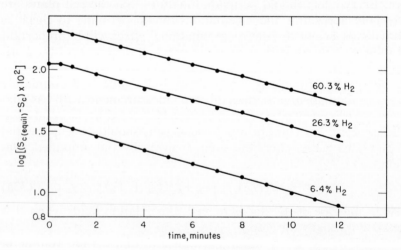

Fig. 18. Approach to equilibrium in the cold bulb of a two-bulb static cell [$H_2$ and $N_2$, Nettley (76)].

atmospheric pressure was reported as 7.7 minutes. Typical data from Nettley's article are reproduced in Figure 18 where $S_c$ is the measured separation in the cold (small) bulb.

Not only do these data confirm the exponential approach to equilibrium as predicted by theory (eq. 57) but the value of the difusion coefficient, $D$, calculated by application of equation 73b agreed within 4% of the value for the $H_2$–$N_2$ system obtained by von Obermayer (77) using ordinary diffusion methods. The nature of this agreement is such as to give strong support to the validity of the assumptions used to develop equations 73a and 73b and to justify their use for design purposes. From the excellent results obtained by Nettley, it can be presumed that the dimensions of his cell were such that convection in the connecting tube did not play an important role.

In summary, two-bulb cells are generally constructed with one large bulb and one small one, the volume of the small bulb being dictated by the method used to determine the composition of the mixture. In addition, if data obtained during the approach to equilibrium are to be used to determine the diffusion coefficient of the gas mixture as suggested by Nettley, the harmonic mean of the volumes of the two bulbs must be several times as large as the volume of the connecting tube. Good results have been obtained in apparatus in which the connecting tube has an inner diameter of about 0.32 cm and a length of 5 cm. Such a connecting tube should inhibit convection effectively without unreasonably increasing the time required to attain equilibrium.

## B. THERMOGRAVITATIONAL COLUMNS

The theoretical analyses presented in Section II-C-3 provide a firm basis for the design of thermogravitational columns. Numerous investigators have demonstrated that experimental results are in excellent qualitative agreement with the theoretical developments. The several distinct bases for investigations which lend support to the theory include: (a) the effect of pressure on the equilibrium separation of gases in batch-thermogravitational columns with reservoirs (72,78,79), (b) the approach to steady-state in batch columns (55,56,58,80), and (c) the effect of throughput on the steady-state separation in continuous-flow columns (21,53,81). Frequent reference will be made to the results of these investigations as the various design variables are discussed in detail.

## 1. Batch Columns

In most applications involving analysis of complex mixtures and for some preparative separations, the batch-type thermogravitational column is to be preferred over the static cell apparatus or the continuous-flow column. Very large separation factors can be achieved in a single column yielding essentially pure components at each end. In general, an excessively long time is required to achieve such separations so that it is necessary to consider the approach to equilibrium as well as the steady-state separation in the design of batch thermal diffusion columns. (Optimum design considerations have been presented in Section II-C-3 and will be illustrated by several design examples in Section IV. The present section is devoted to a qualitative understanding of the influence of the many design variables.)

**Steady-State Separation.** The steady-state separation obtained in a batch thermogravitational column is given by equation 84

$$\ln q = \ln \left\{ [C/(1 - C)]_e / [C/(1 - C)]_s \right\} = 2A = HL/K \quad (84)$$

In order to obtain a better understanding of the effect of the individual factors which influence column operation, equations 82a–d are substituted into equation 84

$$\ln q = [504 \, \alpha D\mu L / \beta_T \overline{T} g \cos \theta (2\omega)^4] \, [1/(1 + K_d/K_c)] \quad (194)$$

where

$$K_d/K_c = 9! \, D^2\mu^2 / [\beta_T^2 g^2 \cos^2\theta (2\omega)^6 \, (\Delta T)^2] \quad (195)$$

In Section II-C-3, it was developed that for gas systems a value of $K_d/K_c = 0.1$ generally represents good design. For liquid systems with $D \cong 10^{-5}$ cm$^2$/sec, mechanical considerations limit the extent to which $2\omega$ can be decreased so that in most columns separating liquid mixtures $K_d/K_c \ll 0.1$. In either case, $K_d/K_c$ is small compared with 1.0 and the term $1/(1 + K_d/K_c)$ can be treated as being essentially independent of column dimensions and operation in order to simplify consideration of the effect of the various parameters.

*Column length.* According to either equation 84 or equation 194, the separation as measured by $\ln q$ is predicted to be directly proportional to the column length. Results of several investigations (55,82) indicate that the effect of column length is as predicted by theory. Data obtained in columns which varied in length from 36.5 cm to 183 cm demonstrate direct proportionality between ln $q$ and $L$ as illustrated in Figure 19 (82). Additional data should be obtained in columns with different plate spacings ($2\omega$) to check this effect because the empirical correlation of Drickamer, Mellow, and Tung (72) indicates deviation from the theoretical relation between length and separation as given by equation 84 (see eqs. 182, 184, 185, and 187).

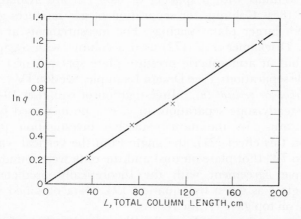

Fig. 19. Steady-state separation in a batch thermogravitational column as a function of column length [$n$-Heptane and Benzene, Crownover and Powers (82)].

Columns varying in length from 5 cm (69) to 10 meters (78) have been described in the literature. In general the shorter columns are used with liquid systems and the longer ones with gases.

*Plate spacing.* By far the most important variable to be considered is that of plate spacing as it enters to the fourth power in equation 194. This relation is in substantial agreement with experimental data, but corrections must be made in order to obtain quantitative agreement between theory and experiment as indicated by the empirical correlations presented in Section II-C-3. In the region where correspondence between the two empirical correlations is established (eqs. 185 and 190) the correction of Drickamer, Mellow, and Tung (72) yields an exponent on $2\omega$ of 3.49 and that of Powers (53) turns out to be 3.52. Recent data by Powers (55) indicates that the exponent may have a value as low as 3.3.

The range of plate spacings which can be used effectively is quite restricted. In columns separating liquid mixtures, plate spacings from 0.02 cm (68) to 0.26 cm (81) have been reported. (See Design Example, Section IV.) With such small spacings, it is essential that uniformity be maintained throughout the column. In flat-plate thermogravitational columns, bending of the plates is a serious problem. In concentric-cylinder columns, spacers are generally provided along the length of the column. Concentric-cylinder columns with a spacing of 0.03 cm are available commerically (85). Columns for separation of gas mixtures generally have much larger plate spacings. For measurements at elevated pressures, Drickamer et al. (72) used a column with a gap of only 0.05 cm but at atmospheric pressure plate spacings of 1 cm give reasonable separations. (See Design Example, Section IV.)

*Angle from the vertical* $(\theta)$.    Investigation of equation 194 reveals that the steady-state separation, ln $q$, can be increased by tilting the apparatus. In the most extensive investigation published to date on this effect (21), the angle from the vertical was varied from 1° to 70° (hot plate on top) and the data were found to be in quantitative agreement with the theoretically predicted effect of the angle $\theta$ as given by equation 194. Data obtained with the cold plate on top gave erratic results.

*Temperature difference.*    According to equation 194, the separation obtained in a batch column at steady-state is independent of $\Delta T$. In the region of usual operation of thermal diffusion columns, this is correct. Unpublished results obtained by the author on several liquid systems in a number of different columns indicates that this prediction is correct only for small values of $2\omega$ ($2\omega <$ 0.07 cm) and for larger values ($2\omega > 0.15$ cm) increasing $\Delta T$ results in an increased steady-state separation. The published data of Heines et al. (81) substantiate this conclusion.

*Pressure of operation.*    Pressure is an important variable in the separation of gas mixtures in thermal diffusion columns. If the effect of pressure on physical properties is taken into account in equations 194 and 195, an equation relating the equilibrium separation in the column to pressure is obtained.

$$\ln q = (a'/P^2)/[1 + (b'/P^4)] \qquad (196)$$

This relation predicts that a maximum separation will occur at $P = (b')^{1/4}$. Several investigators have demonstrated that such a

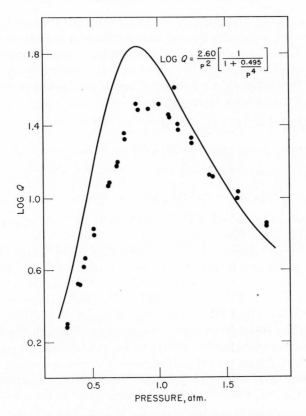

Fig. 20. Steady-state separation in a batch thermogravitational column as a function of pressure [$CO_2$ and $C_3H_8$, Drickamer *et al.* (79)].

maximum exists (78,79). Figure 20 is reproduced from a publication by Drickamer, O'Brien, Bresee, and Ockert (79), and illustrates the nature of agreement between theory and experiment. The curve drawn on Figure 20 is based entirely on the theory. Experiments of this type resulted in the empirical modification of the theory proposed by Drickamer, Mellow, and Tung (72).

**Transient Behavior.** The complicated form of the relations describing the transient behavior of batch thermogravitational columns (eqs. 90 and 106 and Figs. 13 and 14) confuses qualitative considerations. For design purposes, it is sufficient to consider the following two relations for columns with and without reservoirs.

The first should represent the approach to steady-state in a batch column with reservoirs for the entire transient period with the restriction that $C(1 - C) \cong a$. The second equation likewise applies only when $C(1 - C) \cong a$ but, because it is obtained by ignoring all but the first term in an infinite series, it is valid only for $t > t_r$.

Batch column with reservoirs, $[C(1 - C) \cong a]$

$$t_r = (L/K) \ [M_e M_s/(M_e + M_s)]$$

$$= [9' \ D\mu^2 L/(\beta_T{}^2 \rho g^2 \cos^2\theta (2\omega)^7 B(\Delta T)^2)] \ [M_e M_s/(M_e + M_s)] \quad (103)$$

Batch column without reservoirs, $[C(1 - C) \cong a, t > t_r]$

$$t_r = 4mL^2/(\pi^2 K) = 4(9!)D\mu^2 L^2/[\pi^2 \beta_T{}^2 g^2 \cos^2\theta (2\omega)^6 (\Delta T)^2] \quad (197)$$

(The assumption $K_d \ll K_c$ is incorporated in these expressions as discussed in a previous paragraph.)

From these relations, it can be seen that many factors influence the rate of approach to equilibrium in batch columns. The rate is very sensitive to the plate spacing because $t_r$ varies inversely as the seventh power in the first case and as the sixth power for columns without reservoirs. Increasing the temperature difference will increase the rate of approach to steady-state although the final separation will not be greatly influenced by changes in this parameter. Tilting the column ($\cos \theta$) will increase the time required to attain steady-state and will also increase the amount of separation at steady-state (eq. 194). Finally, it is noted that the time required for the separation increases linearly with length for a column with reservoirs but for a column without reservoirs the length parameter enters to the second power.

Jones and Furry (31) present some other approximate expressions for the rate of approach to equilibrium in batch columns. For the case $C(1 - C) \cong C$ and for $t \ll t_r$ an expression attributed to Debye (57) is presented.

Batch column without reservoirs $[C(1 - C) \cong C, t \ll t_r]$

$$C_e/C_f = 1 + 4H[t/(\pi m K)]^{1/2} \quad (198)$$

The interesting features of this expression are that it predicts that the separation between the ends of the column will initially increase in proportion to *the square root of the time* and that the rate of this initial increase in separation will be independent of the column length.

It is to be expected that the above observations are qualitative at best. For example, consideration of Figures 13 and 14 which apply to columns without reservoirs reveals that as $A$ increases the increase in time required to reach steady-state will be less than that estimated by application of equation 197. In addition, in comparing experimental steady-state data with equation 194 in a previous paragraph, it was noted that excellent qualitative agreement was obtained but that empirical corrections must be applied to the terms $H$ and $K$ in order to obtain quantitative agreement. Similar corrections will be required in order to obtain quantitative agreement between experimental transient measurements and the theoretical predictions as represented by equations 90–106 and Figures 13 and 14. Therefore in considering experimental data on the approach to equilibrium as reported in the literature, attention will be focused on determining if the *form* of the equations is correct without requiring that values of $H$ and $K$ used to fit the data also agree precisely with values calculated from equations 82a–d.

Trevoy and Drickamer (86) report data obtained with a liquid mixture in a batch column equipped with reservoirs under conditions which satisfy equations 57 and 103. These data illustrate that the approach to steady-state under such conditions is indeed exponential. The value of $K$ determined from the data by application of equation 103 was approximately 0.4 times as large as that calculated from equations 82b–d but agreed very well with a correlation based on entirely different data (53).

Bardeen (56) compared experimental data on gas mixtures as presented by Nier (78) with the results of a theoretical analysis (eqs. 95–98) and reports satisfactory agreement.

The most extensive investigation of the approach to steady-state in batch columns has been reported by Powers (55,58). It was determined that the form of the theoretically predicted curves was in excellent agreement with experimental results. The nature of this agreement is indicated in Figure 21. The curves shown on Figure 21 were calculated making use of two empirically determined constants. Only one of these constants was derived from the transient data. The other was obtained by analysis of the steady-state separation.

Analysis of data obtained during the approach to equilibrium in a batch column permits one to determine $K$ independent of $H$ and

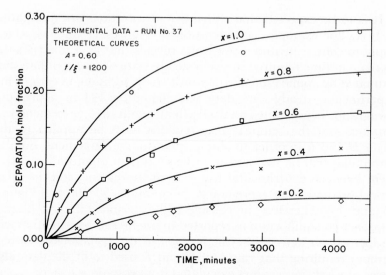

Fig. 21. Approach to equilibrium in a batch thermogravitational column without reservoirs [$n$-Heptane and Benzene, Powers (55)].

therefore separate these two factors. Preliminary results reported by Powers (55) indicate that $H$ is proportional to $(2\omega)^3$ as predicted by equation 82a but that $K_c$ is proportional to $(2\omega)^{6.3}$ instead of $(2\omega)^7$ as given by equations 82b–d. These data also indicate that the effect of temperature difference, $\Delta T$, on $H$ and $K$ is only very slightly different from the squared dependence predicted by equations 82a and 82c and that these differences tend to cancel one another in the case of steady-state separation, equation 84.

## 2. Continuous-Flow Columns

The theoretical results obtained by applying the transport equation to the analysis of the effect of flow rate on separation in a continuous-flow column (eqs. 120–124) are in general too complicated to yield to qualitative reasoning. In order to consider the influence of important parameters, it is convenient to restrict attention to the comparatively simple expression obtained under the restrictions that $C(1 - C) \cong a$, $\sigma_e = \sigma_s = \sigma_f/2$ and $L_e = L_s = L_T/2$.

$$\Delta \equiv C_e - C_s = (4 aH/\sigma_f) [1 - \exp(-\sigma_f L_T/4K)] \quad (127)$$

This relation is shown in dimensionless form in Figure 15.

One interesting conclusion is reached by considering equation 127. As the flow rate, $\sigma_f$, is increased, the exponential term becomes very small when compared with one. Therefore at large flow rates, the separation is predicted to be independent of column length. Published data (21) tend to support this conclusion.

Qualitative consideration of the effect of other parameters is complicated by the fact that such parameters are included in both $H$ and $K$. Additional simplification in form of equation 127 is achieved by expanding the exponential as an infinite series.

$$\Delta = (aHL_T/K) - (aHL_T^2/8K^2)\sigma_f + (aHL_T^3/96K^3)\sigma_f^2 - \dots \quad (199)$$

In the limit $\sigma \to 0$, the intercept $\Delta_0$ and the initial slope, $s_0 = (\partial\Delta/\partial\sigma)_{\sigma\,=\,0}$ are obtained from equation 199 by inspection.

$$\Delta_0 = aHL_T/K = 504a\alpha D\mu L_T/[\beta_T \bar{T} g \cos\theta(2\omega)^4] \quad (200)$$

$$s_0 = -\frac{aHL_T^2}{8K^2} = -\frac{63(9!)a\alpha D^2\mu^3 L_T^2}{\beta_T^3\rho g^3 \cos^3\theta(2\omega)^{11}B(\Delta T)^2} \quad (201)$$

(In order to simplify these expressions, the assumption $K_c \gg K_d$ has been incorporated.)

Comparison of equations 200 and 194 reveals that the separation at zero flow rate, $\Delta_0$, corresponds directly to the separation in a batch column. Consideration of this relation together with the expression for the initial slope, equation 201, gives a qualitative understanding of the effects of the design parameters.

**Length.** The separation at zero flow rate is proportional to the column length but, as flow is increased from a zero rate, the separation decreases at a rate proportional to the square of the column length. At some higher flow rate, the separation is essentially independent of length as discussed previously.

**Plate Spacing.** Both the zero flow separation and the initial slope are strong functions of plate spacing. The former increases as the inverse fourth power of plate spacing but with almost any flow rate at all this initial advantage in separation is obliterated because the separation decreases at a rate inversely proportional to the *eleventh power* of the plate spacing.

**Angle from the Vertical** ($\theta$). The initial advantage in separation that is gained by tilting the column which is proportional to

$(\cos \theta)^{-1}$ is quickly reduced with increasing flow rate because the initial slope is inversely proportional to $(\cos \theta)^{-3}$.

**Temperature Difference.** The zero flow separation is essentially independent of temperature difference, but with flow through the column temperature difference has a marked influence on separation. This is indicated by the fact that the separation initially decreases at a rate inversely proportional to $(\Delta T)^2$.

Experiments carried out in continuous-flow thermogravitational columns (21,81) lend substantial support to the application of the transport equation to the analysis of this type of operation. Better agreement at relatively high flow rates is obtained when the flow correction terms given in Figure 17 are applied (21). As in the case of comparison of theoretical predictions with results obtained from batch column operation, quantitative agreement is obtained only when empirical corrections are applied to the terms $H$ and $K$. In all cases, it has been found that the effect of flow rate on separation was very well predicted by theory. Figure 22 is reproduced from an article by Powers and Wilke (21) to illustrate the nature of the agreement. The solid curve drawn on Figure 22 represents equation 127 with values of $H$ and $K$ chosen to provide the best fit of the data. The dashed curve is the result of applying the corrections for flow as presented in Figure 17. For these particular data the empirical values of $H$ and $K$ are found to be in close agreement with values calculated from equations 82a–d.

Consideration of the selection of an optimum flow rate through the column is given in the next section. Comparison of equations 84 and 147 indicates that the flow rate through the column should be adjusted such that $\ln q$ is just one-half of the value at zero flow rate.

## IV. Design and Application of Large-Scale Equipment

In this section, brief consideration will be given to reports of large-scale application of thermal diffusion which have appeared in the literature and two design illustrations will be presented.

### A. LARGE-SCALE APPLICATIONS

In 1945, H. D. Smyth (87) and M. C. Fox (88) reported that a thermal diffusion plant of gigantic proportions was erected at Oak Ridge, Tennessee, during the late summer of 1944. In this plant,

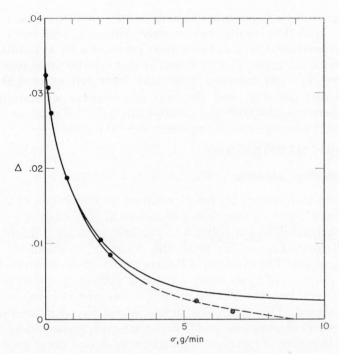

Fig. 22. Separation in a continuous-flow thermogravitational column as a function of flow rate [ethyl alcohol and water, Powers and Wilke (21)].

natural uranium as a liquid $UF_6$ was increased in U abundance from 0.715 to 0.86% and thereby increased the output of the electromagnetic separation plant by 20%. The liquid phase thermal diffusion plant was shut down after less than a year of operation.

In more recent years, a great deal of experimental and pilot plant work has been carried out by the Standard Oil Company (Ohio). The primary objective of this research has been to develop equipment and plant design procedures for the production of lubricating oil with a high viscosity index. A recent report (89) summarizes this work. Equipment costs have been reduced by using concentric-cylinder columns in bundles within a shell as in a shell and tube heat exchanger. A unit 34 feet in length having ten tube sets each with an annular spacing of 0.048 inches (0.11 cm) has been constructed and operated successfully. A similar unit with 96 tube sets has been designed and can be constructed for about $20 per square foot. It is proposed to connect a number of such units in the cross-flow multistage arrangement suggested by Frazier (65) to produce 120 V.I. lubricating oil from a 95 V.I. 140 SEN base stock material. Ten 96-tube, 34-foot bundle units would be expected to yield between 1100 and 2800 gallons of 120 V.I. oil product per day, and the heat consumption is estimated to range between 1,040,000 and 570,000 Btu/gal. The equipment cost of the unit is reported to be approximately $110,000.

## B. DESIGN ILLUSTRATIONS

### 1. Single-Stage Apparatus

Powers and Wilke (21) have presented an illustration of the application of the optimum design equations to the design of a single-stage thermal diffusion column to partially separate a liquid mixture. Krasney-Ergen (32) treats the design of a column to separate a gas pair. The example of Powers and Wilke is presented here.

For purposes of illustration, a thermal-diffusion plant to process 1000 barrels per day of a 50 mole % n-heptane–benzene mixture was designed. This particular design would have no commercial significance, as n-heptane and benzene are easily separated by distillation. However, the process is indicative of separation of aromatics and aliphatics, a difficult separation when applied to lubricating oils.

The design equations which were applied are based on equation 127 and, as a result, are restricted to $0.7 > C > 0.3$ and equal flow rates in each section. Therefore, the overhead product rate is set at 500 barrels per day of 70 mole % n-heptane and the bottom product rate at 500 barrels per day of 30 mole % n-heptane. From these specifications, it follows that

$$\Delta \equiv C_e - C_s = 0.40$$

The problem is further defined by setting reasonable temperature levels.

$$\Delta T = 212°R$$

$$\bar{T} = 565°R$$

Values of the physical properties of the mixture at this mean temperature have been summarized in the literature (58).

$\mu = 0.367$ centipoise        $\alpha = 1.1$

$\rho = 0.7407$ g/cm³        $\beta_T = 0.951 \times 10^{-3}$ g/cm³-°C

$D = 3.15 \times 10^{-5}$ cm²/sec    $k = 0.086$ Btu/hr-ft-°F

The power cost term, $p_c$, was approximated by considering the cost of heating and cooling media to be twice the cost of fuel at 30¢/million Btu.

$$p_c = 2.23 \times 10^{-4} \text{ \$ft/ft}^2\text{-day}$$

The equipment costs, $S$, were assumed to be independent of $2\omega$ and the cost per square foot of area of one plate was estimated to be $60 per square foot. This is ten times the value obtained from cost curves (90) for heat exchange surface and is intended to include cost of auxiliary equipment, design, increase in cost index, etc.

TABLE VIII
Summary of Design Estimates for Hydrocarbon Apparatus
(Plant to process 1000 barrels per day of 50 mole % n-heptane–benzene)

|  | Optimum design | Practical design |
|---|---|---|
| $2\omega$, cm | 0.0182 | 0.0793 |
| (in) | (0.0072) | (1/32) |
| $B$, cm | $1.33 \times 10^{+7}$ | $1.60 \times 10^{+5}$ |
| (ft) | $(4.36 \times 10^{+5})$ | $(5.25 \times 10^{+3})$ |
| (miles) | (82.7) | (1.0) |
| $L$, cm | 1.43 | 514 |
| (ft) | (0.0468) | (16.9) |
| Total area |  |  |
| $(B \times L)$, cm² | $1.90 \times 10^{+7}$ | $8.23 \times 10^{+7}$ |
| (ft²) | $(2.05 \times 10^4)$ | $(8.88 \times 10^{+4})$ |
| Heat load, Btu/hr | $5.27 \times 10^{+8}$ | $5.27 \times 10^{+8}$ |
| Capital investment, $ | 1,230,000 | 5,320,000 |
| Operating costs, per day |  |  |
| Fuel and cooling water, $ | 7,670 | 7,670 |
| Fixed charges | 743 | 3,230 |
| Total, $ | 8,413 | 10,900 |
| Cost per barrel of feed processed, $ | 8.41 | 10.90 |
| Cost per gallon of feed processed, $ | 0.20 | 0.26 |

This figure may be high as indicated by the data of Grasselli *et al.* (89)

$$S = 0.364 \text{ \$/ft}^2\text{-day}$$

These data were used to obtain the dimensions and costs for the "optimum" design listed in Table VIII. The value of the plate spacing, $2\omega$, was calculated from equations 131 and 132. The width of the apparatus was obtained by application of equations 138 and 134 and the length from equation 139.

Even though a column 1.43 cm long and 82.7 miles wide with a plate spacing of 0.0182 cm may be optimum, it would hardly seem practical. An increase in the plate spacing would decrease the column width and increase the column length. The cost would be increased by an increase in plate spacing. (Actually a decrease in fabrication cost with an increase in $2\omega$ would probably offset the predicted increase in cost.) A plate spacing of $1/32$ inch was arbitrarily chosen as a minimum practical plate spacing, and values of $B$ and $L_T$ were calculated from equations 138 and 139. The results of these calculations are listed under Practical Design in Table VIII for comparison with the optimum design. The value of the column length (17 ft) for this arbitrary plate spacing represents a practical construction, and thus no other designs were considered.

The cost data used in these estimates are certainly only approximate, and yet the results should indicate the order of magnitude of the costs involved. It can be seen that thermal diffusion is an expensive process.

### 2. *Multicolumn Apparatus*

Two numerical examples of the design of efficient cascade thermal diffusion apparatus have been presented by Jones and Furry (31). One design considers the use of multicolumn hot-wire apparatus to increase the concentration of $He^3$ from its natural abundance of approximately $10^{-7}$ mole fraction up to a concentration of about $10^{-2}$, a separation factor of $10^5$. It was pointed out in Section II-C-3, that the time required for a single stage apparatus to begin production with such a separation factor is approximately 2000 times that required for the cascaded apparatus, and such a prediction is borne out in the design illustration. The other design illustration presented by these authors deals with the concentration of $C^{13}H_4$ from its natural abundance of 1.08% up to 20% at the rate of approximately 1g/day. This second design example has been abstracted from the presentation of Jones and Furry and is given below as illustration of the application of the multicolumn design equations presented in Section II-C-3.

Nier (78) has worked with separation of a $C^{12}H_4$–$C^{13}H_4$ mixture in a thermal diffusion column and used the following temperatures in his apparatus:

$$T_C = 300°K, \qquad T_H = 573°K$$

therefore

$$\bar{T} = 436.5°K, \qquad \Delta T = 273°K$$

where $\bar{T}$ is the arithmetic average in this case.

The following data are available for the system at the arbitrarily chosen operating pressure of one atmosphere where it behaves essentially as an ideal gas.

$\mu = 1.51 \times 10^{-4}$ poise     $\alpha = 0.007$

$\rho = 4.47 \times 10^{-4}$ g/cm$^3$     $\beta_T = 1.002 \times 10^{-6}$ g/cm-°K

$D = 0.474$ cm$^2$/sec     $k = 1.20 \times 10^{-4}$ cal/cm-sec-°K

For convenience, it is considered that the ratio $B/2\omega$ has the same value as the apparatus used by Nier:

$$B/2\omega = 18.53$$

It remains only to determine an optimum value of $2\omega$ in order to determine values of $H$ and $K$ for the apparatus from equations 82a–d. Jones and Furry point out that near optimum plate spacing can be determined by setting $K_c/K_d = 10$. In this manner, application of the values of physical properties listed above in equations 82c and 82d yields $2\omega = 0.772$ cm. Based on the availability of tubing, the authors choose to complete the design using

$$2\omega = 0.712 \text{ cm}$$

corresponding to the value for the Nier apparatus.

Application of this value for $2\omega$ together with the physical properties previously listed yields the following values for $H$, $K_c$, and $K_d$ from equations 82a–d.

$$H = 2.588 \times 10^{-5} \text{ g/sec}$$

$$K_c = 1.042 \times 10^{-2} \text{ g-cm/sec}$$

$$K_d = 1.994 \times 10^{-3} \text{ g-cm/sec}$$

The authors chose to modify these results slightly. Since equations 82a–d apply rigorously only for the plane apparatus, correction factors were applied in order to correct for the cylindrical shape of the column. In addition, a correction was applied to account for the fact that the physical properties were taken at the arithmetic average temperature. As discussed in Section II-C-3, these corrections are based on the Maxwellian gas case. Application of equations 165–175 yields the following correction terms:

$$H'/H = 1.109$$

$$K_c'/K_c = 1.176$$

$$K_d'/K_d = 0.998$$

where the prime indicates that the values are corrected for cylindrical shape and use of a mean temperature. Therefore,

$$H' = 2.866 \times 10^{-5} \text{ g/sec}$$

$$K_c' = 1.224 \times 10^{-2} \text{ g-cm/sec}$$

$$K_d' = 1.992 \times 10^{-3} \text{ g/cm/sec}$$

In the calculations that follow, the primes will be omitted even through the corrected values will be used.

In addition to the corrections mentioned above, the authors choose to correct for a noted discrepancy between the theory and the data of Nier by adding a term, $K_p$, to $K_c$ and $K_d$ to account for "parasitic remixing." In this case, they found that Nier's data were well correlated if

$$K_p = 2.83 \ K_c$$

and therefore

$$K = K_c + K_d + K_p = 1.771 \times 10^{-2} \text{ g-cm/sec}$$

Now that optimum values of $H$ and $K$ have been determined, the design of an ideal multicolumn apparatus proceeds. Substitution of these values together with the desired product rate of 1g/day enriched from $C_{1f} = 0.0108$ to $C_{Ne} = 0.30$ into equation 155 yields

$$\Lambda_{e,\ \text{ideal}} = 154 \text{ m}$$

From equation 153

$$L_{e,\text{ideal}} = 38.6 \text{ m}$$

By equation 152, the number of tubes in parallel in the first stage is

$$N_{1,\text{ideal}} = 14.3$$

The mass, $M_1'$, is calculated from equation 156

$$M_1' = 1.12 \text{ g}$$

Therefore from equation 157 between 3 and 6 days will be required to start up the ideal cascade apparatus.

Equations 158–164 are applied in order to obtain a practical design. A stepping ratio, $\gamma$, of two is chosen (Fig. 16) and therefore from equation 159

$$N_1 = (^3/_4)\ N_{1,\text{ideal}} = 10.7$$

In order to achieve a stepping ratio of 2 in the actual apparatus, a value

$$N_1 = 8$$

is chosen. This means that only 0.746 g will be produced per day. The complete design is summarized in Table IX.

TABLE IX
Summary of Design Estimate of $C^{13}H_4$ Apparatus
(Apparatus to produce 0.746 g/day of 20% $C^{13}H_4$ from methane containing 1.08% $C^{13}H_4$)

|  | Stage number, $j$ | | | |
|---|---|---|---|---|
|  | 1 | 2 | 3 | 4 |
| $N_j$ | 8 | 4 | 2 | 1 |
| $n_j$ | 0.0377 | 0.0753 | 0.1507 | 0.3013 |
| $C_{je}$ | 0.0207 | 0.0380 | 0.0652 | 0.2000 |
| $q_j$ | 1.936 | 1.870 | 1.763 | 3.582 |
| $A_j$ | 0.662 | 0.629 | 0.572 | 0.806 |
| $\ln q$ | 0.662 | 0.625 | 0.566 | 1.275 |
| $L$, meters | 8.17 | 7.76 | 7.06 | 11.80 |

The values of $N_j$ result from the choice of the stepping ratio, $\gamma = 2$. Equation 163 yields $n_j$ from the known product flow rate and the previously determined value of $H$. Values of $C_{je}$ are calculated from $n_j$ and the stepping ratio $\gamma$ by application of equation 162 and $q_j$ is determined directly from equation 149 using the $C_{je}$ data. These data were likewise used to determine $A_j$ from equation 144. Values of $L_j$ were then calculated from the definition of $A_j$, equation 148. From the definition of $L_e$, equation 160,

$$L_e = \overset{j}{\sum} L_j = 34.8 \text{ m}$$

and similarly from the first part of equation 161

$$\Lambda_e = \overset{j}{\sum} N_j L_j = 122.4 \text{ m}$$

In order to check the validity of these results, Jones and Furry considered three other values of $\sigma_e$ near 0.746 g/day and repeated the enriching section calculations. The results show a very broad efficiency maximum with respect to variation in $\sigma_e$ for a given stepping ratio. The design summarized in Table IX is extremely close to the true efficiency maximum.

The time required to start-up the apparatus is estimated by calculating $M_1' = 1.02$ g from equation 164 and using this value together with $N_1 = 8$ in equation 157. As a result, it is found that between 4 and 8 days will be required to begin production of 20% $C^{13}H_4$ product.

Jones and Furry also considered the design of a single stripping stage with a number of tubes equal to that in the first enriching stage, (Fig. 16). Conditions in the scrubber are uniquely determined once the recovery of $C^{13}H_4$ is specified. They considered two cases, one in which the stripped gas was reduced in composition to $^2/_3$ of its initial value and another involving stripping to $^1/_3$ of the initial value. The results shown in Table X are obtained.

TABLE X

| Case I | Case II |
|---|---|
| $C_s = 2/3$; $C_{1f} = 0.0072$ | $C_s = 1/3$; $C_{1f} = 0.0036$ |
| $q_s = 1.5$ | $q_s = 3.0$ |
| $\sigma_s = 36.4$ g/day | $\sigma_s = 18.2$ g/day |
| $n_s = 1.839$ | $n_s = 0.920$ |
| $A_s = 0.324$ | $A_s = 0.925$ |
| $L_s = 4.00$ m | $L_s = 11.41$ m |

In the calculations summarized in Table X, $q_s$ is defined as in equation 154, $\sigma_s$ is calculated by a simple material balance,

$$\sigma_s = \sigma_e[(C_e-C_{1f})/(C_{1f}-C_s)] \tag{202}$$

$n_s$ results by analogy to equation 163 and $A_s$ is determined from modification of equations 120, 122, 123, or 124. In this particular case, the simplification $C(1 - C) \cong C$ is justified and therefore a modified form of equation 123 applies. The length of the stripping section follows directly from the definition of $A_s$ by analogy to equation 148. Since there are eight tubes in the stripping section $\Lambda_s = 32.00$ m for Case I and $\Lambda_s = 91.28$ m for Case II. As the authors point out, the starting material (methane) is so cheap that recovery will not be a major factor and therefore a long stripping section is probably not justified.

It only remains to estimate the heat load. At these temperature levels, heat transfer will be mainly by conduction and therefore the total heat load, $\dot{Q}$, is given by

$$\dot{Q} = kB(\Lambda_e+\Lambda_s)\Delta T/2\omega = 39.2 \text{ kw}$$

Data of Nier obtained on actual apparatus indicate that losses may increase this value as much as 50%.

## V. Prospects for Future Developments

The fact that the thermal diffusion separation process is based on molecular interactions and size and shape factors should continue to make thermal diffusion a valuable tool for laboratory investigations and might also serve as the basis for practical commercial separations.

Static cells provide the most basic data on the thermal diffusion effect, and such data will be useful for testing theories of the gaseous and liquid states. It seems probable that such investigations may provide the key for extensions of current theories, especially as applied to the liquid state.

The hydrodynamic analysis of thermogravitational columns has proved to be remarkably successful, but it appears that additional theoretical work will be required before quantitative correspondence between theory and experimental results is obtained. Additional experimental investigations will be required to test new theories. The tremendous advance in equipment technology represented by the thermogravitational column will continue to interest investigators in trying to develop new equipment modifications and improved methods of multistaging thermal diffusion apparatus.

It seems surprising that the first commercial application of thermal diffusion (outside of the use by the Atomic Energy Commission) may be in the processing of lubricating oil. Such a product has a relatively low unit value and thermal diffusion is an expensive separation process. It would appear that thermal diffusion might find widespread application in the fine chemical and pharmaceutical fields where unit costs are often quite high. Thermal diffusion as applied to these fields should offer advantages in that processing conditions are very moderate, the separation takes place without change of phase or addition of other agents, trace material can be concentrated for recovery or removal, complex mixtures can be separated easily into many distinct fractions, and exploratory separations can be made easily and with a minimum of expense.

## VI. Summary

Thermal diffusion results from complex interactions between molecules and, as a result, can be predicted theoretically only for pairs of gas molecules which have relatively simple collisions. Static cells are employed for fundamental investigations of the thermal diffusion effect and thermogravitational columns are employed in order to obtain efficient separations. Phenomenological theories of both types of apparatus have been developed and have been found to be in qualitative agreement with experimental data. Theories provide a strong foundation for design and optimization of equipment as has been illustrated by several design examples. Large-scale applications of thermal diffusion has been limited by its high heat requirements to the separation of the uranium isotopes during World War II, but a commercial plant to produce lubricating oil with a high viscosity index has recently been designed. It would be surprising if thermal diffusion did not find some practical application in the preparation of fine chemicals and pharmaceuticals.

**Acknowledgment.** This chapter was improved immeasurably by many constructive criticisms offered by Dr. Edward Von Halle.   He noted several errors thereby contributing a great deal to the accuracy of the material presented.   Mrs. and Mr. C. T. Sciance prepared the manuscript.

## Notation

The following symbols, with few exceptions, are in agreement with the notation of Jones and Furry (31).   A number of symbols which occur only once or twice in the text and which are suitably defined when used, are not included in this listing.   Most of the symbols listed are defined more fully at the point of introduction in the text.

| | |
|---|---|
| $A$ | Defined by equation 47 for static cells and equation 85 for thermogravitational columns |
| $A'$ | Ratio of collision integrals |
| $A_c$ | Cross-sectional area |
| $a$ | Constant (eqs. 32 and 33) |
| $B$ | Width of a thermogravitational column |
| $B'$ | Ratio of collision integrals |
| $b$ | Constant (eq. 33) |
| $C$ | Fraction of component 1 in a binary solution |
| $C$ | Subscript designating cold |
| $C'$ | Ratio of collision integrals |
| $C_0$ | Fraction of component 1 at time equal zero |
| $C_1, C_2$ | Fraction of component 1, 2 in a binary solution |
| $C_P$ | Heat capacity at constant pressure |
| $c$ | Constant (eq. 57) |
| $D$ | Coefficient of ordinary diffusion |
| $D_T$ | Coefficient of thermal diffusion |
| $d_1, d_2$ | Molecular diameters |
| $E_1, E_2$ | Ratio of collision integrals (eqs. 10 and 11) |
| $e$ | Subscript identifying the enriching section of a thermal diffusion column |
| $f$ | Fractional approach to equilibrium (eq. 57) |
| $f$ | Subscript identifying feed to a continuous-flow column |
| $g$ | Local acceleration of gravity |
| $H$ | Coefficient in transport equation defined by equation 82a |
| $H$ | Subscript designating hot |

| | |
|---|---|
| $i$ | Subscript indicating either component in a binary mixture |
| $J_x$ | Net flux of component 1 in the $x$ direction in a nonisothermal solution |
| $J_{x-TD}$ | Flux of component 1 in the $x$ direction in a nonisothermal solution caused by thermal diffusion |
| $j$ | Subscript identifying a section of a thermogravitational column or cascade |
| $K$ | Coefficient in transport equation defined by equation 82b |
| $K_c$ | Defined by equation 82c |
| $K_d$ | Defined by equation 82d |
| $k$ | Thermal conductivity |
| $L$ | Length of a thermogravitational column |
| $l$ | Characteristic length of a static thermal diffusion cell |
| $M_e$, $M_s$ | Total mass in the enriching, stripping reservoir of a batch thermogravitational column |
| $M_1$, $M_2$ | Mass of molecular species 1, 2 (molecular weight) |
| $M_1'$ | Mass of component 1 which must be transported into the enriching section before production can start |
| $m$ | Mass of mixture per unit column length |
| $N$ | Number of identical columns in one stage in a multistage thermal diffusion apparatus |
| $N$ | Subscript identifying the final stage in a multistage thermal diffusion apparatus |
| $n$ | $\sigma/H$ |
| $n_1$, $n_2$ | Volume fraction of the light, heavy component in a binary gas mixture |
| $P$ | Pressure |
| $p_c/2\omega$ | Power cost per unit area per unit time |
| $Q_1$, $Q_2$ | Ratio of collision integrals (eq. 8) |
| $Q_{12}$ | Ratio of collision integrals (eq. 9) |
| $q$ | Enrichment ratio defined in equation 84 |
| $R$ | Gas constant |
| $r_1$, $r_2$ | Radius of outer, inner tube of cylindrical thermal diffusion column |
| $S$ | Amount of fixed charges per unit area per unit time |
| $S_1$, $S_2$ | Ratios of collision integrals (eq. 7) |
| $s$ | Subscript identifying the stripping section of a thermogravitational column |

| | |
|---|---|
| $T$ | Absolute temperature |
| $\bar{T}$ | Mean value of the absolute temperature |
| $T_R$ | Temperature ratio defined as $(T_H/T_C)^\alpha$ |
| $t$ | Time |
| $t_r$ | Relaxation time |
| $V$ | Volume |
| $V_C, V_H$ | Volume of cold, hot bulb |
| $V_e, V_s$ | Volume of reservoir at enriching, stripping end of batch thermogravitational column |
| $V_R$ | Volume ratio defined as $V_C/V_H$ or $V_s/V_e$ |
| $v(x)$ | Velocity function in a thermogravitational column |
| $x$ | Linear coordinate in the direction of the temperature difference |
| $y$ | Linear coordinate in the direction parallel to the plates of a thermogravitational column |
| $Z$ | Dimensionless group $= \sigma_f L_T/4K$ |
| $\alpha$ | Thermal diffusion constant |
| $\beta_T$ | $-\partial\rho/\partial T$ |
| $\Delta$ | $C_e - C_s$ |
| $\Delta T$ | $T_H - T_C$ |
| $\epsilon$ | Energy difference between the separated molecules and the molecules in the configurations for which they have the maximum energy of attraction |
| $\theta$ | Angle of the plates of a thermal diffusion column from the vertical |
| $\Lambda_e, \Lambda_s$ | Total length of tubing in the enriching, stripping section of a multicolumn thermal diffusion apparatus |
| $\mu$ | Viscosity |
| $\nu$ | Repulsive force index |
| $\nu'$ | Attractive force index |
| $\xi$ | Dimensionless time (eq. 94) |
| $\pi$ | Numerical constant 3.141 . . . |
| $\rho$ | Density |
| $\sigma$ | In the case that $\sigma_e = \sigma_s$, then $\sigma \equiv \sigma_e = \sigma_s$ |
| $\sigma_e, \sigma_s$ | Flow of material from the enriching, stripping section of a continuous-flow thermal diffusion column |
| $\sigma_f$ | Flow of feed to a continuous-flow thermal diffusion column |
| $\tau$ | Net transport of component 1 in the $y$ direction in a thermogravitational column |

$\phi$        Defined as $x/l$ for static cells and as $y/L$ for thermogravitational columns

$\omega$        One half of the distance between the plates of a thermogravitational column

## References

1. C. Ludwig, *Wien. Akad. Ber.*, **20**, 539 (1856).
2. C. Soret, *Arch. Sci. phys. nat. (Geneva)*, **2**, No. 3, 48 (1879); *Compt. rend.*, **91**, 289 (1880); *Arch. Sci. phys. nat. (Geneva)*, **4**, No. 3, 209 (1880).
3. C. C. Tanner, *Trans. Faraday Soc.*, **23**, 75 (1927).
4. G. Thomaes, *Physica*, **17**, 885 (1951).
5. N. Riehl, *Z. Electrochem.*, **49**, 306 (1943).
6. E. S. Huse, D. J. Trevoy and H. G. Drickamer, *Rev. Sci. Instr.*, **21**, 60 (1950).
7. W. Nernst, *Z. physik. Chem.*, **4**, 129 (1889).
8. J. H. Van't Hoff, *Z. physik. Chem.*, **1**, 481 (1887).
9. T. Wereide, *Ann. phys.*, **2**, No. 9, 67 (1914).
10. L. J. Tichachek, W. S. Kmak and H. G. Drickamer, *J. Phys. Chem.*, **60**, 660 (1956).
11. S. Whitaker and R. L. Pigford, *Ind. Eng. Chem.*, **50**, 1026 (1958).
12. D. Finn, Private communication, 1960.
13. D. Enskog, *Physik Z.*, **12**, 56, 533 (1911); "Kinetic Theory of Processes in Dilute Gas Masses," Doctoral Dissertation, Uppsala, 1917.
14. S. Chapman, *Phil. Trans.*, **216A**, 279 (1916); *Proc. Roy. Soc. (London)*, **A93**, 1 (1916).
15. S. Chapman and F. W. Dootson, *Phil. Mag.*, **33**, No. 6, 248 (1917).
16. R. S. Mulliken, *J. Am. Chem. Soc.*, **44**, 1033 (1922).
17. K. Clusius and G. Dickel, *Naturwissenschaften*, **26**, 546 (1938).
18. K. Clusius and G. Dickel, *Z. physik. Chem.*, **B44**, 451 (1939).
19. S. H. Jury and E. Von Halle, *Chem. Eng. News*, **34**, 3606 (1956).
20. Howard E. Carr, *J. Chem. Phys.*, **12**, 349 (1944).
21. J. E. Powers and C. R. Wilke, *A.I.Ch.E. Journal*, **3**, 213 (1957).
22. Milton Farber and W. F. Libby, *J. Chem. Phys.*, **8**, 965 (1940).
23. E. Tilvis, *Soc. Sci. Fennica Commentationes Phys.-Math.*, **13**, No. 15 (1947).
24. L. J. Sullivan, T. C. Ruppel and C. B. Willingham, *Ind. Eng. Chem.*, **47**, 208 (1955).
25. P. Debye and A. M. Bueche, *High Polymer Physics*, Chemical Publishing Company, New York, 1948, pp. 497–527.
26. A. K. Brewer and A. Bramley (to the Secretary of Agriculture of the U.S.A. and his successors in office) U. S. 2,258,594, October 14, 1941.
27. Alkhazov, D. G., A. N. Murin, and A. P. Ratner, *Bull. Acad. Sci. U.S.S.R. Classe Sci. Chim.*, **1943**, 3 (1943).
28. J. C. Treacy and R. E. Rich, *Ind. Eng. Chem.*, **47**, 1544 (1955).
29. F. De Maria and R. F. Benenati, *Ind. Eng. Chem.*, **50**, 63 (1958).
30. W. H. Furry, R. C. Jones and L. Onsager, *Phys. Rev.*, **55**, 1083 (1939).
31. R. C. Jones and W. H. Furry, *Rev. Mod. Phys.*, **18**, 151 (1946).

32. William Krasney-Ergen, *Phys. Rev.*, **58,** 1078 (1940).
33. M. Benedict, *Chem. Eng. Progr.* **1,** No. 2, *Trans. Am. Inst. Chem. Engrs.*, **43,** 41 (1947).
34. S. Chapman, *Phil. Mag.* **7,** No. 7,1 (1929).
35. S. P. Frankel, *Phys. Rev.*, **57,** 661(L) (1940).
36. S. Chapman and T. G. Cowling, *The Mathematical Theory of Non-Uniform Gases*, The Cambridge University Press, New York, 1939.
37. K. E. Grew and T. L. Ibbs, *Thermal Diffusion in Gases*, Cambridge University Press, Great Britain, 1952.
38. S. Chapman, *Proc. Roy. Soc. (London)*, **A177,** 38 (1940).
39. S. Chapman, *Mem. Proc. Manchester Lit. & Phil. Soc.*, **66,** No. 1 (1922).
40. J. O. Hirschfelder, R. B. Bird, and E. L. Spotz, *J. Chem. Phys.*, **16,** 968 (1948).
41. H. L. Johnston and K. E. McCloskey, *J. Phys. Chem.*, **44,** 1038 (1939).
42. E. Rammler and K. Breitling, *Die Warme (Z. fur Dampfkessel U. Maschinenbetrieb)* **60,** 620 (1937).
43. C. J. Danby, J. D. Lambert and M. Mitchell, *Proc. Roy. Soc. (London)*, **A239,** 365 (1957).
44. K. Wirtz, *Z. Naturforsch*, **3a,** 672 (1948); **3a,** 380 (1948); *Z. Physik.*, **124,** 482 (1948).
45. I. Prigogine, L. de Broukere, and R. Amand. *Physica,* **16,** 577, 851 (1950).
46. S. R. de Groot, *The Thermodynamics of Irreversible Processes*, Interscience, New York, 1950.
47. S. Glasstone, K. L. Laidler, and H. Eyring, *Theory of Rate Processes*, McGraw-Hill, New York, 1941.
48. E. Von Halle, *AEC Research and Development Report K-1420*, 1959.
49. Harrison Brown, *Phys. Rev.*, **58,** 661 (1940).
50. S. R. de Groot, *Physica*, **9,** 699 (1942).
51. S. R. de Groot, "L'Effet Soret," Thesis, Amsterdam, 1945.
52. D. W. Burton, *United States Atomic Energy Commission Report No. K-1330*, 1957.
53. J. E. Powers, *Univ. of Calif. Rad. Lab. Rept.*, *UCRL-2618*, August, 1954.
54. J. Bardeen, *Phys. Rev.*, **58,** 94(L) (1940).
55. J. E. Powers, *Ind. Eng. Chem.*, **53,** 577 (1961).
56. J. Bardeen, *Phys. Rev.*, **57,** 35 (1940).
57. P. Debye, *Ann. phys.*, **36,** 284 (1939).
58. J. E. Powers, *Proceedings of the Joint Conference on Thermodynamic and Transport Properties of Fluids*, Institution of Mechanical Engineers, London, July, 1957, p. 198.
59. L. Onsager and W. W. Watson, *Phys. Rev.*, **56,** 474 (1939).
60. L. Onsager, *Phys. Rev.*, **55,** 1137(A) (1939).
61. G. G. Vichare and J. E. Powers, *A.I.Ch.E. Journal,* **7,** 650 (1961).
62. A. L. Jones, *Petrol. Processing,* **6,** 132 (Feb., 1951).
63. J. E. Powers and C. R. Wilke, *J. Chem. Phys.*, **27,** 1000 (1957).
64. J. R. White and A. T. Fellows, *Ind. Eng. Chem.*, **49,** 1409 (1957).
65. (a) A. L. Jones, *Petrol. Refiner*, **36,** No. 7, 153 (1957); (b) D. Frazier, U. S., Patent 2,824,647, February 25, 1958; (c) U. S. Patents 2,827,171-2, March 18, 1958.
66. R. Niini. *Suomen Kemistilehti,* **20,** No. 9, 49 (1947).

67. A. H. Emery, Jr., *Ind. Eng. Chem.*, **51**, 651 (1959).
68. S. R. de Groot, W. Hoogenstraaten, and C. J. Gorter, *Physica*, **9**, 923 (1942).
69. S. R. de Groot, D. J. Gorter, and W. Hoogenstraaten, *Physica*. **10**, 81 (1943).
70. I. I. Prigogine, L. de Brouchere, and R. Amand, *Physica*, **16**, 577 (1950).
71. E. W. Becker, *Z. Naturforsch*, **2a**, 441, 447 (1947).
72. H. G. Drickamer, E. W. Mellow, and L. H. Tung, *J*, *Chem. Phys.*, **18**, 945 (1950).
73. K. E. Grew, *Proc. Roy. Soc. (London)*, **A189**, 402 (1947).
74. E. Whalley, E. R. S. Winter, and H. V. A. Briscoe, *Trans. Faraday Soc.*, **45**, 1085 (1949).
75. R. L. Saxton, E. L. Dougherty, and H. G. Drickamer, *J. Chem. Phys.*, **22**, 1166 (1954).
76. P. T. Nettley, *Proc. Phys. Soc. (London)*, **67B**, 753 (1954).
77. J. V. A. E. von Obermayer, *Wien. Ber.*, **81**, 1102 (1880).
78. A. O. Nier, *Phys. Rev.*, **57**, 30 (1940).
79. H. G. Drickamer, V. J. O'Brien, J. C. Bresee, and C. E. Ockert, *J. Chem. Phys.*, **16**, 122 (1948).
80. P. F. Van Velden, H. G. P. Van der Voort, and C. J. Gorter, *Physica*, **12**, 151 (1946).
81. T. S. Heines, O. A. Larson, and J. J. Martin, *Ind. Eng. Chem.*, **49**, 1911 (1957).
82. C. J. Crownover and J. E. Powers, *A.I.Ch.E. Journal*, **8**, 166 (1962).
83. E. Whalley and E. R. S. Winter, *Trans. Faraday Soc.*, **45**, 1091 (1949).
84. A. L. Jones and R. W. Foreman, *Ind. Eng. Chem.*, **44**, 2249 (1949).
85. M. Fink, Co. Cleveland, Ohio.
86. D. J. Trevoy and H. G. Drickamer, *J. Chem. Phys.*, **17**, 1120 (1949).
87. H. D. Smyth, *A General Account of the Development of Methods of Using Atomic Energy for Military Purposes Under the Auspices of the United States Government, 1940–1945*, U. S. Government Printing Office, Washington, D. C., 1945.
88. M. C. Fox, *Chem. & Met. Eng.*, **52**, No. 12, 102 (1945).
89. R. Grasselli, G. R. Brown, and C. E. Plymale, *Chem. Eng. Progr.*, **57**, No. 3, 59 (May 1961).
90. C. H. Chilton, *Chem. Eng.*, **56**, 6, 97 (June, 1949).
91. J. O. Hirschfelder, C. F. Curtiss, and R. B. Bird, *Molecular Theory of Gases and Liquids*, Wiley New York, 1954.
92. B. B. McInteer and M. J. Reisfield, *Los Alamos Laboratory Report LAMS 2517*, February, 1961.
93. E. Von Halle and E. Greene, *United States Atomic Energy Commission Report No. K-1469*, September, 1961.
94. A. O. Nier, *Phys. Rev.*, **56**, 1009 (1939).

# 2

# CHROMATOGRAPHY AND ALLIED FIXED-BED SEPARATIONS PROCESSES

## E. N. Lightfoot, R. J. Sanchez-Palma, and D. O. Edwards

**Contents**

## I. Introduction

The separations techniques discussed below are not new. If they warrant inclusion in the present text it is primarily because their usefulness has not yet been fully appreciated. Our purpose in writing this chapter has therefore been to make the very large body of literature concerning fixed-bed sorption processes more accessible.

Our job has been made easier by the availability of numerous texts and reviews, concerned both with the applications of chromatographic separations techniques and with the details of their quantitative description. References in the first category include the texts of Nachod and Schubert (1), Kunin (2), and Lederer (3). Of particular interest in the latter category is the comprehensive discussion of Vermeulen (4), in which the available solutions to specific chromatographic problems are summarized. This reference provides a key to the extensive work of Hiester and Vermeulen and their associates on ion exchange processes. A second reference deserving of mention is the very excellent text on ion exchange by Helfferich (5). This book provides authoritative up-to-date discussion of ion exchange equilibria and kinetics and also very readable introductions to such allied processes as ion exclusion and ion retardation. Also included are summaries of rate equations and calculation techniques useful for column processes.

It is not out intention here to duplicate the above references or to list the many applications of fixed-bed separations. Rather we have attempted to emphasize the physical nature of the processes involved and the reasons for observed column behavior. We have also tried to provide realistic and detailed examples to familiarize the reader with the equations presented and to give more meaning to our discussion. In accordance with this aim, we have defined mass-transfer coefficients and related quantities in the same way as is usually done for the analogous and better understood steady-state processes.

Finally, we have emphasized some topics that we feel have been neglected. An example is the approximate analysis based on neglect of mass-transfer resistance and other dispersive tendencies, discussed in Section III-B. This type of analysis is simple, can be readily applied to multicomponent systems, and gives a very useful estimate of the potentialities of a proposed process.

Two important topics omitted from the present discussion are the detailed analysis of multicomponent separations and the application of high-speed computers to the numerical solution of chromatographic problems. There has not yet been a great deal done in these fields, and most of the available information was felt to be unsuitable for inclusion in this introductory discussion. Vermeulen (4) has included a brief section on multicomponent adsorption of interfering solutes. The simultaneous adsorption of noninterfering solutes is a relatively trivial problem and can be handled by a straightforward extension of the discussion of Section III-C. This is also discussed by both Vermeulen and Helfferich.

The literature on fixed-bed sorption processes has grown rapidly in the past, and there is every reason to expect this growth to continue. The readers anxious to keep up with recent developments will find numerous reviews in the periodical literature. Of particular interest to engineers are the annual reviews of ion exchange and adsorption in *Industrial and Engineering Chemistry*. The ion exchange reviews in *Annual Review of Physical Chemistry* and *Analytical Chemistry, Annual Review*, may also be helpful. It is our hope that our discussion below will make these and other sources more useful to our readers.

## II. The Nature of Fixed-Bed Separations

A. COMMONLY USED OPERATING PROCEDURES

We shall consider here mass transfer between a nonreactive fluid and a stationary bed of granular solid through which the fluid is flowing. Quite commonly the solid is held in a vertical cylindrical pipe as shown schematically in Figure 1. In the apparatus shown here the fluid moves downward in intimate contact with the solid granules. As it does so, solutes originally present in the fluid tend to be sorbed by the solid, at first on the upper portions of the bed. Similarly, species originally held on the

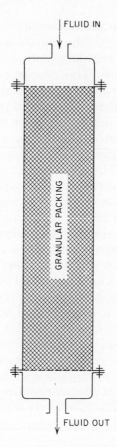

Fig. 1. Schematic representation of a fixed-bed sorption column.

solid tend to be eluted by the flowing fluid, first from the upper portions of the bed. If operation is continued indefinitely the entire bed will become saturated with solute from the feed solution and stripped of sorbates originally present. Operation is thus inherently unsteady, and the solid must be periodically replaced or regenerated, i.e., returned to its original state by heating or other treatment.

A typical effluent curve for the continued feed of solution containing a single solute to an initially solute-free bed is shown in Figure 17. Such S-shaped effluent curves are commonly called "breakthrough curves." Simple saturating operations of the type represented here are used in many industrial separations, for example, drying of air by passage through a desiccant bed, recovery of organic vapors from gases by adsorption on activated carbon, or removal of calcium ions from water in an ion exchange column. The reverse operation, removal of soluble material from the solid, occurs in the extraction of caffeine from coffee beans or in regeneration of the previously mentioned desiccant or carbon beds.

Where it is desired to separate two or more solutes of similar solubility behavior, a somewhat more complicated operation is required. First a limited volume of solution containing all of the solutes is fed to a sorbent column under such conditions that the solutes are concentrated near the feed end of the column. They are then simultaneously eluted by passing a large volume of solvent through the column. The more strongly sorbed solutes migrate more slowly down the column during this elution so that a separation is obtained, based largely upon differences in equilibrium distribution between the fixed and moving phases. The effluent curves for each solute are roughly bell-shaped as indicated in Figure 18. Separations of this type are commonly called "chromatographic" separations, and the zones of high concentration of each solute migrating down the column during the separation are known as "free bands." Chromatographic separations may be further classified according to the conditions of operation.

If high degrees of separation are desired, relatively small amounts of solute are fed to the column, and elution is so carried out that solute concentrations are always very low. Under these conditions the solutes behave very nearly independently of one another, and the equilibrium distributions of solutes between fixed and moving phases are approximately linear. This type of operation is known as "elution chromatography." It is widely used for analytical separations but is too wasteful of solvent and sorbent for most industrial applications.

Where capital and operating costs are important "displacement chromatography" is often employed. Here relatively large amounts of solute are initially fed to the column at high concentration. Elution is then accomplished by passing a concentrated solution of very strongly sorbed material down the column. This eluting solute displaces the solutes originally present and thus forces

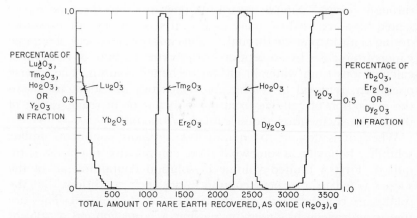

Fig. 2. Separation of the heavier rare earths by displacement chromatography on a semi-industrial scale. Large fractions of Yb, Er, and Dy were obtained directly from this effluent in purity greater than 99.9%. The remaining material can be readily purified further. Adsorbent: Nalcite HCR in H$^+$ form. Eluant: pH 8.0 citrate buffer. (From F. H. Spedding and J. E. Powell in Nachod and Schubert (1).)

them to migrate, and at the high concentrations used, these original solutes tend to displace one another. As a result, they appear in the effluent as a series of overlapping free bands with the least strongly sorbed species appearing first (see Fig. 2).

Displacement chromatography provides a much more economical use of the sorbent column and generally requires less solvent. However, there is a substantial "mixed zone" between each pair of solutes, and the cost of column regeneration may be high. An example of displacement chromatography is the separation of aromatic from paraffinic hydrocarbons using silica gel as adsorbent. The aromatic constituent is the more strongly adsorbed in this case, and it is used as the eluting agent. The column is regenerated by heating.

Many actual separations are intermediate between these two limiting cases, for example, the salt-glycerine separation discussed in Example 2.

B. APPLICABILITY OF FIXED-BED SORPTION TECHNIQUES

Before proceeding to a quantitative description of these processes we consider briefly the factors affecting their suitability for a given

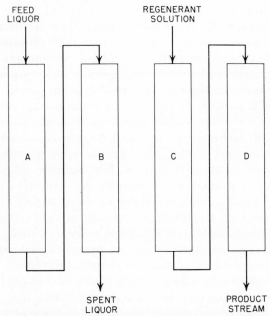

Fig. 3. A simple four-column sorption unit. This apparatus provides very nearly continuous flow of almost constant composition. An automatically timed or manual flow-switching system is required to provide the following four-stage cycle:

| | ─────Absorption───── | | ─────Desorption───── | |
| Stage | Primary | Secondary | Primary | Secondary |
|---|---|---|---|---|
| 1 | A | B | C | D |
| 2 | B | C | D | A |
| 3 | C | D | A | B |
| 4 | D | A | B | C |

Many other flow arrangements are possible, all of them variants of the old "ring" system. A very common arrangement is a three-column system, similar to that shown except that desorption (regeneration) is accomplished in a single stage.

separation problem. This discussion is purposely kept short as there are a number of excellent references available (1,2,6).

Fixed-bed techniques offer a number of important advantages to the engineer, one of the most important of which is the availability of a wide variety of highly selective sorbents. These often permit a high degree of separation of chemically similar materials. Of particular interest is the growing number of materials tailored to individual applications. A good example of these is provided by the so-called "molecular sieves," which have specific affinities for water vapor or other small molecules (7). Other advantages commonly include long sorbent life, with small losses of sorbent per cycle and negligible contamination of the fluid stream being processed. Frequently it is possible to consider a sorbent as part of the capital equipment of the plant, rather than as a reagent. This is true, for example, of ion exchange resins in many applications. Equipment is generally simple and reliable, and operation can usually be carried out over a wide range of flow rates. For example, while 2 gal/ft³-min is about a normal space velocity for industrial mixed-bed deionizing columns, rates five times or more higher can be used (1). As a result of this flexibility, fixed-bed units can often be operated at much higher than normal capacity during periods of peak load. Finally the batch nature of fixed-bed techniques is well adapted to the resolution of multicomponent mixtures.

These techniques do, however, suffer from two severe limitations. First, they are inherently batch operations and may, therefore, be difficult to integrate into otherwise continuous processes. This drawback, most serious when the cycle is short, can be minimized by automatic cycle timing and multicolumn operation (see for example Fig. 3). Second, and often more serious, the solute-holding capacity of industrial sorbents is typically rather small. As a result, investment cost per unit mass of solute treated tends to be high. Fixed-bed systems operate most favorably then in the removal of small amounts of unwanted solutes or in the recovery of relatively valuable materials from dilute solution. An outstanding exception is the case of ion exclusion where solute-holding capacity is high.

Costs of column regeneration vary widely. They can be very low, as in ion exclusion and ion retardation, where the regeneration process consists simply of passing water through the column. In ion exchange, the cost of regeneration depends primarily upon the amount of solute sorbed and not upon its concentration. In thermal regeneration, on the other hand, the high heat load represented by the heat capacity of the sorbent, is serious. For example, heating cost tends to restrict economic operation of fixed-bed air dryers to the production of very low dew-point air.

To show the relative importance of the above-mentioned

economic considerations, we consider briefly four applications for which fixed-bed techniques have been successful: water demineralization, antibiotic recovery, separation of salt and glycerine by ion exclusion, and resolution of rare earth mixtures.

## 1. Water Demineralization

Here the cost per unit mass of solute removal is high, largely because of the cost of reagents, but the cost per unit volume of water treated is small. Thus, to remove $CaSO_4$ from water at 50–500 ppm, on an industrial scale, the typical costs are about three to ten cents per pound of $CaSO_4$ (8). However, this corresponds to only about seven to twenty cents per thousand gallons of water, very considerably less than distillation, for example. It is also possible to keep capital costs low here since relatively high flow rates are permissible (see above). These high flow rates are possible in part because of the high selectivity of the resins.

## 2. Recovery of Streptomycin from Fermentation Broths

Streptomycin and other polyvalent basic antibiotics are removed from filtered fermentation broth by absorption in cation exchange resins, for example, the carboxylic acid resin Amberlite IRC50. The key to the success of this process was the development of a sorbent of high capacity (see Table I) and good selectivity for

TABLE I
Approximate Capacities of Some Typical Adsorbents for Streptomycin[a]

| Adsorbent | Capacity, mg streptomycin/g adsorbent |
|---|---|
| Sulfonated phenol-formaldehyde | 10 |
| Sulfonated coal | 12 |
| Activated carbon | 20 |
| Fuller's earth | 50 |
| Poly acrylic-methacrylic acids | |
| 5% divinylbenzene | 600–1500 |
| 10% divinylbenzene | 300–800 |
| Carboxylic phenol-formaldehyde | |
| resins (9) | 500–900 |

[a] Presented by N. Lengborn (10) for rough comparative purposes only.

streptomycin. Selectivity is enhanced by the low concentration of sorbable solutes, which increases resin preference for ions of high valence (see Section II-C-2). The chief interference in this case is from the divalent calcium ion; it is usually precipitated or sequestered prior to absorption. Because of the high capacity and selectivity of the resins used, it is possible to process on the order of $10^2$ resin-bed volumes of fermentation broth per cycle. Under these conditions, just as in water demineralization, the cost per unit volume of solution is very low.

### 3. Ion-Exclusion Separation of Sodium Chloride and Glycerine

Ion exclusion is an ingenious and economical method of separating strong electrolytes from weak ones or from nonelectrolytes. It owes its success to the fact that electrolytes are strongly excluded from ion exchange resins, in accordance with the Donnan principle, whereas nonelectrolytes often distribute about evenly between the stationary and moving phases.

The separation of salt and glycerine is of considerable economic interest and has been studied rather thoroughly (see Ex. 2). Operation in this system contrasts strongly with water treatment or antibiotic recovery. Here less than half a column volume of feed can be introduced to the resin bed before elution is started. Such a short cycle greatly complicates equipment design in that mixing in the headers must be minimized to produce sharp separations. In addition, lower flow rates must be used than in the previous two systems discussed because mass-transfer resistance and viscosity are higher. Nevertheless, ion exclusion is very economical and is quite often the method of choice where applicable. This is because it offers a number of important advantages:

1. The difference in distribution coefficients between electrolyte and nonelectrolyte is large.
2. Very high nonelectrolyte concentrations may be achieved in the stationary phase.
3. Regeneration is achieved simply by passage of water through the partially saturated bed. Direct regeneration costs are very low.

In addition, careful header design and the development of automatic cycle timers have offset much of the disadvantage of the short cycle.

According to Baumann, Wheaton, and Simpson (11), the originators of this process, it is possible to separate over 1 pound of glycol per hour per cubic foot of column from a feed 10% glycol and 10% salt by weight.

## 4. Separation of Rare Earths

Separation of the rare earths has long presented a challenge to the chemist, and more recently to the chemical engineer. Although widely distributed, they normally occur as multicomponent mixtures, for example, in monazite sand. This material is processed for its content of thorium, cerium, and lanthanum, but also contains substantial amounts of neodymium, samarium, europium, and gadolinium. Most of the rare earths exist in solution or crystalline salts in a hydrated trivalent form, and their chemical and solubility behavior change only slightly from element to element. In addition, since their atomic radii do not differ greatly, they tend to form solid solutions in one another on crystallization.

The classic methods of separation, used up to about 1945, were very tedious: fractional crystallization, fractional decomposition, etc. Effective resolution of mixtures required literally thousands of individual staged operations. It became obvious that, if pure rare earths were to become readily available, methods would have to be developed whereby these multiple operations could be performed automatically.

Chromatographic techniques are clearly very well suited to "automation" of this sort, and chromatography over ion exchange resins of the sulfonic acid type has proven a very effective method of resolving rare-earth mixtures. It is important to note that the success of chromatography in this application results from its inherent characteristics, and not from any unusual affinities of the resins for individual rare earths.

Detailed description of procedures used are discussed by Spedding and Powell (12). Both elution and displacement techniques have been used. The former is effective for separating minute or tracer quantities of rare earths, but is not competitive for large-scale isolation. Here displacement chromatography is the method of choice. An effluent curve for separation of the heavier rare earth ions by displacement with an ammonia-citric acid buffer is shown in Figure 2.

It should be emphasized here that the chromatographic separation of these very similar materials is slow and expensive. Examples are given by Spedding and Powell (12) from the operation of a pilot plant at Iowa State College, Ames, Iowa. In an apparently typical operation, adsorption of the mixture to be resolved took about 8 hours, and, during elution, the band of rare earths moved down the ion exchange bed at a rate of about $3^1/_2$ feet per day. Reagent costs are also considerable. Here then the attractiveness of chromatographic separations is primarily due to the unattractiveness of other available techniques.

## C. REQUIREMENTS OF A QUANTITATIVE DESCRIPTION

In order to describe any of the above operations quantitatively we must:

1. Decide upon a geometric model to represent the actual system. This model must be simple enough to permit analysis but realistic enough to provide useful results.

2. Set up a differential equation and boundary conditions based upon this model to provide a mathematical description of the system.

3. Integrate this differential equation.

As we shall see below the difficulty of step 3 has limited analysis to a relatively few simple model systems.

### 1. Approximation of System Geometry

We base all further discussion on the apparatus pictured in Figure 1: fluid percolating downward through a granular solid bed held in a vertical cylindrical pipe. It may easily be shown that the detailed behavior of such a system is too complicated to permit quantitative description, however, and we therefore must set up a simplified model. Actual and model behavior are contrasted in Figure 4. We define our model system by means of these figures and the following assumptions:

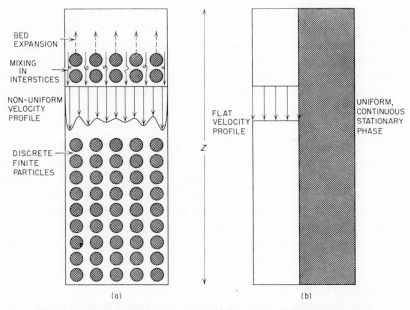

Fig. 4. Schematic representation of (a) real and (b) model systems.

1. The fixed and moving phases are continuous in the direction of flow and exist side by side, in contact with one another over an interfacial area $a$ per unit packed volume of bed.

2. The fluid flows straight down the column without back-mixing, and the fluid velocity is constant over any column cross section.

3. The concentration profiles in the direction of flow are continuous curves not appreciably affected by placement of individual packing particles.

4. The fluid phase occupies a constant volume fraction of the column, and the densities of the fixed and fluid phases remain constant.

Of these assumptions, number 2 is probably the most unrealistic: both the nonuniformity of the velocity and the interparticle mixing shown in Figure 4a result in movement of solute relative to the average fluid velocity, i.e., an axial dispersion of solute in the column. This point is further discussed in Section II-C-2 below.

Assumption 4 may be quite poor in many cases, but as yet there is no reliable way to estimate the errors caused by its use. Assumptions 1 and 3 appear to be quite reasonable, except that, in ignoring the detailed column behavior, we lose the possibility of *a priori* determination of mass transfer coefficients and friction factors.* These quantities must be determined by the methods of dimensional analysis.

### 2. Mathematical Description of the Simplified Model

In order to describe our model system we must first derive partial differential equations relating the concentrations of each species in each phase with position in the column and time; we shall see that these are expressions of conservation of mass, commonly called "equations of continuity." To integrate these differential equations we shall need, in addition to initial and boundary conditions, expressions for the equilibrium distribution of each solute between the fixed and moving phases, and for the rate of transfer of solutes between phases.

**a. The Equations of Continuity for Fixed-Bed Separations.** We may develop these equations by considering a column segment of length $\Delta z$, as shown in Figure 5. To do this we write a mass balance expression for any solute A in the form:

(rate of A in) $-$ (rate of A out) $=$

(rate of accumulation of A)    (1)

The solute A will enter section $\Delta z$ both by convection, i.e., by virtue of the bulk fluid motion, and by "diffusion," i.e., by movement relative to the bulk fluid velocity.

[We may then write** the rate of transfer of A into the system at $z$ as:

$$\epsilon S[v_z c_A - \mathfrak{D}_{Aa}(\partial c_A/\partial z)\,|_{z,t}]$$    (2)

---

* It appears that such *a priori* determination of mass-transfer coefficients may be possible for some packings, e.g., uniform spheres (13).

** Material enclosed in heavy brackets [ ] is primarily mathematical in nature and may be avoided by those interested only in using the results. Important equations and definitions of symbols may occasionally appear in this material, however.

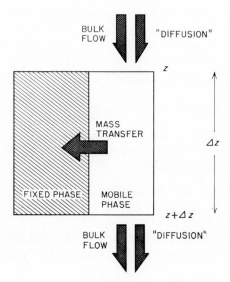

Fig. 5. Segment of column over which a mass-balance is made.

Here $S$ is the column cross section, $\epsilon S$ is the cross section available for flow, and $v_z$ is the interstitial fluid velocity. The concentration $c_A$ is the bulk, or volume-average, concentration of A in the moving phase at the cross section of interest. The vertical line is to be read "evaluated at," and $\mathfrak{D}_{A_a}$ is the apparent diffusivity of the solute in the system. If assumption 2 in Section II-C-1 correctly described the flow pattern, the apparent diffusivity would be the effective binary (molecular) diffusivity* of the solute A through the mixture, $\mathfrak{D}_{Am}$. To take into account the additional transport of solute resulting from back-mixing and nonuniformity of velocity it is customary to add to the molecular diffusivity a "dispersion coefficient" $E_A$ so that:

$$\mathfrak{D}_{A_a} \equiv \mathfrak{D}_{Am} + E_A \qquad (3)$$

where $\mathfrak{D}_{A_a}$ is the effective diffusivity of solute A *in the direction of flow*. The mechanisms by which mass leaves the system at $z + \Delta z$

* For a discussion of the effective binary diffusivity in multicomponent mixtures see R. B. Bird, W. E. Stewart, and E. N. Lightfoot (14, Section 18.4). For dilute multicomponent systems with solvents, the effective binary diffusivity may be taken as the true binary diffusivity for A alone in $s$, $\mathfrak{D}_{As}$.

are clearly the same as those by which it enters at $z$. We may then write the left side of equation 1 as:

$$\epsilon S\{ [v_z c_A - \mathfrak{D}_{Aa}(\partial c_A/\partial z)] \,|\, z - [v_z c_a - \mathfrak{D}_{Aa}(\partial c_A/\partial z)\,|z + \Delta z\} \quad (4)$$

The rate of accumulation of solute in the volume element $s\,\Delta z$ is:

$$S\Delta z[\epsilon(\partial c_A/\partial t) + (1 - \epsilon)(\partial c_{As}/\partial t)]z_{\mathrm{avg},\,t} \quad (5)$$

Here $c_{As}$ is the bulk concentration of component A in the stationary phase. We now combine equations 4 and 5, divide through by $S\Delta z$, and rearrange to obtain

$$\mathfrak{D}_{Aa}\{ [(\partial c_A/\partial z)\,|z + \Delta z_{,t} - (\partial c_A/\partial z)\,|_{z,t}] \} \,/\Delta z = v_z(c_A\,|z + \Delta z_{,t}$$

$$- c_A\,|z_{,t})/\Delta z + \{(\partial c_A/\partial t) + [(1 - \epsilon)/\epsilon](\partial c_{As}/\partial t)\}|z_{\mathrm{avg},\,t} \quad (6)$$

We now let the distance $\Delta z$ become very small and take advantage of the definitions of first and second partial derivatives to write equation 6 as

$$\mathfrak{D}_{Aa}(\partial^2 c_A/\partial z^2) = v_z(\partial c_A/\partial z) + (\partial/\partial t)\{c_A + [(1 - \epsilon)/\epsilon]c_{As}\} \quad (7)]$$

Equation 7 is the equation of continuity for solute A. We may write similar equations for all other components of the solution. In order to integrate this equation to obtain $c_A(z,t)$ we must relate the concentrations in the two phases, $c_A$ and $c_{As}$. To obtain such a relation we will need the equilibrium and rate data discussed in the next two subsections.

Before going on to these topics, however, we stop to say a few words about the dispersion coefficient $E_A$. The dispersion represented by this term results from several different effects:

1. Interparticle or "cell" mixing of the fluid in the interstices of the bed.

2. "Channeling," i.e., the result of gross nonuniformity of fluid velocity over the bed cross section.

3. "Taylor diffusion," i.e., axial dispersion resulting from the combined effect of local lateral gradients in the fluid velocity and axial gradients in the solute concentration.

There are, however, many cases in which not all of these effects are important. For example, it appears that channeling is negligible in carefully packed beds of small particles.

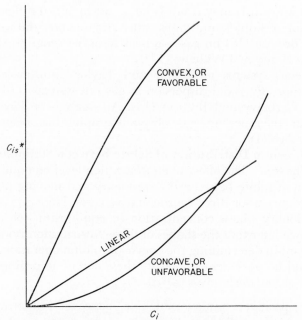

Fig. 6. Classification of equilibrium distribution isotherms.

If in addition the percolating fluid is a liquid, the effects of intra-particle mixing will normally be much greater than those of molecular and Taylor diffusion. A number of investigations have been made under these conditions, and somewhat conflicting results have been obtained. The results of most investigators (15,16) working with liquids, yield axial effective Péclet numbers, $\text{Pé}_E = D_p v_z / \mathfrak{D}_{Aa}$, of about 0.3–1.0 for particle Reynolds numbers $(D_p v_z \rho / u)$, of about $10^{-2}$ to $10^2$. For Reynolds numbers greater than 100, this Péclet number increases and appears to approach a limiting value of 2. McHenry and Wilhelm (17), working with gases, found the effective Péclet number to be about 1.88 and Reynolds number independent over a Reynolds number range about $10–10^3$. They further showed that this Péclet number should be 2 if the bed acted as a series of $n$ perfect mixers, with $n$ the number of layers of particles between inlet and outlet of the column. These experimental Péclet numbers of McHenry and Wilhelm are clearly much higher than those of other investigators; the reasons for this are not yet known. It may result from an unexplained difference in the behavior of liquids and gases, since fragmentary data of Carberry and Bretton (15) on gases appear to agree roughly with the result of McHenry and Wilhelm (17).

For gaseous systems molecular and Taylor diffusion are frequently important. Axial dispersion in gaseous systems is discussed briefly by Carberry and Bretton (15). An analysis of Taylor diffusion with reference to gas chromatography has been given recently by Aris (18).

**b. Equilibrium Distribution of Solute between Stationary and Moving Phases.** The effect of concentration level on equilibrium distribution of solute between the stationary and moving phases is shown in Figure 6 for three representative cases. Here $c_{As}{}^* = f(c_A)$ is the stationary phase concentration in equilibrium with $c_A$. It will be shown later that the shapes of these "distribution isotherms" are important in determining the course of column operation. Thus, we shall find it convenient to classify these curves according to the signs of the second derivatives $(\partial^2 f/\partial c_A{}^2)_{T,p}$

$(\partial^2 f/\partial c_A{}^2)$ positive: "unfavorable" or "concave" isotherm    (8a)

$(\partial^2 f/\partial c_A{}^2)$ negative: "favorable" or "convex" isotherm    (8b)

$(\partial^2 f/\partial c_A{}^2)$ zero: linear isotherm    (8c)

The reasons for the terms "favorable" and "unfavorable" are discussed in some detail in Section III-B. It may be noted here that the sorbate affinity of most solids tends to decrease with increasing sorbate concentration; hence, most distribution isotherms are convex or "favorable." An outstanding exception to this rule is the sorption of an electrolyte $M^+X^-$ by an ion exchange resin of the form $M^+R^-$ or $R^+X^-$. Here the Donnan exclusion of electrolyte becomes less effective at high electrolyte concentrations. Linear behavior is often, *but not always*, approached at low concentrations. Inflected isotherms also occur in many systems of interest. A special case of such an isotherm is discussed in Example 3.

Prediction of column behavior is, of course, greatly facilitated if simple analytic expressions are available to describe quantitatively the distribution isotherms of interest, and consequently a great deal of effort has been expended to develop such expressions. A few of the most generally applicable ones are discussed below. There are, however, many systems for which these simple expressions are of little value, especially in the case of multicomponent solutions of interfering solutes. For some of these at least, other types of expressions may be preferable; such a case is illustrated in Example 2.

*Correlation of adsorption data* (19–21). In a very large number of fixed-bed separations solutes are held on the stationary phase by adsorption. Some widely used model isotherms for this case are given in Table II. Most of these were developed for adsorption of gases, but they have proven useful for liquid systems as well. Of them, the simple empirical Freundlich expression has probably

TABLE II

Expressions Commonly Used for Correlating Adsorption Equilibria[a]

*Single component*

Langmuir

$$c_{As} = \frac{K' c_A Q}{1 + K' c_A}$$

Freundlich

$$c_{As} = k c_A^{1/n}$$

Brunauer, Emmett, and Teller

$$c_{As} = \frac{B_1 B_2 c_A}{\left(1 - \frac{c_A}{c}\right)\left[1 + (B_2 - 1)\frac{c_A}{c}\right]}$$

Koble and Corrigan

$$c_{As} = \frac{L K' c_A^n}{1 + K' c_A^n}$$

*Multicomponent*

Langmuir

$$c_{As} = \frac{k' k_A c_A}{1 + \sum_{i=A}^{n} k_i c_i}$$

[a] Where $c_{As}$ is the concentration of A in the solid phase (moles of A/unit volume of solid); $c_A$ is the concentration of A in the fluid phase (moles of A/unit volume of solution); and $B_1, B_2, k, n, L, K', L_A, k', k_i, Q$ are constants to be determined empirically.

been the most widely used; it appears to be particularly successful for correlating data for adsorption on activated carbon over limited concentration ranges. Note that the Freundlich expression does not predict linear isotherms in the limit of zero concentration. The Langmuir equation, based on the assumption of single-layer adsorption on a fixed number of equivalent adsorption sites, has also been useful over limited concentration ranges. The remaining equations represent extension of Langmuir's original development to more complicated systems: polymerizing or dissociating solutes in the case of the Koble and Corrigan equation, multilayer adsorption in the case of the Brunauer, Emmett, and Teller equation, and multisolute single layer adsorption in the case of the multicomponent equation. The derivations and applicability of these and other model isotherms are discussed in the above-mentioned references.

*Correlation of partition data.* In many fixed-bed separations the solid portion of the stationary phase is inactive and serves only to immobilize an extracting liquid. In such systems the solutes are distributed or "partitioned" between two fluids, one moving and one stationary. In many gas chromatographies, for example, the stationary phase consists of a low-volatile liquid solvent, e.g., dibutylphthalate, immobilized in a porous pellet of some inert solid such as diatomaceous earth. Examples of liquid–liquid partition systems include paper chromatography, where the cellulose fibers swell to form an aqueous gel, and ion exclusion, where the swollen resin acts as a concentrated electrolyte solution. Frequently the distribution isotherms in such systems are approximately linear. This is especially likely at low concentrations, as are normally used in paper and gas chromatography. A rough idea of the reliability of the assumption of linear distributions for ion exclusion systems may be obtained from examining the glycerine distribution data in Example 2. There are, however, three cases of considerable importance in which linear behavior does not occur, even at low concentration: (a) Dissociating or polymerizing solutes. (b) Solutes which react with at least one solvent. (c) Solutes excluded by Donnan effects. We now consider some examples of such systems.

Dissociating or polymerizing solutes. Consider a solute which undergoes a change in molecular weight in passing from one solvent to another according to the reaction:

$$n\mathrm{A}_m(\text{soln, solvent 1}) \rightarrow m\mathrm{A}_n(\text{soln, solvent 2}) \qquad (9)$$

We may write an equilibrium constant for this reaction as:

$$K_{\mathrm{eq}} = (a_{\mathrm{A}_n})_1{}^m / (a_{\mathrm{A}_m})_2{}^n \qquad (10)$$

If we assume activity coefficients to be independent of concentration, equation 10 simplifies to:

$$c_{\mathrm{A}2} = K c_{\mathrm{A}1}{}^r \qquad (11)$$

where $c_\mathrm{A}$ refers to the solute concentration expressed as the monomer A. The subscripts 1 and 2 refer to solvents one and two, respectively, $r = n/m$, and $K$ is a constant. It may then be seen that Henry's law does not describe this system adequately even at low concentration. For example, the distribution of picric acid between benzene (solvent B) and water (solvent W) at $18\,^\circ\mathrm{C}$ may be represented (22) by the empirical expression:

$$C_{\mathrm{PW}} = 0.084 C_{\mathrm{PB}}{}^{05.32}$$

where picric acid concentration is in gram moles per liter. This expression predicts the ratio of picric acid concentrations in the two solvents within about 5% for concentrations in benzene from $10^{-4}$ to $2 \times 10^{-1}$ g.-moles/liter. Note that this empirically determined exponent is close to one-half, suggesting that the acid exists in benzene as a dimer of the aqueous form.

Reactive systems. In a number of common vapor–liquid systems departures from Henry's law can be quatitatively explained on the basis of chemical reaction between solute and solvent. A common example is the distribution of ammonia between an inert gas and water. Here we may consider the solution of ammonia to take place according to the following sequence:

$$\mathrm{NH_3\ (g)} \rightleftharpoons \mathrm{NH_3\ (aq)} \overset{\mathrm{H_2O}}{\rightleftharpoons} \mathrm{NH_4OH} \rightleftharpoons \mathrm{NH_4}^+ + \mathrm{OH}^- \qquad (12)$$

We may write equilibrium expressions for each step of this sequence as follows:

$$[\mathrm{NH_3(aq)}] = H p_{\mathrm{NH_3}} \qquad (13)$$

$$[\mathrm{NH_4OH}] = K_1 [\mathrm{NH_3(aq)}][\mathrm{H_2O}] \qquad (14)$$

$$[\mathrm{NH_4}^+][\mathrm{OH}^-] = K_2 [\mathrm{NH_4OH}] \qquad (15)$$

Combining equations 13–15, and assuming constant activity co-efficients, we may write:

$$c_{NH_3} = Hp_{NH_3}(1 + K_1 c_{H_2O}) + (Hp_{NH_3})^{1/2}(K_1 K_2 C_{H_2O})^{1/2} \quad (16)$$

Here $c_{NH_3}$ is the total concentration of ammonia in aqueous solution, including free $NH_3$, $NH_4OH$, and $NH_4^+$. Equation 16 is claimed to give a good representation of this system (23,24). At 25 °C the three equilibrium constants are: $H \approx 2.6 \times 10^{-3}$ moles/liter, mm Hg; $K_1 \approx 0.5$ liter/g-mole; $K_2 \approx 6.5 \times 10^{-5}$ g-moles/liter.

Other reactive systems that have been extensively investigated include $Cl_2$, $SO_2$, and the oxides of nitrogen, in water (25). An understanding of the effect of chemical reaction in these systems is especially important when the reaction rates are low or the hold-up time in the liquid phase is short. Under such circumstances the chemical reaction may not occur to a significant extent, and the apparent solubility may be expressed approximately (25) as $c_A = p_A H$.

Donnan exclusion of electrolytes from ion exchange resins (5). We consider here the distribution of a one to one electrolyte $M^+X^-$ between water and an ion exchange resin containing as its counterions either $M^+$ or $X^-$. For an example we choose the cation exchange resin $M^+R^-$, where $R^-$ represents the resin matrix and its fixed negative charges. The equilibrium distribution of electrolyte in this system is subject to the following requirements:

1. The chemical potential of $M^+X^-$ must be the same in the resin and the external solution.

2. Electroneutrality: neither the resin nor external solution may carry a measurable net charge with respect to the other.

In addition we shall assume here for simplicity that the activity coefficients of $M^+X^-$ are unity in both phases. We may then write:

$$c_E^2 = c_{Es}^2 + c_{Es} c_R \quad (17)$$

where $c_E$ is the concentration of the electrolyte $M^+X^-$ in the external solution, $c_{Es}$ is the concentration of $M^+X^-$ in the resin (stationary) phase, and $c_R$ is the concentration of fixed ions in the resin phase. The ratio of electrolyte concentrations in the two phases is then:

$$K_D = c_{Es}/c_E = [(c_R^2/4c_E^2) + 1]^{1/2} - c_R/2c_E \qquad (18)$$

Equation 18 correctly predicts that $K_D$ is quite small for low concentrations of $M^+X^-$ in the external solution and that it increases with concentration. It is only qualitatively correct, however, and does not take into account the effects of resin crosslinkage, ion size, or the nonideality of the system. These topics are discussed at some length by Helfferich (5, pp. 132–138), who also treats the case of electrolytes containing multicharged ions. In general, one may say that the exclusion of external electrolyte is greatly increased by an increase of resin crosslinkage, and is somewhat greater for larger than for smaller ions if chemical activity coefficients are equal. Data for the system water–sodium chloride–Dowex 50–Na$^+$ are presented in Example 3.

*Correlation of ion exchange data* (5, Chap. 5).   Ion exchange equilibria have been very extensively studied in recent years, and a large number of theoretical and empirical model expressions have been developed for data correlation. The more widely used of these expressions are presented in a review by Högfeldt (26). The theoretical bases for them are discussed in detail by Helfferich (5, Chap. 5). Our purpose here is merely to present the salient features of ion exchange behavior and to prepare for the developments in later sections of this chapter.

As a basis for discussion we consider the exchange of a cation $A^{w+}$ in aqueous solution with a second cation $B^{z+}$ in an ion exchange resin. We may represent this process by means of the equation.

$$zA^{w+}(aq) + wB^{z+}(res) \rightleftharpoons zA^{w+}(res) + wB^{z+}(aq) \qquad (19)$$

Here the terms (aq) and (res) refer to the external (or aqueous) and resin phases, respectively. The equilibrium constant for this reaction may be written (27,28) in the form:

$$RT\ln[(a_B^w/a_A^z)_{aq}(a_A^z/a_B^w)_{res}] = \pi(w\bar{V}_B - z\bar{V}_A) \qquad (20)$$

where $a_i$ = chemical activity of species $i$ at the prevailing chemical composition and at the osmotic pressure in the external solution; $\pi$ = osmotic pressure in the resin phase relative to that in the external solution; and $\bar{V}_i$ = partial molal volume of species $i$, assumed independent of composition and pressure (27,28). This choice of reference pressure for activity, first suggested by H. P. Gregor (27,28), is a very convenient one because it shows explicitly the effect of osmotic pressure on ion exchange equilibria. This effect is important as resin osmotic pressures are typically quite high, frequently on the order of several hundred atmospheres.

Equation 20 may be written in more familiar form as:

$$(x_B{}^w/x_A{}^z)(y_A{}^z/y_B{}^w) = (c_{aq}/c_{res})^{(z-w)} K_c = K_x \qquad (21)$$

$$K_c = (\gamma_A{}^z/\gamma_B{}^w)_{aq}(\gamma_B{}^w/\gamma_A{}^z)_{res} \exp \pi(w \bar{V}_B - z \bar{V}_A)/RT \qquad (22)$$

where $x_B$ = the cation equivalent fraction of B in the external solution = $c_B/c_{aq}$; $c_B$ = the concentration of B in the external solution, equivalents per unit volume; $c_{aq}$ = the total concentration of cations in the external solution, equivalents per unit volume; $y_B$ = the cation equivalent fraction of B in the resin phase = $c_B(\text{res})/c_{res}$; $c_{res}$ = the total concentration of cations in the resin, equivalents per unit volume of matrix-free solution; and $\gamma_i$ = activity coefficient of compound $i = a_i/c_i$

Equation 22 correctly predicts the effects of external solution concentration and of chemical compositions of the two phases on the relative distribution of ions between external solution and resin. It also shows correctly that, if activity coefficients are equal, the smaller of two ions will be preferentially adsorbed by the resin. It is important to note here that it is the hydrated ionic volume that counts; thus potassium will normally be more strongly adsorbed than sodium. This equation is not by itself sufficient to describe all of the osomtic effects, however, because the osmotic pressure $\pi$ is affected by the chemical nature of the resin, by the extent of resin cross linkage, and by the fractions of the two cations in the resin. We satisfy ourselves here by pointing out that the selectivity of a given resin for the smaller of two ions is enhanced by increasing the extent of resin cross linkage or by increasing the fraction of the larger ion in the resin. The significance of osmotic effects is discussed at some length by Helfferich (5) and by Gregor (27,28).

The effect of external solution concentration is of particular importance in ion exchange separations and warrants some attention here. Let us consider as an example the feed of sodium chloride solution to a cation resin containing only copper as counterion.

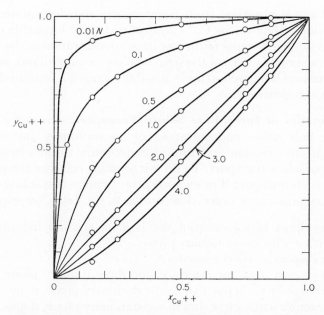

Fig. 7.  Effect of solution normality on the distribution of $Cu^{++}$ between Dowex 50 X-8 and aqueous $CuCl_2$-$NaCl$ solutions.    Note the greatly increased affinity of the resin for copper at low external solution concentrations.    (From H. C. Subba Rao and M. M. David, *A.I.Ch.E. J.*, **3**, 187 (1957)).

If we consider $Na^+$ as ion A and $Cu^{2+}$ as ion B we may write equation 21 as:

$$(y_{Na^+}^{2}/y_{Cu^{2+}})(x_{Cu^{2+}}/x_{Na^+}^{2}) = (c_{aq}/c_{res})K_c = K_x \qquad (23)$$

It may easily be shown that the distribution isotherm will be favorable (convex) for the adsorption of $Na^+$ if $K_x$ in equation 23 is greater than unity and unfavorable if the $K_x$ here is less than unity. Now, it may be noted that $K_c$ and $c_{res}$ in equation 21 will not vary greatly with external solution concentration; for our present purposes we may consider them as essentially constant. Then $Na^+$ adsorption will be favored by a high external solution concentration and be hindered by a low one. In fact, as shown by Figure 7, the distribution isotherm may be made either favorable or unfavorable for $Na^+$ adsorption by appropriate adjustment of $c_{aq}$. Similar behavior is taken advantage of in home water softeners where $Ca^{2+}$ is absorbed from water onto a resin containing $Na^+$ counter-ions. Here $K_x$ for $Ca^{2+}$ adsorption is very favorable during water treatment because of the low ionic concentration in the water, $c_{aq}$. During regeneration of the resin bed, on the other hand, adsorption of sodium is favored so far as possible by using a saturated NaCl solution as regenerant.

**c. Kinetics of Interphase Solute Transport.**    In order to relate the bulk solute concentrations of the stationary and moving phases at any position and time it is necessary to understand the kinetics of solute transport. To do this we must consider the mechanism of such transport. For example, the sorption of a solute by the stationary phase may proceed according to the following sequence:

1. Transport of solute from the bulk of the moving phase to the interface with the stationary phase.
2. Transport across the interface.
3. Transport from the interface into the stationary phase.
4. Adsorption on active sites in the stationary phase, if any.
5. Reaction with active sites in the stationary phase, if any.

Desorption, of course, occurs in the reverse order, and in the special case of ion exchange the sorption of one species is always accompanied by desorption of another. It is assumed in writing this sequence that no reaction occurs in the moving phase.

The various models used to describe solute transport differ both in the relative importance ascribed to the individual steps of the sorption and desorption processes and in the behavior assumed in each step. In many cases the behavior implied is not realistic, but the model may nevertheless be useful if considered as an empirical basis for data correlation. This is usually true of the "reaction-rate model," for example (see Section III-D-2). In all cases the resistance to solute transport across the interface between the stationary and moving phases can be safely neglected, and the interfacial compositions of the two phases may be assumed to be in equilibrium.

Some of the most widely used models are described immediately below. In choosing among them it should be kept in mind that it is not always necessary to know the precise shapes of effluent curves. Consider, for example, the breakthrough curve shown in Figure 20.

It is of greatest importance to know $V_a$, the effluent volume at which solute would first appear in the absence of dispersive forces. This information, which usually gives one a rather good idea of column capacity, can be obtained by assuming instantaneous equilibration between phases and no axial dispersion—the simplest possible model.

*Equilibrium models.* The simplest way to obtain a relation between the bulk concentrations of the two phases is to assume them to be in equilibrium with each other, that is, to neglect entirely the driving forces required for mass transfer, adsorption, and chemical reaction. In addition, we may assume the effective diffusivity in the direction of flow to be either finite or zero.

The assumption of zero diffusivity (29). If we assume zero effective diffusivity in the direction of flow in addition to interphase equilibrium, we have neglected all dispersive forces except that caused by the shape of the equilibrium isotherm. The resulting model provides an accurate description of column behavior only in exceptional cases (see Ex. 1), but it is nonetheless very useful:

1. Calculations based on these assumptions predict the sharpest possible separation and thus indicate the maximum potentialities of a proposed process. This limiting separation is approached in very long columns, especially if very small particles are used for the stationary phase.

2. These assumptions permit approximate prediction of the positions of free bands and breakthrough curves, and thus give a good idea of column capacity.

3. This model is the only one generally useable for multicomponent solutions of interfering solutes or to nonisothermal systems, except for numerical analysis.

A practical advantage of this model is that it requires far less calculation effort than any of the more realistic ones discussed below. In addition, it can be used to determine equilibrium distribution isotherms from breakthrough curves (30–32). The usefulness of this model is illustrated in Section III-B.

The assumption of finite longitudinal diffusivity. Frequently it is possible to obtain a good description of column performance by assuming interphase equilibrium and a finite effective diffusivity in the direction of flow. In some cases, particularly in gas chromatography, these two assumptions may be justified, and the assumed model may accurately represent the behavior of the system. More commonly, however, the success of the model results from the similarity of the effects of longitudinal diffusion and mass-transfer resistance on column operation: a spreading of the solute front as it passes down the column. That is, both longitudinal diffusion and resistance to solute transport are dispersive "forces." For these cases the values of the effective diffusivity that must be used to correlate the data successfully are larger than those predicted by equation 3; $E_A$ must then be considered an empirical parameter to be determined separately. For the specific case of linear distribution equilibria and long columns, it is possible to predict the required value of the effective diffusivity from knowledge of the mass-transfer resistances in the system (see the next section, *Quasi-steady-state models* and *Example 4*). The main application of this model is in fact to such linear systems, where its use leads to very simple and convenient expressions for the shapes of effluent curves. In particular, it should be used to replace the "plate" theories of chromatography; this point is further discussed in Section III-C.

*Quasi-steady-state models* (*5, p. 265*). Here we discuss models for correlation of instantaneous mass transfer rates in terms only of physical properties and bulk solute concentrations of the two phases. Clearly these models cannot give exact descriptions in unsteady-state systems since mass transfer rates depend upon the solute concentration profiles in the two phases and not directly upon average concentration. That is, they are dependent upon past history. Nevertheless, these models have proven very useful, and it is doubtful if it is often worthwhile to consider the concentration profiles in detail (33).

Mass-transfer coefficients.  For systems in which the rates of mass transport are determined primarily by molecular diffusion and convection, it is convenient to express these rates in terms of local mass-transfer coefficients defined by the equations:*

---

* In writing equations 24–27, it has been assumed that the net rate of mass transfer to the particles is small. This will be true where solute concentration is low, e.g., most analytical applications, or when the inflow of one solute is nearly balanced by the outflow of another, e.g., ion exchange. Where this restriction is not met,

$$\partial c_{As}/\partial t = k_f S_0 (c_A - c_{Ai}) \qquad (24)*$$

$$= k_s S_0 (c_{Asi} - c_{As}) \qquad (25)$$

$$= K_f S_0 (c_A - c_A^*) \qquad (26)$$

$$K_f = [(1/k_f) + (1/mk_s)]^{-1} \qquad (27)$$

Here: $k_f$ = the fluid-phase mass-transfer coefficient; $k_s$ = the stationary-phase mass-transfer coefficient; $K_f$ = over-all mass-transfer coefficient; $c_{Ai}$ = interfacial concentration in the moving phase; $c_{Asi}$ = interfacial concentration in the stationary phase; $m = (c_{As} - c_{Asi})/(c_A^* - c_{Ai})$ where $c_A^*$ is the fictitious moving-phase concentration in equilibrium with $c_{As}$. Note that $m$ is the average slope, $dc_{As}^*/dc_A$, of the equilibrium distribution isotherm between $c_{As}$ and $c_{Asi}$; $S_0 = a/(1 - \epsilon)$ = particle specific surface, particle surface divided by particle volume.

Equations 24–27 are written according to the usual convention for steady-state operations, and they may be used in much the same way as for steady-state systems. However, it should be noted that it is not, in general, possible to relate the bulk, or volume-average, concentrations $c_A$ and $c_{As}$ in advance. It is therefore not possible to predict $m$ as a function of $c_A$ accurately unless the distribution expression is linear.** It should also be noted that while the mass-transfer coefficients for the two phases are defined in a very similar way they represent two quite different situations; we shall therefore discuss them separately.

In the case of the moving phase, present knowledge of mass-transfer coefficients to beds of particles is probably best summarized

---

the mass transfer coefficients defined here will be complex functions of concentration, and the forms of these equations will not be convenient. The reader interested in the case of high mass transfer rates is referred to Bird, Stewart, and Lightfoot (14), Section 21–4. The definitions given in equations 24 and 25 are equivalent to the definition of $k_L$ in equation 21.4–46 of this reference.

* For particles of unknown specific surface, it is common practice to write equation 24 as:

$$\partial c_{As}/\partial t = (k_f a) (c_A - c_{Ai})/(1 - \epsilon). \qquad (24a)$$

Equations 25 and 26 may be written analogously.

** For an exception to this rule, see Examples 6 and 7.

TABLE III
Particle Shape Factors for Packed-Bed Correlations (35)

| Particle shape | $\psi$ |
|---|---|
| Spheres | 1.00 |
| Cylinders | 0.91 |
| Flakes | 0.86 |

by means of the following empirical correlation,[*] widely used for both steady- and unsteady-state processes:

$$j_D = 0.91\psi\text{Re}^{-0.51} \quad (\text{Re} < 50) \tag{28}$$

$$j_D = 0.61\psi\text{Re}^{-0.41} \quad (\text{Re} > 50) \tag{29}$$

Here the Colburn factor, $j_D$, and the bed Reynolds number, Re, are defined as:

$$j_D = (k_f/\epsilon v)(\text{Sc}_{\text{A}m})_f^{2/3} \tag{30}$$

$$\text{Re} = G_0/a\psi\mu_f \tag{31}$$

where $G_0$ = superficial mass velocity of fluid through the bed, is independent of density changes. $G_0 = \epsilon\rho v_z$, where $\rho$ is the fluid density; $\mu_f$ = the "film" fluid viscosity, defined as the viscosity for a fluid at the "film composition," that is at the arithmetic average of bulk and interfacial compositions; $(\text{Sc}_{\text{A}m})_f$ = the film Schmidt number for component A = $(\mu/\rho\mathfrak{D}_{\text{A}m})_f$, defined analogously to $\mu_f$; the shape factor $\psi$ is a constant characteristic of the shape of the packing particles (see Table III for a few sample values).

The estimation of mass-transfer coefficients in the stationary phase is more complicated than that in the moving one for two reasons:

1. The mechanisms of solute transport are more complex (5, Chap. 6; 36–38).

2. There is no closely analogous steady-state situation to draw upon for a model.

[*] F. Yoshida, private communication (December, 1959). See also Hougen, Watson, and Ragatz (34). The $j$-factor and mass-transfer coefficients in these references are obtained through division of ours by $\psi$. A similar relation for ion-exchange resins is given by Moison and O'Hern (7).

We limit discussion here to those systems in which solute transport can be described by Fick's second "law":

$$\partial c_{As}(x,y,z)/\partial t \ = \ \mathfrak{D}_{As}\nabla^2 c_{As}(x,y,z) \tag{32}$$

where $c_{As}(x,y,z)$ is the concentration of A at any point $(x,y,z)$ in a given particle, and $\mathfrak{D}_{As}$ is an apparent diffusivity of solute A through the stationary phase. Column operations in such systems have been extensively studied and a number of empirical expressions have been developed to describe approximately the rate of mass transport in the fixed phase. One very simple and reasonably satisfactory expression for spherical particles (5, p. 265) which has found widespread use is:

$$k_s \ = \ 10\mathfrak{D}_{As}/D_p \ = \ (5/3)(S_0\mathfrak{D}_{As}) \tag{33}$$

For nonspherical particles, $D_p$ may be replaced by $6/S_0$. A number of other expressions have been suggested (5, p. 265; 33) but these are more difficult to use and have apparently not found wide acceptance in analysis of unsteady-state column separations.

The combined effects of longitudinal diffusion and resistance to mass transfer. It is very difficult to integrate the equation of continuity, equation 7, for systems in which both longitudinal diffusion and mass-transfer resistance must be considered. As a result the usual practice is to consider only one of these two dispersive forces explicitly, and to make an approximate allowance for the other. Thus one may neglect $\mathfrak{D}_{Aa}$ in equation 7 if one decreases the actual mass transfer coefficient by an amount equivalent to the effect of longitudinal diffusion. Alternatively one may assume interphase equilibrium if the apparent longitudinal diffusion coefficient is increased sufficiently to account for the effect of mass-transfer resistance. Such approximate procedures, discussed by Vermeulen (39) for the general case of nonlinear isotherms, have been found to be satisfactory for most practical purposes.

An exact analysis may be made for one limiting case: passage of a solute exhibiting a linear isotherm through a long column. For such a system, discussed in some detail in Section III-C, the dispersive effects due to longitudinal diffusion and mass-transfer resistance are additive (40). We may then define Péclet numbers or over-all mass-transfer coefficients modified to account for the total dispersive tendencies of the system:

$$\frac{1}{\text{Pé}_{\text{tot}}} = \frac{\mathfrak{D}_{Aa}}{vD_p} + \left[\frac{(1 - \epsilon)K_D}{\epsilon + K_D(1 - \epsilon)}\right]^2 \left(\frac{v}{K_f S_0 D_p}\right)\left(\frac{\epsilon}{1 - \epsilon}\right) \quad (34)$$

$$\frac{1}{K_{f,\text{tot}}} = \frac{1}{K_f} + \left(\frac{1 - \epsilon}{\epsilon}\right)\left(\frac{S_0 \mathfrak{D}_{Aa}}{\epsilon v^2}\right)\left[\frac{\epsilon + K_D(1 - \epsilon)}{K_D(1 - \epsilon)}\right] \quad (35)$$

Here then $\text{Pé}_{\text{tot}}$ is the Péclet number to be used in III-C-2 if the effect of mass transfer is to be taken into consideration, and $K_{f,\text{tot}}$ is the over-all mass-transfer coefficient that should be used in III-C-3 if longitudinal diffusion is to be accounted for. Clearly either equation 34 or 35 may also be used to determine the relative importance of these two dispersive tendencies. The applicability of equations 34 and 35 can best be understood in the light of the discussions in Sections III-C and D.

The Thomas or chemical-reaction model. In practice it has been found that the rate-controlling steps in interphase transfer are usually the physical processes just discussed. For example, in ion-exchange and most adsorption processes, the adsorption on active sites appears to be extremely rapid and may be assumed without serious error to be instantaneous. Nevertheless, it is commonly desirable to postulate a chemical reaction as the rate-limiting step in two important cases: exchange of ions of equal valence in an ion-exchange resin, and the adsorption of a single solute on an adsorbent exhibiting a Langmuir adsorption isotherm for the solute. This is done because of the greater mathematical simplicity of the resulting rate expressions; in these cases the assumption of a rate-limiting chemical reaction of the type described below permits calculation of the shape of a free band of solute. Use of the mass-transfer model, except for linear systems, is limited to the calculation of a few simple breakthrough curves. The usefulness of the reaction-rate model is increased by the fact that an approximate relation is available between the chemical rate constant and the physical mass-transfer coefficients just described. This approximate relation becomes exact as the equilibrium distribution isotherm approaches linearity.

We begin discussion here by presenting two special cases to which the chemical-reaction model may be applied. We then show how each may be reduced to a common form and how this resulting general expression may be related to the mass-transfer model.

*Case 1:* Exchange of ions of equal valence. Consider here the feed of a solution of ion $A^+$ to an ion-exchange column originally containing only $B^+$. Assume the cation concentration of the solution and resin phases to be constant at $c_0$ and $c_{s0}$, respectively. If we then postulate a bimolecular reaction as the rate-controlling step for the exchange reaction, we may write:

$$\partial c_{As}/\partial t = (k_i/c_{s0})[c_A c_{Bs} - (1/K_c)(c_{As}c_B)] \qquad (36)$$

Here $k_i$ is the chemical rate constant, and both it and the equilibrium constant $K_c$ are assumed not to vary significantly as the exchange process proceeds.

*Case 2:* Langmuir adsorption. Consider now the feed of a solution of some solute A at constant concentration $c_{A0}$ to an initially solute-free sorbent column. Assume that the equilibrium distribution of A between phases may be expressed according to Table II as:

$$c_{As} = K'c_A Q/(1 + K'c_A) \qquad (37)$$

If we assume the rate expressions originally used by Langmuir, and neglect mass-transfer resistance, we may write:

$$\partial c_{As}/\partial t = (k_i/Q)[c_A(Q - c_{As}) - c_{As}/K'] \qquad (38)$$

In the ensuing discussion we shall assume both $K'$ and $Q$ to be constant.

*The Generalization of Thomas.* It has been shown by Thomas (41) that equations 36 and 38 can be reduced to a single expression

TABLE IV

| Variable | Ion exchange | Langmuir adsorption |
|---|---|---|
| Concentration of A in mobile phase, $x_A$ | $x_A = c_A/c_0$ | $x_A = c_A/c_{A0}$ |
| Concentration of A in stationary phase, $y_A$ | $y_A = c_{As}/c_{s0}$ | $y_A = c_{As}(1 + K'c_{A0})/K'Qc_{A0}$ |
| | | $= c_{As}/c_{As0}$ |
| Equilibrium parameter, $r$ | $r = 1/K_c$ | $r = 1/(1 + K'c_{A0})$ |

by introduction of the modified concentration and equilibrium parameters in Table IV.

Note that the definitions of $x_A$ and $y_A$ are similar for the two cases. In each, $x_A$ is the ratio of concentration of solute A in the fluid phase to that in the feed, and $y_A$ is the ratio of solute concentration in the stationary phase to that in equilibrium with the feed. These definitions are thus generalizations of those given in connection with equation 21. The treatment given below can be extended to columns with a uniform initial loading through the use of similar modified variables (42). We now write equations 36 and 38 as:

$$\partial y_A / \partial t = k_i (c_{A0}/c_{As0})[x_A(1 - y_A) - r y_A(1 - x_A)] \quad (39)$$

It may easily be shown that the corresponding form of equation 26 is:

$$\partial y_A / \partial t = (K_f S_0)(c_{A0}/c_{As0})(x_A - x_A^*) \quad (40)$$

We may now obtain a relation between the chemical rate constant and the over-all mass-transfer coefficient by equating these two expressions:

$$\beta = k_i / K_f S_0 = (x_A - x_A^*)/[x_A(1 - y_A) - r y_A(1 - x_A)] \quad (41)$$

The ratio $\beta$ is a function* of both $x_A$, $x_A^*$, and $r$. The effect of $x_A$ appears explicitly and also implicitly, through the dependence of $K_f$ on the local slope of the equilibrium curve, $m = dc_{As}/dc_A$ (see eq. 27). For analytic integration of the equation of continuity through use of equation 39, it is necessary to assume $k_i$ to be constant; that is to neglect the effects of $x_A$ on $\beta$ and to assume a relation between $x_A$ and $x_A^*$ (or equivalently between $x_A$ and $y_A$). It can be shown (39), however, that for moderately curved isotherms* the value of $\beta$ does not depend very strongly upon these assumptions. It is common practice to calculate $\beta$ for $x_A = 0.5$ and for a $y_A(x_A)$ dependent upon conditions of absorption. If $r < 1$ (convex isotherm), it is usually assumed that $y_A = x_A$ (see Ex. 6); if $r > 1$, it is usually assumed that $y_A = y_A^*(x_A)$. The value

---

* The ratio $\beta$ is closely related but not identical to the $b$ of Hiester and Vermeulen (43). The definition used here is chosen for convenience: since the local slope $m$ of the equilibrium curve appears only in the definition of $K_f$, graphical and trial and error determinations are avoided. The slope $m$ should be evaluated at the composition $x_A$ for which $\beta$ is to be calculated.

of $\beta$ may then be readily calculated, using l'Hôpital's rule for $r > 1$:

| $r$ | $\beta(= k_i/K_f S_0)$ |
|-----|------------------------|
| $r < 1$ | $2/(r + 1)$ |
| $r > 1$ | $(r + 1)/2r$ |

For the linear case, $r = 1$, $\beta$ is identically unity, and the chemical-reaction model is exactly equivalent to the mass-transfer model.

*Unsteady-state models.* If one takes into account the effect of past history on the instantaneous mass-transfer coefficients, considerable additional difficulty is encountered; a thorough discussion of this situation is outside of the scope of the present article. Up to the present time, the only available treatments (44,45,61) assume pseudo-steady-state behavior in the fluid phase and Fick's second "law" in the stationary phase. They include linear and Langmuir distribution isotherms and ignore longitudinal diffusion.

### III. Determination of Effluent Curves and Column Concentration Profiles

A. INTRODUCTORY REMARKS

In this section we show how effluent curves and column concentration profiles may be determined. That is, we show how the mass-balance equation of Section II-C-2-a has been integrated for a number of practically important sets of operating conditions. The purpose of this section is to demonstrate practical calculation techniques rather than to give mathematical justification of the results presented. We have emphasized the most useful "working" equations by printing very brief descriptions immediately beneath them in lightface italic type. Furthermore, we have worked out detailed numerical examples which serve to illustrate the meanings of the equations and the variables that appear in them. Mathematical manipulations are minimized, and the more tedious of them are set apart from the rest of the text by the use of heavy brackets. Such sections may be omitted by the reader without great loss, except that the definitions of some variables will be found in them. Organization is according to assumed system behavior.

We begin in Section III-B by considering equilibrium operation with negligible dispersive forces. These conditions exist only as a limiting case and are seldom closely approximated in industrial applications. However, calculations based on such an analysis are easily obtained and quite useful. Coupled with estimates of measurable operating conditions, obtainable from such references as Nachod and Schubert (1), they give a fair idea of the potentialities of a proposed separation process. In addition, a good understanding of equilibrium operation provides considerable insight into the behavior of fixed beds. Of particular interest here are the concepts of "self-sharpening" and "self-broadening" solute fronts. The behavior of "equilibrium" systems is discussed at some length in Section III-B, and at least the qualitative portion of this discussion is strongly recommended.

We next consider the behavior of linear systems with appreciable dispersive tendencies, in Section III-C. We consider these separately because of the great mathematical simplifications resulting from linearity, and because linear behavior is often closely approximated in practice. Of particular interest here are the discussions of the physical significance of linearity, III-C-1, and the close equivalence of the "longitudinal-dispersion" and "mass-transfer" models, Example 5. For most calculation purposes the simpler longitudinal dispersion model is to be preferred.

In the final section, III-D, we consider nonlinear systems with appreciable dispersion. Here it is important to become familiar with the concept of "asymptotic" or "constant-form" fronts. The assumption of such a front, reasonable for the analysis of over half of the breakthrough curves encountered in practice, permits a very considerable simplification. It may be noted here that constant-form fronts are very closely related to the self-sharpening fronts of Section III-B. Where constant-form fronts cannot reasonably be assumed, one must usually resort to the Thomas model. It is shown in Example 7 that this model gives a useful description of the behavior of many systems, in spite of the unrealistic assumptions made in its development.

## B. EQUILIBRIUM OPERATION WITH NEGLIGIBLE LONGITUDINAL DISPERSION

In this section we describe fixed-bed separations carried out under such conditions that both mass-transfer resistance and $\mathfrak{D}_{Aa}$, the effective diffusivity in the direction of flow, are negligible, i.e., equilibrium nondispersive operation. We begin with a qualitative explanation of the behavior observed under these conditions and then consider three representative special cases: single-solute isothermal, multi-solute isothermal, and single-solute adiabatic operations.

## 1. The Characteristic Features of Equilibrium Nondispersive Operation

There are two factors of importance governing the behavior of fixed-bed sorbers under these conditions:

1. The independence of column behavior on time, or equivalently, upon solute velocity through the sorbent bed.
2. The effect of the shape of the equilibrium distribution isotherm on the sharpness of solute fronts in the bed (column isochrones) and effluent curves.

Among the first to recognize the importance of these factors was de Vault (29), who has given a very readable and authoritative discussion of the single-solute isothermal case.

The independence of column behavior on time follows directly from neglect of all kinetic factors. It is important in often allowing us to write expressions for solute concentration in terms of a single independent variable

$$\phi = s/z \tag{42}$$

rather than the two independent variables, $s$ = volume of solution fed to column divided by (empty) column cross section; and $z$ = distance along column from upstream end in direction of flow.

By combining variables in this way we reduce the equation of continuity from a partial to an ordinary differential equation, a very useful simplification as we shall see. The variable $\phi$ may be considered as a dimensionless volume: the ratio of volume of solution fed to the column to the total column volume (i.e., of both fixed and moving phases) contained within a distance $z$ of the column inlet. The replacement of $s$ and $z$ by $\phi$ is permissible in all nondispersive equilibrium operations provided that the required initial and boundary conditions are expressible in terms of

$\phi$. The validity of this statement may easily be demonstrated by means of a simple thought experiment: the feed of equal volumes of a given solution to two uniformly loaded sorbent columns differing only in cross section. Although the solute will have penetrated the column of smaller cross section to a greater depth, solute concentrations at equal values of $\phi$ are the same. This must be true since the geometric configuration of the column can influence only the rate

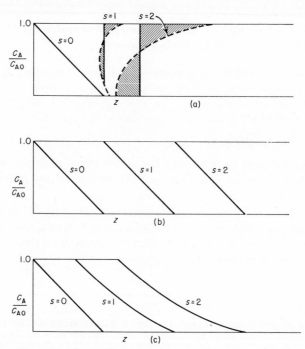

Fig. 8. The effect of isotherm shape on column concentration profiles. Solute exhibiting (a) a convex isotherm; (b) a linear isotherm; (c) a concave isotherm.

of equilibration. It should be noted that the above statements are in no way limited to single-solute or isothermal systems.

The effect of the shape of the equilibrium distribution isotherm may be briefly described as follows. Consider the continued feed of solution of constant composition to a column initially nonuniformly loaded with solute (see Fig. 8). The changes of the solute concentration profiles in the column with amount of solution fed will then be as shown in Figure 8 (a–c) for solutes exhibiting "favorable," linear, and "unfavorable" isotherms, respectively. That is:

1. If the distribution isotherm is "favorable," $d^2f/dc_A^2$ negative, the column concentration profile will become increasingly sharp and approach a step function.

2. If the distribution isotherm is linear, the concentration profile will be displaced toward higher $z$ with no change in shape.

3. If the distribution isotherm is "unfavorable," the column concentration profile becomes more diffuse, without limit.

The reasons for such behavior lie in the effects of concentration level on average rate of solute travel. Under equilibrium conditions the average linear rate of solute travel, $v_A$, at any column cross section is clearly

$$v_A = v \times \text{ fraction of total solute in moving phase}$$

$$= v\epsilon c_A / [\epsilon c_A + (1 - \epsilon)c_{As}] \tag{43}$$

where $v$ is the interstitial velocity of the solution as previously defined. Now, for solutes exhibiting a favorable isotherm, the ratio $c_A/c_{As}$ increases with $c_A$; that is, the solute is moving more rapidly where the concentration is higher. Then the solute in regions of higher concentration tends to overtake that in regions of lower concentration, and the solute front becomes sharper. In the case of linear isotherms, the rate of solute travel is independent of concentration, and there is no tendency for either a sharpening or broadening of the solute front. In the case of unfavorable isotherms, the progressive broadening of the solute front results from the higher rate of movement of solute in the regions of lower concentration. It follows from the above discussion that the reverse behavior takes place during elution of a solute:

1. There will be a progressive broadening of the solute front during elution of a solute with a "favorable" distribution isotherm.

2. There will be no change of shape of the solute front during elution of a material with a linear distribution isotherm.

3. The solute front will become sharper and approach a step function for elution of a material with an "unfavorable" isotherm.

During elution then the terms "favorable" and "unfavorable" are misleading.

Whereas the effects of distribution isotherm shape are most pronounced in nondispersive equilibrium operation, they also occur in the presence of dispersive forces. Thus, as discussed quantitatively in Section III-D, the sharpening effect noted during sorption of a solute with a "favorable" isotherm opposes the dispersive effects of mass-transfer resistance and longitudinal diffusion.

## 2. Isothermal Sorption and Elution of a Single Solute

We begin our discussion of equilibrium behavior by modifying the equation of continuity for this simple case. We consider the feed of solution of a single solute A at constant concentration to a column of constant cross section initially containing an arbitrary monotone distribution of A expressible as $c_A(z,0)$. Note that specification of the distribution of A in the fluid phase is sufficient, since under the assumed conditions $c_{As} = f(c_A)$, and also that $\partial c_{As}/\partial t = (\partial c_A/\partial t)(dc_{As}/dc_A) = (\partial c_A/\partial t)f'(c_A)$.

[We may then write the equation of continuity in the form*:

$$0 = v(\partial c_A/\partial z) + (\partial c_A/\partial t)\{1 + [(1 - \epsilon)/\epsilon]f'(c_A)\} \qquad (44)$$

For equilibrium operation we may replace time by $s$, the volume of solution fed to the column per unit (empty) cross section, since start of operation. Thus we may write:

$$ds/dt = \epsilon v \qquad (45)$$

and

$$s = \int \epsilon v dt \qquad (46)$$

For the usual case of constant feed rate, $s = \epsilon vt$. We now combine equations 44 and 45 to obtain:

$$0 = (\partial c_A/\partial z) + (\partial c_A/\partial s)[\epsilon + (1 - \epsilon)f'(c_A)] \qquad (47)$$

Now, for any initial loading and feed schedule $c_A = c_A(z,s)$, and therefore

---

* Material set in heavy brackets is primarily mathematical in nature and may be avoided by those interested only in using the results. Important equations and definitions of symbols may occasionally appear in this material, however.

$$dc_A = (\partial c_A/\partial z)dz + (\partial c_A/\partial s)ds \tag{48}$$

$$\partial s/\partial z = -(\partial c_A/\partial z)/(\partial c_A/\partial s) \tag{49}$$

We may then combine equations 47 and 49 to write the equation of continuity as:

$$(\partial s/\partial z)_{c_A} = [\epsilon + (1 - \epsilon)f'(c_A)] \tag{50}$$

Equation 50 may be readily integrated for constant feed concentration, $(c_A(0,t) = $ a constant) to give:

$$s/[\epsilon + (1 - \epsilon)f'(c_A)] = z - z_0(c_A) \tag{51}$$

Here $z_0$ is the distance corresponding to any $c_A$ at the start of operation. We may then define a time-distance variable for each concentration $c_A$ as

$$\phi(c_A) = s/(z - z_0)$$

and write

$$\phi(c_A) = [\epsilon + (1 - \epsilon)f'(c_A)] \tag{52}]$$
*concentration profile, broadening front*

Equation 52 just says that the distance down the column to a region of any given solute concentration is directly proportional to the amount of solute fed, but that the proportionality constant may be different for each concentration.

The $s - z - c_A$ and $\phi - c_A$ relations for sorption of solute with an "unfavorable" isotherm are shown graphically in Figure 9a. Note that, in accordance with our introductory discussion, the solute front becomes increasingly diffuse on continued solution feed. It may also be seen that equation 52 provides a very compact description of column behavior.

This equation must, however, be used with care in the case of sharpening fronts, that is, for sorption of a solute with a "favorable" isotherm or for elution of one with an "unfavorable" one: if used blindly it will predict the occurrence of multivalued curves, such as those indicated by dotted lines in Figure 8a, on continued solution feed. Such double-valued curves have no physical meaning, and they should be replaced by the solid lines shown in the figure. The determination of the proper curve shapes is discussed in detail

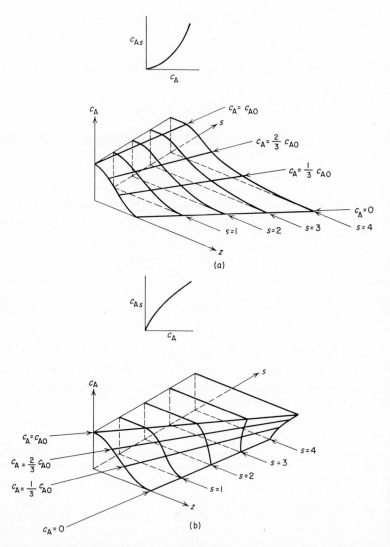

Fig. 9. Graphical presentation of equation 51 for two simple nonlinear isotherms: (a) "concave" isotherm; (b) "convex" isotherm. In each case, solute
at constant concentration is being fed to an initially partially saturated column.
Note that the predicted behavior is physically realistic in the first case but
not in the second (from D. de Vault (29)).

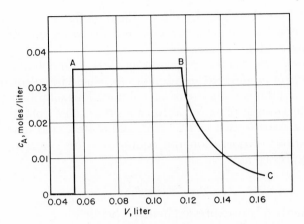

Fig. 10. Purification of lauric acid on a charcoal column (adapted from D. de Vault (29)). See Example 1.

by de Vault (29), but it is seldom of practical interest. We content ourselves here by pointing out that on the feed of sufficient solute to the column the solute front will become a step function as shown in Figure 10. We may find the position of the concentration discontinuity for this limiting case very simply through use of a material balance.

[Thus, we may write:

$$\underset{\text{solute fed}}{c_{A0}s} + \underset{\text{solute initially present}}{\int_0^\infty \{\epsilon c_A(z,0) + (1 - \epsilon)f[c_A(z,0)]\}\,dz}$$
$$= \underset{\text{solute in column}}{[\epsilon c_{A0} + (1 - \epsilon)f(c_{A0})]z_d} \qquad (53)$$

Here $c_{A0}$ is the solute concentration in the feed and $z_d$ is the position of the discontinuity corresponding to a feed volume per unit column cross section of $s$. For the very common case of an initially empty column, equation 51 may be written

$$\phi_d = s/z_d = [\epsilon + (1 - \epsilon)f(c_{A0})/c_{A0}]$$
$$\text{position of discontinuity for a sharpening front} \qquad (54)]$$

Equation 54 is used in the following example. For columns with initially uniform solute loadings all breakthrough curves, or isochrones, are described by either equation 52 or 54. The former must be used for broadening fronts and the latter for those which are self-sharpening.

*Example 1: Purification of lauric acid (29).* One hundred cubic centimeters of an $0.035M$ solution of lauric acid in petroleum ether are fed to a small activated-carbon column. This solution is followed by a large volume of pure petroleum ether. The column is 3 cm long, has a cross section of 1.32 cm², and is 40% void space. Under the conditions of operation the equilibrium distribution isotherm may be expressed as:

$$c_{As}{}^* = 2.26c_A{}^{0.324} \tag{55}$$

where $c_A$ and $c_{As}{}^*$ are expressed in moles per liter.

Calculate the effluent curve for this operation assuming local equilibrium and no longitudinal dispersion.

*Solution.* We begin by considering the absorption of lauric acid from the feed solution. The isotherm for this case is convex, and the column initially contains no solute. We may then use equation 54 to describe column behavior and write for the position of the concentration discontinuity:

$$\phi_d = s/z_d = 0.4 + 0.6 \times 2.26(0.035)^{0.324-1} = 0.4 + 13.1 = 13.5 \tag{56}$$

We see that for this case the hold-up of solute in the column is negligible. Then

$$s_d = 3 \text{ cm} \times 13.5 = 40.5 \text{ cm} \tag{57}$$

and the effluent volume at which solute first appears is

$$V_d = 1.32 \, s_d \text{ cm}^2 = 1.32 \times 40.5$$

$$V_d = 53.5 \text{ cm}^3 \tag{58}$$

This "solute front" is shown in the effluent curve for the system pictured in Figure 10, at A.

We next consider the elution of lauric acid from the column. Since the elution of a solute exhibiting a concave isotherm results in a diffuse concentration profile, we use the integrated form of equation 52 directly. However, it will be convenient to replace $s$ by $V/1.32$ cm². Remembering that

$$V = 100.0 \text{ cm}^3 \qquad \text{at } z = 0 \qquad (59)$$

$$\text{for } 0 < c_{A0} < 0.035$$

where $V$ = effluent volume measured from start of lauric acid adsorption, we obtain:

$$V - 100 \text{ cm}^3 = [0.4 + 0.6(dc_{As}/dc_A)]1.32z \text{ cm}^2 \qquad (60)$$

Putting in 3 cm for $z$ and using the given equilibrium distribution isotherm we may write equation 60 as:

$$V = (101.6 + 1.74c_A{}^{-0.676}) \text{ cm}^3 \qquad (61)$$

$$\text{for } 0 < c_A < 0.035$$

Equation 61 relates effluent concentration from the column with effluent volume. This relationship is shown in Figure 10 as line B-C. We know from the above discussion of adsorption behavior that line A-B must be as shown in the figure. Note that equation 61 predicts that an infinite amount of solvent is required for complete elution. This follows from the slope of the distribution isotherm, which becomes infinite at zero concentration. For a solute exhibiting an isotherm with a finite limiting slope, for example, a Langmuir isotherm, our development would predict complete elution with a finite solvent volume.

### 3. Isothermal Sorption or Elution of Two or More Interfering Solutes

We begin by considering the simultaneous feed of $n$ interfering solutes to an initially solute-free column. As stated in the introduction to this section, the concentration of any solute, $c_i$, is a function only of $\phi$. It then follows that for any $c_i$, the total composition of the solution, i.e., the concentrations of each of the other $(n - 1)$ species, is fixed, and therefore that $c_{is}$ is a function only of $c_i$ and the composition of the feed solution. For any feed composition we may then use the results of Section III-B-2 if we can determine the relation between $c_{is}$ and $c_i$.

This determination may be made as follows. For each component we write

$$\phi = \epsilon + (1-\epsilon)(dc_{is}/dc_i) \qquad (62)$$

and therefore, for any point in the column

$$(dc_A/dc_{As})_R = (dc_B/dc_{Bs})_R = \ldots = (dc_n/dc_{ns})_R \qquad (63)$$

Here the subscript $R$ indicates that these derivatives are restricted to the initial and feed conditions of operation. For simplicity we now limit ourselves to two solutes, A and B; the following treatment may be readily extended to more complex systems, at least in principle.

[We begin by recognizing that the fixed-phase concentration of either species may be expressed as a function of $c_A$ and $c_B$:

$$c_{As} = c_{As}(c_A, c_B) \qquad (64a)$$

$$c_{Bs} = c_{Bs}(c_A, c_B) \qquad (64b)$$

We may then write

$$dc_{As} = (\partial c_{As}/\partial c_A)dc_A + (\partial c_{As}/\partial c_B)dc_B \qquad (65a)$$

$$dc_{Bs} = (\partial c_{Bs}/\partial c_A)dc_A + (\partial c_{Bs}/\partial c_B)dc_B \qquad (65b)$$

Then for any chosen initial and feed conditions we obtain:

$$(dc_{As}/dc_A)_R = (\partial c_{As}/\partial c_A) + (\partial c_{As}/\partial c_B)(dc_B/dc_A)_R \qquad (66a)$$

$$(dc_{Bs}/dc_B)_R = (\partial c_{Bs}/\partial c_A)(dc_A/dc_B)_R + (\partial c_{Bs}/\partial c_B) \qquad (66b)$$

We now use equation 63 to eliminate $(dc_{As}/dc_A)_R$ and $(dc_{Bs}/dc_B)_R$ between these equations and to solve for $(dc_B/dc_A)$:

$$\left(\frac{dc_B}{dc_A}\right)^2 + \left\{\frac{(\partial c_{As}/\partial c_A) - (\partial c_{Bs}/\partial c_B)}{(\partial c_{As}/\partial c_B)}\right\}\left(\frac{dc_B}{dc_A}\right) - \frac{(\partial c_{Bs}/\partial c_A)}{(\partial c_{As}/\partial c_B)} = 0 \qquad (67)$$

Solving this quadratic expression for $(dc_B/dc_A)$ we get:

$$dc_B/dc_A = {}^1/_2[Q \pm (Q^2 + 4R)^{1/2}] \qquad (68)$$

where $Q = (\partial c_{Bs}/\partial c_B - \partial c_{As}/\partial c_A)/(\partial c_{As}/\partial c_B)$ and $R = (\partial c_{Bs}/\partial c_A)/(\partial c_{As}/\partial c_B)$.

Equation 68 is a first-order, ordinary differential equation relating $c_A$ and $c_B$. It may be integrated if $c_A$ is known for any value of $c_B$. For the sorption operation under discussion, this information is obtained from the composition of feed to the column. In the elution of solutes from a uniformly loaded column with pure solvent, this information is obtained from the initial solute concentrations in the column.

It may be seen that equation 67 is a quadratic expression and therefore that there are two mathematically possible solutions to it, as indicated in equation 68. A choice between these two possibilities must be made on physical grounds.]

We find then the restrictions imposed by the requirement of local equilibrium permit us to determine a unique relation between $c_A$ and $c_B$.

We may now make use of this information to simplify equations 64a and b:

$$c_{As} = [c_{As}(c_A)]_R \qquad c_{Bs} = [c_{Bs}(c_B)]_R \qquad (69a,b)$$

*Equivalent binary isotherms. Explicit forms to be obtained from integration of equation 68.*

Again the subscript $R$ is used to denote restriction of these relations to some specific set of initial and feed conditions. Once equations 69a and b have been obtained one may proceed just as in Section III-B-2. Solutions of equation 67 have been obtained for some specific simple cases, but for most systems the direct integration of equation 67 or 68 is very difficult. Under these circumstances it is frequently preferable to write equation 63 in difference form and obtain a $c_A - c_B$ relation by a trial and error procedure: thus we may write equation 63 as:

$$(c_{A2} - c_{A1})/(c_{As2} - c_{As1}) = (c_{B2} - c_{B1})/(c_{Bs2} - c_{Bs1}) \qquad (70)$$

Here the subscripts 1 and 2 refer to any two values of $\phi$. The procedure is then as follows:

1. Choose point 1 as at $\phi = 0$ or $\phi = \infty$ where $c_A$ and $c_B$ are both known.
2. Pick a value of $c_A$ for which the corresponding value of $c_B$ is desired.
3. Find a value of $c_B$ which will satisfy equation 70 as well as equations 64a and b.

Again two $c_A - c_B$ relationships are obtained, one of which must be discarded on physical grounds. Note again that the procedure here is just like that for one-solute systems, except in the determination of the $c_A - c_{As}$ and $c_B - c_{Bs}$ relations.

*Example 2: Ion-exclusion separation of salt and glycerine.* Ionic solutes can be effectively separated from nonelectrolytes without chemical or thermal regeneration by the process of ion exclusion, a separations technique pioneered by Wheaton and Bauman.* In this process a predetermined volume of the mixture to be separated is fed to a solute-free ion-exchange column, and is then washed out with pure water. The solutes to be separated pass down the column as interfering free bands with separation occurring because they travel at different rates.

We consider here in detail only the sorption step, in this case the feed of NaCl and glycerine to a column of a sulfonic-acid resin in the Na$^+$ form. In this system, the salt is strongly excluded by the Donnan effect discussed in Section II-C-2. The glycerine on the other hand distributes relatively evenly between the fixed and moving phases and moves down the column more slowly than the NaCl.

We shall assume the following to describe the system**:

Feed solution: 50% glycerine and 10% salt by weight.
Volume of solution fed: 40% of empty volume of column.
Equilibrium data:

$$Y_S = 0.484(0.0286X_S + 1.408X_S^2 + 1.102X_GX_S^2)$$

$$Y_G = 0.484(0.5687X_G + 0.4472X_G^2 + 2.30X_GX_S - 1.13\ X_G^2X_S)$$

Column void fraction, $\epsilon = 0.38$.
Average density of resin phase (47), $\rho_s \approx 1.385$ g cm$^{-3}$.
Average density of moving phase (47), $\rho \approx 1.17$ g cm$^{-3}$.
Here $Y$ = weight fraction of solute in resin phase; $X$ = weight fraction of solute in moving phase; and the subscripts S and G refer to salt and glycerine, respectively.

---

* See for example, Bauman, Wheaton, and Simpson. For separation of similar mixtures by ion retardation see Hatch, Dillon and Smith (46); also Helferich (5, p. 393).

** The indicated distribution equilibria are approximately correct for commercial Dowex 50 resin with 8% cross-linkage, i.e., 8% divinylbenzene. They are close approximations of the data of Shurts and White (48), simplified for convenience of presentation here.

Note that for the high solute concentrations being considered here the neglect of density variation may introduce an appreciable error.
*Solution:*

a. Relation between salt and glycerine concentrations in solution. We begin by writing expressions analogous to equations 66a and b:

$$(dY_s/dX_s)_R = 0.484[0.0286 + 2.816\ X_s + 2.204X_GX_s$$
$$+ 1.102X_s^2(dX_G/dX_s)_R]\quad (71a)$$

$$(dY_G/dX_G)_R = 0.484[0.5687 + 0.894X_G + 2.30X_s$$
$$+ 2.30X_G(dX_s/dX_G)_R - 2.26X_GX_s - 1.13X_G^2(dX_s/dX_G)_R]\quad (71b)$$

We now equate these two expressions to obtain:

$$) = 0.5401 - 0.516X_s + 0.894X_G - 4.468X_GX_s$$
$$+ (dX_s/dX_G)_R(2.30X_G - 1.13X_G^2) - 1.102X_s^2(dX_G/dX_s)_R\quad (72)$$

This equation may be integrated numerically by iteration, starting at $X_s = 0.1$, $X_G = 0.5$. Here we may write equation 72 as:

$$) = 0.5401 - 0.0516 + 0.447 - 0.2234$$
$$+ (1.15 - 0.28)\ (dX_s/dX_G) - (0.01102)\ (dX_G/dX_s)$$
$$= 0.712 + 0.87(dX_s/dX_G) - 0.01102\ (dX_G/dX_s)\quad (73)$$

Putting this expression in the standard quadratic form we obtain:

$$(dX_s^2/dX_G) + 0.818(dX_s/dX_G) - 0.0127 = 0\quad (74)$$

We may then write:

$$dX_s/dX_G = [-0.818 \pm (0.668 + 0.051)^{1/2}]/2$$
$$= -0.83 + 0.015\quad (75)$$

The second of these two solutions is found to be the physically correct one by suppressing the terms showing the effect of glycerine on salt distribution. In the limit as these terms approach zero the negative solution remains large, which is unrealistic physically, while the positive solution approaches zero, as should occur for the correct solution.

We now assume this value of $dX_S/dX_G$ to be correct over a finite concentration range, say to $X_G = 0.4$. Then for $X_G = 0.4$ we may write

$$X_S = 0.100 - (0.50 - 0.40)(dX_S/dX_G)\big|_{x_G=0.50}$$

$$= 0.0985 \qquad (76)$$

The value of $dX_S dX_G$ is now recalculated at the new $X_G$ and $X_S$ and the above process repeated. In this way we obtain the coexisting concentrations shown in Table V. The last of these may be very easily checked through use of equation 70. This check yields a value of $X_S$ of 0.0920.

TABLE V
$X_S - X_G$ Relationship During Sorption Step

| $X_G$ | $X_S$ | $dX_S/dX_G$ |
|-------|-------|-------------|
| 0.5 | 0.100 | +0.015 |
| 0.4 | 0.099 | 0.016 |
| 0.3 | 0.097 | 0.016 |
| 0.2 | 0.095 | 0.017 |
| 0.1 | 0.094 | 0.018 |
| 0 | 0.092 | 0.019 |

b. Determination of column concentration profiles (isochrones). From the above results, one can show that the distribution equilibria, equations 69a and b, are concave. We may thus express the concentration profiles according to equation 52, but for our present purposes it will be convenient to think of $\phi$ somewhat differently than before:

$$\phi = V^*/z^*$$

where $V^*$ = number of (empty) column volumes of solution introduced to column = 0.4 for our conditions; $z^*$ = fractional distance along column. We may then write equation 52 as:

$$z^* = 0.4/[0.38 + (1 - 0.38)(1.385/1.17)(dY_i/dX_i)_R] \qquad (77)$$

where the subscript $i$ can refer to either salt or glycerine. Equation 77 is now used with equations 71a and b, and Table V, to obtain the concentration profiles shown as solid lines in Figure 11. Note

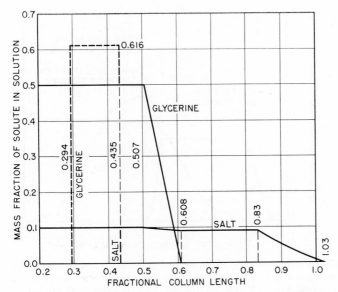

Fig. 11. Ion-exclusion separation of salt and glycerine:    equilibrium analysis.
See Example 2.

that the regions $0 < z^* < 0.507$ and $0.6086 < z^* < 0.83$ are not
described by equation 77. However, it is clear from the physical
nature of the problem that these lines must be as shown.

c. Note on the elution step.*    Elution of the saturated column
with water can be handled analogously to the sorption step just
discussed. Only two major differences will be encountered:

1. The $X - Y$ relationship will be different; that is, the other
of the two mathematical solutions is the physically realistic one for
elution.

2. Both the salt and glycerine fronts will be sharp, and therefore
equation 54 should be used rather than equation 52.

The result of feeding 0.2 column volumes of water to a column
saturated with the salt-glycerine mixture just discussed is shown as
dotted lines in Figure 11. Note that by combining these dotted

* In estimating the position of the sudden increase in glycerine concentration the
proper equivalent to equation 54 is $\phi_d = [\epsilon + (1 - \epsilon)\,(\Delta f(c_A)/\Delta c_A)]$ where $\Delta$ indicates the difference in the value of the appropriate quantity across the discontin-
uity.

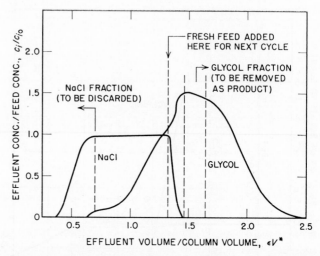

Fig. 12. Intermittent-continuous separation of NaCl and ethylene glycol by ion exclusion. Shown is the effluent curve from the column after a cyclic steady state has been established. The glycol- and salt-poor fractions are removed, and the remainder of solution recycled to the column, this recycle being interrupted at about 1.3 column volumes to permit introduction of fresh feed. Note that the glycol removed is nearly half again as concentrated as that fed. Feed is 0.26 column volumes of 10% NaCl and 10% ethylene glycol by weight. Resin is Dowex 50 X-8 in Na$^+$ form. (From W. C. Bauman, R. M. Wheaton, and D. W. Simpson in Nachod and Schubert (1).)

lines with the appropriate solid lines one may describe the result of following 0.2 column volumes of salt-glycerine with 0.2 column volumes of water.

The elution step is of particular interest here because of the concentration effect: elution under equilibrium conditions in this system results in glycerine concentrations higher than in the feed to the column. This effect occurs also under nonequilibrium conditions as well, as shown in Figure 12. This effect is of considerable possible economic importance and has been investigated by Wheaton and Bauman (11).

### 4. Single-Solute Adiabatic Operation

We consider here the feed of a solution of constant composition and enthalpy to an adiabatic column of uniform composition and nthalpy. To describe such a system completely we must use an nergy balance in addition to our equations of continuity for each omponent. It may easily be shown that the energy balance may )e expressed as:

$$0 = (\partial H/\partial z) + (\partial H/\partial s)[\epsilon + (1 - \epsilon)(dH_s/dH)_R]  \quad (78)$$

vhere: $H$ = specific enthalpy of moving phase, energy per unit nass or per mole of solution, or solvent; $H_s$ = specific enthalpy of tationary phase. The major conditions required for the derivation )f equation 78 are: 1. Heat losses from the column to the surround- ngs are negligible. 2. Potential and kinetic energy changes are mall compared to changes in enthalpy. These conditions are net in most industrial equipment of the type being considered in this ·hapter, for example, air dryers. In addition, we must of course issume equilibrium nondispersive operation: negligible resistance o heat transfer and negligible axial movement of heat relative to he fluid motion.

[We may now manipulate equation 78, just as for equation 47, to )btain:

$$(\partial s/\partial z)_H = [\epsilon + (1 - \epsilon)(dH_s/dH)_R]  \quad (79)$$

'or the specific case of a one-solute system, we may equate $(\partial s/\partial z)_H$ vith $(\partial s/\partial z)_{cA}$, from equation 50 to obtain:

$$\left(\frac{dH}{dc_A}\right)^2 + \left\{\frac{[(\partial c_{As}/\partial c_A) - (\partial H_s/\partial H)]}{(\partial c_{As}/\partial H)}\right\} \left(\frac{dH}{dc_A}\right) - \frac{(\partial H_s/\partial c_A)}{(\partial c_{As}/\partial H)} = 0$$

$$(80)$$

)r

$$(H_{s2} - H_{s1})/(H_2 - H_1) = (c_{As2} - c_{As1})/(c_{A2} - c_{A1})  \quad (81)]$$

These expressions correspond to equations 67 and 70 and may be ised for the analogous purpose: to find the $H - c_A$ relation for the :olumn. One may then write expressions analogous to equations i9a and b:

$$H_s = [H_s(H)_R]  \quad (82a)$$

$$c_{As} = [c_{As}(c_A)]_R  \quad (82b)$$

TABLE VI

Humidificauon Conditions Used in Example 3

---

Entering air:    dry-bulb temperature = 80°F
                 wet-bulb temperature = 67°F
Initial condition of desiccant bed:
  temperature = 220°F
  moisture content, $Y_S = 0$
Salt content of desiccant bed, $R = 0.12$ lb MX/lb inert carrier
Equilibrium absolute humidities over solutions of MX and over MX·$H_2O$
  see Figure 13
Enthalpy-concentration diagram for the system MX-$H_2O$:
  see Figure 14
Heat capacity of inert carrier = 0.25 Btu/lb°F
Psychrometric data for the system air-water taken from Chemical Engineer's
  Handbook, John H. Perry, ed., 3rd ed., McGraw-Hill, New York (1950)

---

We may then proceed to determine the enthalpy and concentration profiles separately using the methods of Section III-B-2.

*Example 3: Drying of air in a desiccant bed* (49). We consider here the dehumidification of air by passage through a desiccant bed, a common industrial operation of some importance, and one in which temperature changes are important. The results of the following analysis can also be applied, with minor modification, to the drying of beds of moist solids, for example, the drying of grains or the maintenance of low relative humidity in storage bins.

We consider specifically the passage of cool moist air through an initially hot dry solid. The solid consists of an inert porous carrier impregnated with a hygroscopic salt, MX, under the conditions summarized in Table VI. Under the conditions of operation, the salt can form only a single stable hydrate, MX·$H_2O$.

*Solution*

Our procedure for solving this problem will be essentially that used in Section III-B-3, with the following modifications:

1. It will be convenient to express moisture content as pounds of moisture per pound of inert carrier or per pound of dry air. We therefore define: $X$ = absolute humidity, pounds of water per pound of bone-dry air; $Y$ = moisture content of bed, pounds of water per pound of inert carrier; $R$ = salt content of bed, pounds of MX per pound of inert carrier; $H_s$ = Btu per pound of inert carrier; $H$ = Btu per pound of bone-dry air.

2. The moisture or enthalpy of the air in any region of the bed will be small compared to those in the solid phase in the same region.

3. It will be convenient to replace $\phi$ and $\phi_d$ of equations 52 and 54 with $\Phi$ and $\Phi_d$, pounds of dry air passed through any cross section of the bed divided by the total mass of desiccant upstream of the cross section.

With these modifications equations 52 and 54 may be written* as:

$$\Phi = (dY/dX)_R = (dH_s/dH)_R \qquad (83a,83b)$$

$$\Phi_d = (\Delta Y/\Delta X)_R = (\Delta H_s/\Delta H)_R \qquad (84a,84b)$$

Note that in neglecting the holdup of mass and enthalpy in the gas phase we have not only simplified our mass- and heat-balance expressions, we have also lost the need to neglect swelling.

We are now ready to determine the temperature-concentration relationship and the concentration and temperature profiles for this operation, using much the same procedures as in Example 2. The major results of such calculations are shown in Figures 13, 15, and 16.

The $X$-$T$ relation, part of which is shown in Figure 13 is most readily obtained from equation 81 since the available equilibrium data are not easily expressible algebraically. The trial and error determination of this relation is not difficult. The portion of the $X$-$T$ curve shown can be adequately expressed as a straight line and is not far from a line of constant adiabatic saturation temperature. The calculation is carried out as follows, choosing as point one the entrance to the column where $\Phi = \infty$.

1. From an air-water psychrometric chart we find that for the entering air, $X = X_1 = 0.0112$ lb $H_2O$/lb dry air and $H = 23.8$ Btu/lb dry air when $T = T_1 = 80°F$.

2. Then at the inlet end of the dehumidifier, where the solid is in equilibrium with the air, we find from Figure 13, $Y = Y_1 = (2.83$ lb $H_2O$/lb MX$)(0.12) = 0.34$ lb $H_2O$/lb carrier.

3. From Figure 14, for $Y = Y_1 = 0.34$ and $T = T_1 = 80°F$, we find $H_s = H_{s1} = -7.32$ Btu/lb carrier.

* See footnote to Example 2.

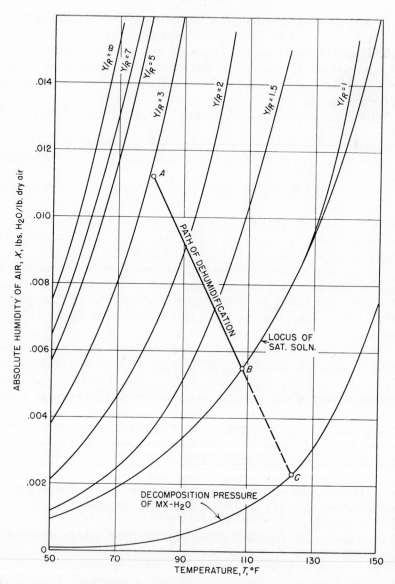

Fig. 13. Psychrometric data for the system air-MX-H$_2$O at one atmosphere total pressure.

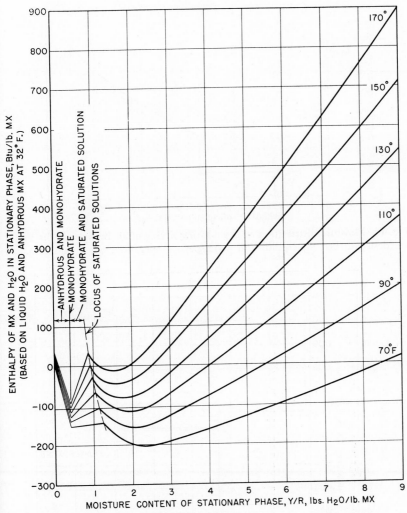

Fig. 14. Enthalpy-concentration diagram for the system MX-H₂O.

4. We may then use equation 81 to write:

$$(0.34 - Y_2)/(0.0112 - X_2) = (-7.32 - H_{s2})/(23.8 - H_2) \quad (85)$$

where the subscript 2 represents any other value of $\Phi$ in the column. This expression was used to obtain the dehumidification path, line

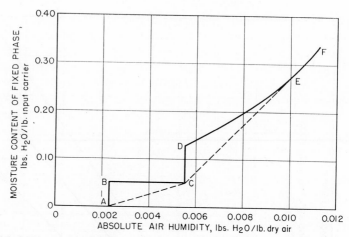

Fig. 15. Moisture distribution relation during drying of air by passage through a desiccant bed for equilibrium nondispersive operation. See Example 3.

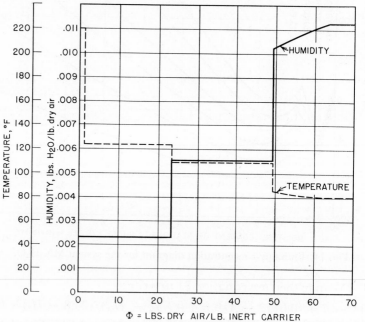

Fig. 16. Concentration profiles in the drying of air by passage through a desiccant bed, calculated for equilibrium nondispersive operation. See Example 3.

ABC of Figure 13. Some care must be exercised in using this curve, however: between points B and C the stable phase is $MX \cdot H_2O$ and the $X$-$T$ points on this portion of the curve do not represent equilibrium partial pressures of $H_2O$. There is instead an abrupt transition from B to C in the column; this behavior is shown more clearly in Figures 15 and 16. A similar abrupt change takes place at C, when the dehumidification line reaches the decomposition-pressure curve for $MX \cdot H_2O$. To the right of the latter curve the column is anhydrous and acts solely as a sensible heat exchanger.

The $X$-$Y$ relation may be very simply obtained as before once the $X$-$T$ relation is known, but, as mentioned above, care must be used in the region to the right of the saturated solution curve. This $X$-$Y$ relation, shown in Figure 15, is of considerable interest in that it has the equivalent of two inflections.

To use Figure 15 to obtain the $\Phi$-$X$ and $\Phi$-$T$ relations shown in Figure 16 one must recognize that the portions ABC and CDE of this curve are "convex," and that in this interval equation 84a must be used, for reasons discussed in Section III-B-3. Here E is the point of tangency of curve DEF with a straight line through C. Alternatively one may recognize that for constant feed to a uniformly loaded column, the $\Phi$-$X$ relation will be the same for a convex curve and for a straight line joining the end points of the convex curve. Thus, one may replace the actual $X$-$Y$ curve, ABCDEF, with the equivalent uninflected curve, ACEF, and use equation 83a for the whole concentration range. Clearly once the relation between $\Phi$ and $X$ is known, one may use curve ABC of Figure 13 to obtain a relation between $\Phi$ and $T$.

## C. LINEAR SYSTEMS WITH APPRECIABLE DISPERSIVE FORCES

It may be noted that the equation of continuity, equation 7, is linear with respect to $c_A$ and $c_{As}$. That is, if $c_A$ and $c_{As}$ are replaced by the multiples $ac_A$ and $ac_{As}$ where $a$ is any constant, the equation will still be valid. We consider here those cases in which the equilibrium distribution expression is also linear, that is

$$c_{As}{}^* = K_D c_A$$

where $K_D$ is a constant. For such a case the rate expressions that we have so far considered are linear with respect to concentration too. Our reasons for devoting a section to these special cases are two.

First, the behavior of linear systems is in many respects very simple, and second, the assumption of linear behavior is commonly made in a large number of important fixed-bed separation processes. We consider here only two kinetic models in detail: equilibrium operation with longitudinal dispersion, and the "mass-transfer coefficient" model without longitudinal dispersion. These appear to be the most useful models available, and both find wide application. The equilibrium model is the simpler and probably the more widely used. It has been shown that it gives a good description of non-equilibrium operation if the "effective diffusivity" $\mathfrak{D}_{Aa}$ is suitably redefined (see equations 34 and 35).

*1. Application of the Principle of Superposition to the Analysis of Linear Column Processes*

The characteristic behavior of linear systems may be simply illustrated by comparison of the effluent curves for two common column processes:

1. A very large volume of solution of constant composition $c_{A0}$ is fed to an initially solute-free column of length $L$, at a uniform volumetric rate.

2. A limited volume $V^0$ of the same solution is fed to an identical column at the same volumetric rate. This solution is then followed by a large volume of the same solvent, solute free, at the same volumetric rate.

Clearly the effluent curve for the first process will be an $S$-shaped breakthrough curve of the general shape shown in Figure 17. The effluent curve for the second process will be roughly bell-shaped as shown in Figure 18. We shall now write an expression for the shape of the effluent curve for the second process in terms of that for the first.

We begin by defining the concentration profile for the first process as:

$$x_A = c_A/c_{A0} = X(z,V) \tag{86}$$

We assume that this function has already been determined, either experimentally or otherwise, for the given flow rate. The effluent curve is just this function evaluated at the end of the column;

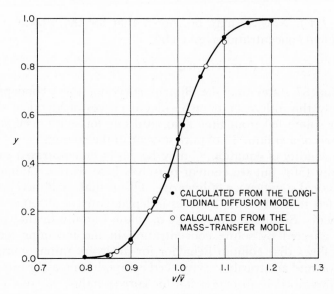

Fig. 17. Comparison of the longitudinal-diffusion and mass-transfer models. See Example 5.

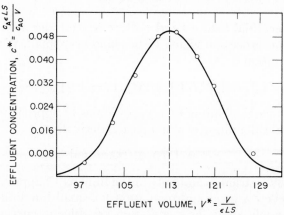

Fig. 18. Elution of a preformed band. Elution of praseodymium from a pre-formed band containing praseodymium and cerium. Resin: Dowex 50, $H^+$ form. Adsorption from solution of $PrCl_3$ and $CeCl_3$. Elution by a citrate buffer under such conditions that distribution isotherms for the rare earths were linear and noninterfering. Circles represent experimental data. The curve is a plot of equation 103. See Example 4.

i.e., $X(L,V)$. Now, it may be shown that for the second process the effluent concentration is given by

$$x_A{}^0 = X(L,V) - X(L,V - V^0) \tag{87}$$

Equation 87 states that the effluent curve for the second process is simply the difference of two effluent curves of identical shape, one for solute fed from time zero, and one for solute feed started after feed of a volume $V^0$ of pure solvent to the column.

The validity of equation 87 may be easily demonstrated mathematically (50), but we content ourselves here with a statement of the physical significance of linearity. This is that each increment of solute fed to the column behaves independently of all other solute increments. Similarly, movement of solute initially in the column is not affected by solute concentration in the incoming feed. It then follows that column behavior for arbitrary initial solute distribution and arbitrarily varying feed composition may be quantitatively described if an expression for corresponding to equation 86 is known. In the remainder of this section we show in detail how such general descriptions are obtained. In the next sections we give some examples for specific kinetic models.

[a. **Differential Solute Feed.**   Here we consider a limiting case of the second process in which $V^0$ becomes very small. We begin by writing equation 87 as:

$$x_A{}^0 = \{ [X(L,V) - X(L,V - V^0)]/V^0 \} V^0 \tag{88}$$

If we now take the limit of this expression as $V^0$ approaches zero we obtain, by the definition of a first partial derivative:

$$x_A{}^0 = V^0(\partial/\partial V)[X(L,V)] \tag{89}$$

Equation 89 is strictly valid only in the limit as $V^0$ approaches zero. It is, however, a good approximation for small but finite $V^0$, and it is commonly used for calculation of effluent curves in chromatographic separations.

b. **Elution from a Solute-Containing Column.**   *A uniformly loaded column.*   We consider here the feed of pure solvent to a column initially uniformly loaded with solute at mobile phase concentration $x_A = 1$. Our present situation is then clearly just the reverse of that described by equation 86, and we may therefore write:

$$x_A(L,V) = 1 - X(L,V) \qquad (90)$$

Here $X(L, V)$ is the $x$ of equation 86, the effluent curve for continued feed of solution at $x_A = 1$ to an initially solute-free column.

*A partially loaded column.* We now consider a column containing solute at $x_A = 1$ from $z = 0$ to $z = L^0$ and no solute from $z = L^0$ to $z = L$. The effluent curve for continued solute feed to this column is

$$x_A{}^0(L,V) = [1 - X(L,V)] - [1 - X(L - L^0,V)] \qquad (91a)$$

$$= X(L - L^0,V) - X(L,V) \qquad (91b)$$

The first term on the right in equation 91a is the effluent curve from a fully loaded column of length $L$; the second term is the contribution that would have been obtained from the solute-free portion of the column had it contained solute at unit concentration. The analog to equation 88 for this case is just:

$$x_A{}^0 = L^0\{[X(L - L^0,V) - X(L,V)]/L^0\}$$

$$\doteq -L^0(\partial/\partial L)[X(L,V)] \qquad (92)$$

Like equation 89, this expression is frequently used for finite $L^0$. Equations 89 and 92 can be used to write effluent curve expressions for any variable feed and initial conditions (14, pp. 710 and 711).]

## 2. Application of the Longitudinal-Dispersion Model

Here we consider operation under such conditions that local equilibrium may be assumed but longitudinal diffusion cannot be neglected. We shall also assume that the column being used is very long (51,52). The results we shall obtain from our development are, however, useful even where these restrictions are violated. We shall consider here only the continued feed of solution of constant composition $c_{A0}$ to an initially solute-free column at a uniform rate. Column behavior for other boundary conditions can then be obtained through use of the relations developed in the previous section.

We may describe the system being considered in terms of the following differential equation and boundary conditions:

$$(\mathfrak{D}_{Am} + E_A)(\partial^2 x_A/\partial z^2) = v(\partial x_A/\partial z)$$
$$+ (\partial x_A/\partial t)\{1 + [(1 - \epsilon)/\epsilon](c_{As0}/c_{A0})\} \quad (93)$$

$$\text{at } z = 0, \quad x_A = 1 \quad \text{for } t > 0 \quad (94)$$

$$\text{at } z = \infty, \quad x_A = 0 \quad \text{for } t > 0 \quad (95)$$

$$\text{at } t = 0, \quad x_A = 0 \quad \text{for } z > 0 \quad (96)$$

Equations 93–96 have been solved by Lapidus and Amundsen (52). For all columns of reasonable length, the result may be adequately expressed as*:

$$x_A = c_A/c_{A0} = \frac{1}{2}\left\{1 + \text{erf}\left[\frac{z - \dfrac{vt}{1 + [(1 - \epsilon)/\epsilon](c_{As0}/c_{A0})}}{\left(\dfrac{4(\mathfrak{D}_{Am} + E_A)t}{1 + [(1 + \epsilon)/\epsilon](c_{As0}/c_{A0})}\right)^{1/2}}\right]\right\} \quad (97)$$

This expression can be written more conveniently through introduction of the following new quantities: $V = \epsilon v St =$ volume of solution fed to a column of (empty) cross section $S$ in time $t$ at an interstitial velocity $v$; $\overline{V} = Sz[\epsilon + (1 - \epsilon)(c_{As0}/(c_{A0})]$: = volume of solution required to saturate a column of length $z$ in the absence of dispersive tendencies; $\text{Pé}_z = zv/(\mathfrak{D}_{Am} + E_A) =$ a length Péclet number for the column. In terms of these variables, equation 97 may be written:

$$x_A = c_A/c_{A0} = 1/2\{1 + \text{erf}[(\text{Pé}_z)^{1/2}(V - \overline{V})/2(V\overline{V})^{1/2}]\} \quad (98)$$

*Shape of a breakthrough curve*

Equation 98 as written describes the concentration profile in a sorbent column as a function of feed volume. If $\text{Pé}_z$ and $\overline{V}$ are evaluated at the end of the column $(z = L)$, the equation describes the effluent concentration from the column as a function of feed volume. Equation 98 has been widely used to describe effluent curves. It is equivalent to the expression developed by Glueckauf (62) for a column consisting of a number of discrete stages or "plates." Glueckauf's work is particularly useful because he presents working equations for predicting the degree of separation of two non-

* The error function, erf $u = -\text{erf}(-u)$, of any quantity $u$ is defined as erf $u = 2/\pi^{1/2} \int_0^u \exp(-\xi^2)d\xi$. Tabulated values of this function are readily available.

interfering solutes in a column of known $\bar{V}$ and $\text{Pé}_z$. If the product $V\bar{V}$ in equation 98 is approximated by $\bar{V}^2$, the resulting expression corresponds to that developed by Mayer and Tompkins (53) for a discrete-stage system similar to that of Glueckauf's. Equation 98 may also be used to describe nonequilibrium column behavior with $\text{Pé}_z$ redefined as discussed earlier.

This equation is written for constant-rate feed of solution of constant composition to an initially solute-free column. It can be used to describe more complicated processes through use of the expressions developed in Section III-C-1. We consider here two simple cases: differential solute feed and elution of a thin, preformed band. Both of these situations are frequently approximated in practical operations.

**a. Differential Solute Feed.**  We consider here the feed of a small volume $V^0$ of solution at concentration $c_{A0}$ to an initially solute-free column. We wish to describe the effluent curve that results if this solution is followed by a large volume of pure solvent. That is we wish to describe "the second process" of Section III-C-1. For simplicity we will let $V^0$ be much smaller than $\bar{V}$, the minimum saturating volume, so that we may use equation 89.

[Differentiating equation 98 with respect to $V$, we obtain:

$$\frac{\partial x_A}{\partial V} = \frac{\text{Pé}_z^{1/2}}{2\pi^{1/2}} \cdot \frac{\exp\left\{-(\text{Pé}_z/4)[(V - \bar{V})^2/V\bar{V}]\right\}}{(V\bar{V})^{1/2}} \cdot$$

$$\left[1 + \frac{1}{2}\left(\frac{V - \bar{V}}{V}\right)\right] \quad (99)$$

Usually $(V - \bar{V})/2V$ is small compared to 1 and can be neglected for the concentration range of interest. With this simplification we may write equation 89 as:

$$x_A^0 \doteq (1/2)(V^0/\bar{V})(\text{Pé}_z/\pi)^{1/2} \exp\left[-\text{Pé}_z(V - \bar{V})^2/4V\bar{V}\right] \quad (100)$$

**b. A Thin Preformed Band.**  In some separations, for example, of rare earth or amino acid mixtures, it is the practice to first adsorb the materials to be separated in a very thin band at the top of the column, using a solvent favoring absorption. In such cases it is usually assumed that the concentration is uniform in the adsorption band and that this band is thin compared to the length of the column. The elution behavior can then be described in terms of equation 92. For the kinetic model now being described this equation may be written in the form:

$$x_A^0 = (1/2)(L^0/L)(Pé_z/\pi)^{1/2}$$
$$\exp\{-(Pé_z/4)[(V - \bar{V})^2/4V\bar{V}]\} \cdot [\bar{V}/(V\bar{V})^{1/2}] \quad (101)$$

This expression can also be simplified by use of the approximation $V \doteq \bar{V}$. We thus obtain:

$$x_A^0 = (1/2)(L^0/L)(Pé_z/\pi)^{1/2}\exp\{-(Pé_z/4)[(V - \bar{V})^2/V\bar{V}]\} \quad (102)$$

This approximation will clearly be excellent in the neighborhood of maximum concentration. It may be shown (62) that it is a good approximation for the whole concentration range of practical interest whenever the equilibrium distribution ratio $(1 - \epsilon)c_{As0}/\epsilon c_{A0}$ is much greater than unity.

It may be seen that equations 100 and 102 are quite similar. In fact, when the initial fractional loading of the column is small, the shape of the effluent curve depends very little on the method of solute addition. Under these conditions, quite common in elution chromatography, we may replace both equations 100 and 102 with the single more general expression:

$$c_A^0 = (\alpha c_{A0}/2)(Pé_z/\pi)^{1/2} \exp\{-(Pé_z/4)[(V - \bar{V})^2/V\bar{V}]\} \quad (103)$$

*Approximate generalized effluent curve for small fractional column loadings.*

Here $\alpha$ is a measure of fractional column loading. For differential solute feed $\alpha = (V^0/\bar{V})$; for elution of a sharp preformed band $\alpha = (L^0/L)$. More generally we may write for a preformed band:

$$(\alpha c_{A0}) = 1/L \int_0^L c_A(z, 0)dL \quad (104)$$

where $c_A(z, 0)$ is the solute distribution in the fluid phase just prior to elution. By using equations 103 and 104 we may predict the shapes of effluent curves knowing only the total solute content of the column immediately prior to elution, and of course $Pé_z$ and $\bar{V}$. The prediction will be reasonable, however, only if the solute is originally concentrated very near the inlet end of the column; e.g., when $L^0/L$ or $V^0/\bar{V}$ is much less than unity.

*Example 4: Praseodymium elution.**   In Figure 18 we have repro-

* Adapted from: "Ion Exchange as a Separations Method, IV. A Theoretical Analysis of the Column Separations Process," Mayer and Tompkins (54).

uced an effluent curve obtained by Harris and Tompkins (53) for
he elution of praseodymium from Dowex 50 with a pH $=$ 3.0
itrate buffer. Our intention in the following discussion is to show
ow such an effluent curve can be used to determine the equilibrium
istribution coefficient and to characterize the dispersive forces in
he system. We base our discussion on equation 103 and, following
he suggestion of Mayer and Tompkins (54), we shall approximate
$V\bar{V}$) as $\bar{V}^2$. In terms of the reduced variables of Figure 18, we
nay then write:

$$c^* = {}^1\!/_2(\text{Pé}/\pi)^{1/2}(1/\bar{V}^*) \exp\left[-(\text{Pé}/4)(V^* - \bar{V}^*)^2/\bar{V}^{*2}\right] \quad (105)$$

Here we have used the relation $L^0/L = V^0/\bar{V}$.

a. Determination of the column affinity for Pr.   At the point
f maximum effluent concentration we may write

$$\bar{V}^* = V^* = 113 \tag{106a}$$

$$\bar{V} = 113\epsilon Ls \tag{106b}$$

This is as far as we can proceed without more complete data. We
nay, however, write a formal expression for the distribution co-
fficient from the definition of $\bar{V}$ just below equation 97:

$$113\epsilon LS = LS[\epsilon + (1 - \epsilon)(c_{As0}/c_{A0})]$$

$$K_D = c_{As0}/c_{A0} = 112\epsilon/(1 - \epsilon) \tag{107}$$

The fractional void space in a resin bed is commonly around 0.3–
.4. In any event equation 106a gives a reliable measure of column
apacity as packed.

b. Determination of the Péclet number.

$$\text{Pé}_z^{1/2} = c^*_{max} \cdot 2(\pi)^{1/2} \cdot \bar{V}^*$$

$$= (0.0505)(2)(\pi)^{1/2}(113)$$

$$= 11.4(\pi)^{1/2}$$

$$\text{Pé}_z = 408 \tag{108}$$

Mayer and Tompkins measure dispersion in terms of the "number
f theoretical plates" in the column, $N = \text{Pé}_z/2 = 204$. It might
•e noted here, that where equation 105 is valid, band width,
.e., volume between any two arbitrarily chosen effluent concen-

trations varies as the $1/2$-power of $\text{Pé}_z$, $N$, or equivalently, column length. This dependence is always approached in long columns fo linear systems, whatever the kinetic behavior.

c. Test of equation 103 for data correlation. A plot of equation 103 for $\bar{V}^* = 113$ and $\text{Pé}_z = 408$ is shown as a solid line in Figure 18 It can be seen by comparison with the experimental datum points shown as circles, that this equation gives a good description of the experimental results.

Sample calculation for $\bar{V}^* = 129$.

$$c^*/c^*_{\max} = \exp\left[-102(16)^2/113\right] = 0.10$$

$$c^* = 0.005$$

The usefulness of equation 103 for predicting dispersion is discussed in the next section.

### 3. Application of the Linearized Mass-Transfer Model

We begin once again by considering the feed of a solute at uni concentration to an initially solute-free column. Here we show how the linearized mass-transfer model (eq. 26) can be used to describe column concentration profiles and effluent curves. Note that the effect of axial dispersion may be included in such an analysis if the mass-transfer coefficient is defined as in equation 35.

The solution to this problem appears to have first been obtained by Anzelius (55) for an analogous situation in unsteady-state heat transfer. It may be expressed as:

$$x_A = J(\zeta, \tau) \tag{109}$$

Here

$\zeta = z(K_f a/\epsilon V)$
$\quad$ = reduced distance along column
$\tau = [K_f a/K_D(1 - \epsilon)](t - z/v)$
$\quad$ = reduced time
$J = $ the $J$-function of Brinkley, Hiester and Vermeulen, and others.*

* The $J$-function is: $J = 1 - \int_0^\zeta \exp\left[-(\tau + \xi)\right] J_0\left[i\,(4\tau\xi)^{1/2}\right]d\xi$ where $J_0$ is zero-order Bessel function of the first kind and $i$ is the square root of $-1$.

Note that $(t - z/v)$ is time for any point in the column, measured from first contact with solvent from the feed solution. Graphical expressions for the $J$-function are available in a large number of references.[*] Clearly equation 109 can be used to develop expressions for the shapes of free bands, just as was done in Section III-C-2 for the model discussed there.

We shall see in Section III-D that a very similar expression to equation 109 can be used for many nonlinear systems. We shall see here how such an expression can predict the shape of an effluent curve. Here we content ourselves with comparing the shapes of effluent curves based on equations 98 and 109.

*Example 5: Comparison of the longitudinal-dispersion and mass-transfer models.* Here we consider again the praseodymium-pH 3.0 buffer-Dowex 50 system of Example 4. This time we shall estimate the shape of the breakthrough curve obtained on continuous feed of solution at unit praseodymium concentration to an originally empty column. The calculation shall be made by two methods:

1. Through use of the longitudinal-diffusion model and the calculations of Example 4.

2. Through use of the mass-transfer model, using equation 35 and the results of Example 4.

The results of these two procedures are compared in Figure 17.

It may be seen that the two models yield practically identical curves. This is generally true except for very short columns. As a result, the simpler longitudinal-dispersion model is preferred for practical calculations. Equations 139–141 may also be approximated in terms of error functions.

*Solution:*

a. The longitudinal-diffusion model.   Here our starting equation is:

$$x_A = y = (^1/_2)[1 + \mathrm{erf}\{(P\acute{e}_z^{1/2}/2)[(V^* - \bar{V}^*)/\bar{V}^*]\}]$$
$$= (^1/_2)[1 + \mathrm{erf}\{10.1[(V^*/113) - 1]\}] \qquad (110)$$

We may now evaluate $y(V^*)$ with the results given in Table VII.

* See for example, Hougen and Watson (37, p. 1086). Their $y/y_0$, $b\tau$, and $aZ$ correspond to our $x_A$, $\tau$, and $\zeta$.

TABLE VII

| $V^*$ | $y$ |
|---|---|
| 90.5 | 0.01 |
| 96 | 0.015 |
| 102 | 0.08 |
| 107.5 | 0.24 |
| 110.5 | 0.35 |
| 112 | 0.44 |
| 113 | 0.50 |
| 114 | 0.56 |
| 116 | 0.64 |
| 118.5 | 0.75 |
| 124 | 0.92 |
| 130 | 0.985 |
| 135.5 | 0.99 |

Note that this expression for $y(V^*)$ is antisymmetrical about $V^* = 113$.

b. The mass-transfer model. In order to construct the effluent curve for this model we must first obtain expressions for $\zeta$ and $\tau$ in terms of known quantities, in particular $\text{Pé}_z$ and $V^*$. We begin by summarizing relations useful for this purpose.

From equation 35,

$$K_f a = K_f S_0 (1 - \epsilon) = $$
$$[\epsilon v^2/(E_A + \mathfrak{D}_{Am})]\{(1 - \epsilon)K_D/[(1 - \epsilon)K_D + \epsilon]\}^2 \quad (111)$$

From the definitions following equation 97:

$$V = \epsilon v S t \quad (112)$$

$$\bar{V} = Sz[\epsilon + (1 - \epsilon)(c_{As0}/c_{A0})] = Sz[\epsilon + (1 - \epsilon)K_D] \quad (113)$$

We may now write, from the definitions of $\zeta$ and $\tau$ given in this section:

$$\zeta = z(K_f a)/\epsilon v$$
$$= \text{Pé}_z\{(1 - \epsilon)K_D/[(1 - \epsilon)K_D + \epsilon]\}^2 \quad (114)$$

$$\tau = (K_f a)[t - (z/v)]/K_D(1 - \epsilon)$$
$$= \text{Pé}_z(\epsilon v/z)[t - (z/v)](1 - \epsilon)K_D/[(1 - \epsilon)K_D + \epsilon]^2$$
$$= \text{Pé}_z[(V - S\epsilon z)/\bar{V}]\{(1 - \epsilon)K_D/[(1 - \epsilon)K_D + \epsilon]\} \quad (115)$$

'or the conditions of this problem: $Pé_z = 408$, $\bar{V}^* = 113$, and $\epsilon/(1 - \epsilon)K_D] = 112^{-1} \cong 0.01$. We may then write:

$$\zeta = 408/1.02 = 400 \tag{116}$$

$$\tau = 404[(V^*/113) - 0.01] \tag{117}$$

Ve now use equations 116 and 117 along with a graphical presen- ation* of equation 109 to calculate $y$ and $V^*$ for several $\tau$:

| $\tau$: | 340 | 350 | 360 | 375 | 380 | 390 | 400 | 405 | 410 | 425 | 440 |
|---|---|---|---|---|---|---|---|---|---|---|---|
| $y$: | 0.015 | 0.03 | 0.07 | 0.20 | 0.25 | 0.35 | 0.47 | 0.50 | 0.60 | 0.80 | 0.90 |
| $V^*$: | 96 | 98 | 102 | 106 | 107 | 110 | 113 | 114 | 116 | 120 | 124 |

It may be seen from Figure 17, where the models are compared, hat the two starting equations give nearly identical results. ?oorer agreement would have been obtained in a shorter column or more precisely for smaller $Pé_z$) or for less strong adsorption of he praseodymium into the resin (that is, for smaller $K_D(1 - \epsilon)/\epsilon$). Ve see then, that for long columns, the models are very nearly :quivalent. Most actual columns can probably be considered long rom this standpoint without serious error.

## ). NONLINEAR SYSTEMS WITH APPRECIABLE DISPERSIVE FORCES

We now consider briefly those situations for which both non- inearity and dispersion must be considered. For simplicity, we imit ourselves to a few analytic solutions for single-solute problems. Ve discuss some of the more widely used of these, and for con- venience, we divide them into two groups: (1) asymptotic solutions or arbitrary kinetic models and (2) solutions based on the Thomas model. These two groups are discussed separately below.

The first consists of limiting solutions approached in long columns when the shape of the equilibrium distribution isotherm favors formation of a sharp solute front—sorption of a solute with a "con- vex" ("favorable") isotherm or elution of a solute with a concave one. Under these conditions the sharpening effect discussed in Section III-B acts in opposition to the dispersive tendencies result- ing from longitudinal diffusion and mass-transfer resistance. In an initially uniformly loaded column fed at constant rate and com- position, these opposing tendencies ultimately come to balance,

* As prepared and first presented by Hougen and Watson (37).

and the solute front travels down the column without change in shape. Strictly speaking, such "constant-form fronts" are only approached asymptotically in very long columns; in practice they can often be considered to be reached even in very short ones (see Ex. 7). As we shall see, these asymptotic fronts are quite easy to describe quantitatively for a wide variety of kinetic models. They also offer the advantage of yielding "conservative" estimates of column performance in that actual fronts in short columns must be sharper than the asymptotic limits.

Clearly constant-form fronts will not be approached in those cases where the shape of the distribution isotherm tends to cause dispersion or in the case of free bands. No generally applicable description is available for these. Solutions are available, however, for solutes following the Thomas model, and as described in Section II-C-2, this model can be used to approximate the behavior of many real systems.

### 1. Assumption of Asymptotic or "Constant-Form" Fronts

Here we consider the limiting shapes of column concentration profiles, or effluent curves, that are obtained under conditions producing sharp discontinuous fronts in the absence of dispersive tendencies. For simplicity we shall consider only sorption in initially solute-free columns and elution with pure solvent. In this asymptotic state, the *shape* of the concentration profile ceases to change with time. Rather all portions of the solute front are displaced down the column at the same rate, and it may easily be seen that this rate of movement is the same as that of $z_d$, the position of the concentration discontinuity in the absence of dispersive forces. We may then write that $c_A = c_A(z^*)$ where:

$$z^* = z - z_d = z - \{ \epsilon v t / [\epsilon + (1 - \epsilon)(c_{As0}/c_{A0})] \} \quad (118)$$

[If we now rewrite the equation of continuity in terms of $z^*$ and $t$ and neglect changes of concentration with respect to time at constant $z^*$ we get:

$$d^2 x_A / d z^{*2} = (v/\mathfrak{D}_{Aa})\{(1 - \epsilon)(c_{As0}/c_{A0})/[\epsilon + (1 - \epsilon)(c_{As0}/c_{A0})]\}$$

$$(d/dz^*)(x_A - y_A) \quad (119)$$

Equation 119 is the equation of continuity as modified to express

onditions far down the column where concentration depends only
upon $z^*$; it is inexact except for finite $z^*$ and infinite $z$. In this
equation $x_A = c_A/c_{A0}$ and $y_A = c_{As}/c_{As0}$. Since $x_A = y_A = 1$ for
large negative $z$, we may at once integrate this equation to obtain:

$$x_A/dz^* = (v/\mathfrak{D}_{Aa})$$
$$\{(1 - \epsilon)(c_{As0}/c_{A0})/[\epsilon + (1-\epsilon)(c_{As0}/c_{A0})]\}(x_A - y_A) \quad (120)$$

To integrate further we need a kinetic model.  For an example we
choose the linearized mass-transfer model, equation 36.  For this
model we may write:

$$y_A/dz^* = -(\partial y_A/\partial t)\{[\epsilon + (1 - \epsilon)(c_{As0}/c_{A0})]/\epsilon v\}$$
$$= \{[\epsilon + (1 - \epsilon)(c_{As0}/c_{A0})]/\epsilon v\}[K_f a/(1 - \epsilon)](c_{A0}/c_{As0})(x_A^* - x_A)$$
$$(121)$$

Equations 120 and 121 may be combined and integrated to obtain
column concentration profiles (56); particularly simple expressions
are obtained when the dispersive effects of either $\mathfrak{D}_{Aa}$ or $(K_f a)$ may
be neglected (57). We present here the results for small $\mathfrak{D}_{Aa}$ as these
are probably of greatest practical interest.

If $\mathfrak{D}_{Aa}$ is very small, it follows from equation 120 that $x_A = y_A$.
We may then write from equation 121:

$$z_2^* - z_1^* = \{(1 - \epsilon)(\epsilon v)(c_{As0}/c_{A0})/[\epsilon + (1 - \epsilon)(c_{As0}/c_{A0})](K_{fa})\}$$
$$\cdot \int_{x_{A1}}^{x_{A2}} dx_A/[y_A^*(x_A) - x_A] \quad (122)$$

Here subscripts 1 and 2 refer to any two cross sections in the column.
Equation 122 is clearly very similar to corresponding descriptions
for steady-state column operations. Note, however, that this expression does not give us the position of the solute front relative to the inlet end of the column. This is because we have not considered the
formation of the front in our development. We may position the
front precisely through use of a material balance, as illustrated in
the following example. Usually, however, we may obtain a sufficiently accurate positioning by assuming $x_A$ to be $1/2$ at $z^* = 0$.]
   Then for most systems, we may relate concentration of solute with
position in the column by:

$$z^* \doteq \{(1 - \epsilon)(\epsilon v)(c_{As0}/c_{A0})/[\epsilon + (1 - \epsilon)(c_{As0}/c_{A0})](K_f a)\}$$
$$\cdot \int_{1/2}^{x_A} dx_A/[y_A^*(x_A) - x_A]$$

*Concentration profile for a constant-form front, mass-transfer resistance con-
trolling.*                                                                (123)

Some idea of the error introduced in assuming the lower limit of in tegration to be $1/2$ may be obtained from Example 6. Note tha equation 123 is written for the commonly encountered case of mass transfer resistance as the controlling cause of dispersion.

*Example 6: Adsorption of sodium ions in an ion-exchange resin.** Her we illustrate the application of the equations presented above to specific case—removal of $Na^+$ from a dilute aqueous solution b passage through an ion-exchange bed. We shall consider the ion ex changer to be Nalcite HCR, a strong-acid resin, in the $H^+$ form Sodium is more strongly adsorbed than hydrogen in this system and the distribution equilibria may be expressed with sufficient accuracy for our present purposes as:

$$y_A^*/(1 - y_A^*) = 1.2 \ [x_A/(1 - x_A)] \qquad (124$$

where $y_A$ and $x_A$ are the cation fractions of $H^+$ in the resin and solu tion phases separately.

Since the equilibrium constant for this exchange reaction i greater than unity, conditions are favorable for formation of a con stant-form front. We may then use equation 122 to describe the sol ute fronts produced on feeding sodium solution to the column. In this example we shall illustrate the use of this equation for the follow ing conditions: total resin in bed $= 0.26$ eqts; bed length $L =$ 33.5 cm; bed cross section (empty) $S = 3.80$ cm²; bed void fractio $\epsilon = 0.42$ (approx); feed solution: $0.120N$ NaCl at $25\,°C$; superficia liquid velocity $\epsilon v = 0.62$ cm/sec.

*Solution*

1.   Calculation of effective column capacity.

We begin by calculating the column concentration profile and the volume of solution fed to the column when the effluent sodium con centration is $0.006N$. The concentration profile is describe by equa tion 122 with $y_A = x_A = 0.05$ at $z = 33.5$ cm. We may thus write:

$$z = 33.5 \text{ cm} = \{(1 - \epsilon)(\epsilon v)(c_{As0}/c_{A0})/[\epsilon + (1 - \epsilon)(c_{As0}/c_{A0})]$$
$$\times (K_f a)\} \cdot \int_{0.05}^{x_A} dx_A/(y_A^*(x_A) - x_A) \qquad (125$$

For the given system and conditions of operation it has been foun experimentally by Michaels (58) that:

* Adapted from data of Michaels (58).

$$(1 - \epsilon)(\epsilon v)(c_{As0}/c_{A0})/[\epsilon + (1 - \epsilon)(c_{As0}/c_{A0})](K_f a) = 0.915 \text{ cm} \tag{126}$$

Using equations 124 and 126, we may rewrite equation 125 as

$z = 33.5$ cm

$$+ \; 0.915 \text{ cm} \int_{0.05}^{x_A} \{x_A - [1.2/(1.2 - 1.0)]\}dx_A/x_A(1 - x_A) \tag{127}$$

Performing the indicated integration we obtain:

$$z = 17.3 \text{ cm} + 0.915 \, [5 \ln (1 - x_A) - 6 \ln x_A] \text{ cm} \tag{128}$$

Equation 128 is shown graphically in Figure 19. Note that the column under consideration is very short, and consequently the predicted concentration at the inlet is appreciably less than unity. The actual concentration at the inlet will be unity in the absence of appreciable longitudinal diffusion. The use of such a short column is clearly a very severe test of a constant-form-front model.

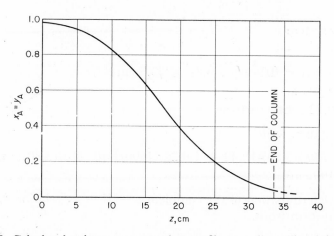

Fig. 19. Calculated column concentration profile at sodium "breakthrough." See Example 6.

To determine the volume of solution fed up to this point, we equate the amount of sodium fed to that in the column. To take into account the sodium that has passed into the effluent we consider for the moment that the column extends indefinitely beyond its actual length. We may then write

$$c_{A0}V = S[\epsilon c_{A0} + (1 - \epsilon) c_{As0}] \int_0^\infty x_A dz \qquad (129)$$

where $V = S \epsilon vt$ = volume of solution fed since start of operation. In writing this equation we have taken advantage of the fact that $x_A = y_A$. It will be more convenient to integrate by parts and write:

$$c_{A0}V = S[\epsilon c_{A0} + (1 - \epsilon)c_{As0}] \int_0^{0.978} z dx_A \qquad (130)$$

Here 0.978 is the value of $x_A$ at $z = 0$ as calculated from equation 128. We now use equation 130 to write:

$$\int_0^{0.978} z dx_A = \int_0^{0.978} \{17.3 + 0.915 [5 \ln (1 - x_A) - 6 \ln x_A]\} dx_A$$
$$= 17.3(0.978)$$
$$+ 0.915 \{5(1 - x_A)[1 - \ln (1 - x_A)] - 6 x_A [\ln x_A - 1]\}\Big|_0^{0.978}$$
$$= 16.92 - 4.44 + 5.50 = 17.98 \qquad (131)$$

We may then write:

$$V = 17.98 S[\epsilon + (1 - \epsilon)(c_{As0}/c_{A0})] \qquad (132)$$

For this system

$\epsilon \doteq 0.42$

$(1 - \epsilon) c_{As0} = 0.26$ eqts./$3.80 \times 33.5$ cm

$S = 3.80$ cm$^2$

$c_{A0} = 0.120$ eqts/1000 cm$^3$

We may then write:

$$V = (17.98)(3.80) \{0.42 + [(0.26)(1000)]/[(0.210)(3.80)(33.5)]\}$$
$$= 1190 \text{ cm}^3 \qquad (133)$$

2. Determination of the complete $z - V - x_A$ relation for the constant-form front.

We may also use the above results to write expressions for $z^*(x_A)$. Thus we may write from equation 118:

$$z^* = z - V/S[\epsilon + (1 - \epsilon)(c_{As0}/c_{A0})] \qquad (134)$$

We now substitute into equation 134 the previously calculated results for $V = 1190$ cm$^3$, thus obtaining

$$z^* = 17.3 \text{ cm} + 0.915 \: [5 \ln (1 - x_A) - 6 \ln x_A] \text{ cm} - 17.98 \text{ cm}$$
$$= 0.915 \: [5 \ln (1 - x_A) - 6 \ln x_A] \text{ cm} - 0.7 \text{ cm} \qquad (135)$$

Equation 135 is the complete $z$ versus $x_A$ relation for the constant-pattern front. It is the equivalent of equation 122 for $x_{A1} = 0.05$.

We are now in a good position to compare this "exact" $z^* - x_A$ relation with the approximate expression given by equation 123. This latter equation may be rearranged to give:

$$z^* \doteq \{ v\epsilon(1 - \epsilon)(c_{As0}/c_{A0}) / [\epsilon + (1 - \epsilon)(c_{As0}/c_{A0})] K_f a \}$$
$$\cdot \int_{1/2}^{x_A} (x_A - 6) \, dx_A / x_A (1 - x_A)$$
$$= 0.915 \: \{ 5 \ln (1 - x_A) - 6 \ln x_A - \ln (1/0.5) \}$$
$$= 0.915 \text{ cm} \: [5 \ln (1 - x_A) - 6 \ln x_A] - 0.6 \text{ cm} \qquad (136)$$

The discrepancy of 0.1 cm between the expressions for $z^*$ given by equations 135 and 136 is not significant. Then for this example, the $z^* - x_A$ relation, and all of the results of the preceding part (1) could have been obtained as well, and with much less work, by starting from equation 123. In the limit as the distribution isotherm

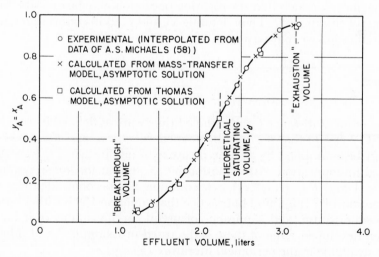

Fig. 20. Comparison of the mass-transfer and Thomas models with experimental results. See Examples 6 and 7.

approaches linearity equation 123 becomes exact. It becomes less reliable as the distribution isotherm becomes more strongly curved, but it is a satisfactory expression for most actual cases.

3. Construction of an effluent curve. An effluent curve is simply the $z - V - x_A$ relation evaluated for $z$ equal to the column length. We may then write from equation 135:

$$33.5 \text{ cm} - V/(3.80)(17.4)\text{cm}^2 = 0.915 \text{ cm} [5 \ln (1 - x_A) - 6 \ln x_A] - 0.7 \text{ cm} \quad (137)$$

The $V - x_A$ relation is then:

$$V = 2260 \text{ cm}^3 - 60.5[5 \ln (1 - x_A) - 6 \ln x_A]\text{cm}^3 \quad (138)$$

This equation is expressed graphically in Figure 20 along with Michael's (58) experimental results and the calculated results of the next example.

### 2. Applications of the Thomas Model

We begin by considering the feed of a solution of a single solute, A, to an initially solute-free column at constant rate and composition. We assume the shape of the equilibrium isotherm and the kinetic behavior to be such that the sorption operation may be described in terms of equation 39. Then defining $x_A$ and $y_A$ as in connection with this equation we may write:

$$x_A(\zeta,\tau) = 1/\{1 + G \exp [(r - 1)(\tau - \zeta)]\} \quad (139)$$

where

$$G = [1 - J(\zeta, r\tau)]/J (r\zeta, \tau) \quad (140)$$

The reduced distance $\zeta$ and reduced time $\tau$ are as defined in Section III-C-3 except that $K_D$ must be defined as $c_{As0}/c_{A0}$, and $K_f a/(1 - \epsilon)$ must be multiplied by $\beta$. The measure of nonlinearity, $r$, is as defined in connection with equation 39. Note that for linear systems $[r = 1$ and $K_D = c_{As}^*(c_A)/c_A]$, equation 139 becomes identical to equation 141. It is found in practice that equation 139 is rather cumbersome to use, and a number of useful simplifications of it have been developed. One of these is discussed in Example 7 and others are available in the periodical literature (59, 60).

We next consider a process similar to the above except that at $\tau = T$, pure solvent feed is substituted for the solution of A. We assume that the physical properties and flow rate of the pure solvent are the same as those of the fluid being replaced. Equation 139 may still be used in the form given above for $\tau \leq T$. For $\tau \geq T$, it may be used if $G$ is redefined:

$$G = \frac{\{1 - J(\zeta,r\tau) + J[\zeta, (r\tau - rT)]\exp[(1 - r)T]\}}{\{J(r\zeta,\tau) - J[r\zeta, (\tau - T)]\}} \quad (141)$$

Again more convenient approximate relations are available.

Equations 139–141 can also be modified to describe a process similar to the above, but in which the column originally contained a finite uniform loading of the solute in question. The procedure for doing this is described in some detail by Vermeulen (4).

*Example 7: Comparison of the mass-transfer and Thomas models.* Here we shall recalculate the shape of the effluent curve for the system of Example 6, this time using the Thomas model. In this way we can compare the effluent curves obtained from these two kinetic models.

*Solution*

a.   Calculation of $\zeta$ and $\tau$.

$$\zeta = \beta(K_f a)z/\epsilon v \quad (142)$$

$$\beta = 2/(1 + 0.833) = 1.09$$

$$K_f a = [(1 - \epsilon)(c_{As0}/c_{A0})\epsilon v]/\{(0.915)[\epsilon + (1 - \epsilon)(c_{As0}/c_{A0})]\}$$
$$= (7.0)(0.62)/(0.915)(17.42)$$
$$= 0.66 \text{ sec}^{-1}$$

$$\zeta = (1.09)(33.5)(0.66)/(0.62) = 39.0 \quad (143)$$

$$\tau = \beta(K_f a)[t - (z/v)]/[(1 - \epsilon)(c_{As0}/c_{A0})] \quad (144)$$

Making use of the relation $V = \epsilon v t S$ we then obtain:

$$\tau = (1.09)(0.66)[(V/2.36) - (0.42 \times 35/0.62)]/(17.0)$$
$$= 0.0179V \text{ cm}^{-3} - 0.96 \quad (145)$$

b.   Calculation of the shape of the effluent curve.   The effluent curve may be plotted directly from equations 139 and 140 with the aid of equations 144 and 145. However, for large values of $\zeta$ it may be shown (59,60) that the effluent curve may be approximated as:

$$x_A = 1/\{1 + \exp[(\zeta - \tau)(1 - r)]\} \quad (146)$$

Equation 146 is the "final-form front" approximation of equation 139. This may be seen more readily be rewriting:

$$\zeta - \tau = [\beta(Ka_f)/\epsilon v] \, [(V_d - V)/S(1 - \epsilon)(c_{As0}/c_{A0})] \quad (147)$$

It may thus be seen that $x_A$ in equation 146 depends only upon $(V_d - V)$ and not upon $V_d$, hence not on column length. For the system being considered here

$$(\zeta - \tau)(1 - r) = (39.0 - 0.0179V \, \mathrm{cm}^{-3} + 0.96)(1/6)$$

$$= 0.00298 \, \mathrm{cm}^{-3} \, (V_d - V) \quad (148)$$

where $V_d = (39.0 + 0.96)/(0.0179) = 2230 \, \mathrm{cm}^3$.

It may be seen from Figure 20 that for these conditions, equation 146 agrees almost exactly with the corresponding expression for the mass-transfer model, equation 122.

## Notation

Dimensions are given in terms of mass $m$, length $l$, and time $t$. Symbols that appear infrequently are not included.

$c_A$ = concentration in mobile phase, $ml^{-3}$

$c_{As}$ = concentration in stationary phase, $ml^{-3}$

$c_{As}{}^*$ = stationary phase concentration in equilibrium with $c_A$, $ml^{-3}$

$c_{A0}$ = solute concentration in feed solution, $m/l^3$

$\mathcal{D}_{Aa}$ = apparent (axial) diffusivity of species A, $l^2 t^{-1}$

$\mathcal{D}_{Am}$ = effective binary diffusivity of species A in mobile phase, $l^2 t^{-1}$

$D_p$ = particle diameter, $l$

$f(c_A)$ = $c_{As}{}^*$, $ml^{-3}$

$G$ = dimensionless function

$J$ = dimensionless function

$K_D$ = distribution coefficient, dimensionless

$K_f$ = over-all mass-transfer coefficient, $lt^{-1}$

$k_f$ = fluid-phase mass-transfer coefficient, $lt^{-1}$

$k_s$ = stationary-phase mass-transfer coefficient, $l \, t^{-1}$

$k_i$ = Thomas-model rate constant, $t^{-1}$

$L$ = column length, $l$

$L^0$ = length of column originally containing solute, $l$

$Pé_E$ = particle diameter-based Péclet number for axial dispersion, dimensionless

$Pé_{tot}$ = $Pé_E$ corrected to account for mass-transfer resistance, dimensionless

$Pé_z$ = length Péclet number, dimensionless = $Pé_{tot}(L/D_p)$

$S$ = column cross section, $l^2$

$S_0$ = particle specific surface, $l^{-1}$

$s$ = penetration depth of solvent, $l$

$t$ = time, $t$

$V$ = volume of solution fed to column, $l^3$

$\bar{V}$ = minimum saturating volume, $l^3$

$V^0$ = volume of solution originally fed to column, $l^3$

$v$ = $v_z$ = interstitial fluid velocity, $lt^{-1}$

$x_A$ = $c_A/c_{A0}$, dimensionless

$x_A^0$ = shape of a free band, dimensionless

$y_A$ = $c_{As}/c_{As}*(c_{A0})$, dimensionless

$y_A*$ = $c_{As}(c_A)/c_{As}*(c_{A0})$, dimensionless

$z$ = distance from column inlet in direction of flow, $l$

$z_d$ = value of $z$ at a concentration discontinuity, $l$

$z*$ = $(z - z_d)$, $l$

$E_A$ = axial dispersion coefficient for solute A, $l^2 t^{-1}$

$\epsilon$ = fractional void space in column, dimensionless

$\zeta$ = dimensionless distance along column

$\tau$ = dimensionless time

$\phi$ = $s/z$, dimensionless

$\phi_d$ = $s/z_d$, dimensionless

## References

1. F. C. Nachod and J. Schubert, eds., *Ion Exchange Technology*, Academic Press, New York, 1960.
2. Robert Kunin, *Ion Exchange Resins*, 2nd ed., Wiley, New York, 1958.
3. E. and M. Lederer, *Chromatography*, Elsevier, New York, 1957.
4. T. Vermeulen, "Separation by Adsorption Methods," *Advances in Chemical Engineering*, Vol. II, T. B. Drew and J. W. Hoopes, Jr., eds., Academic Press, New York, 1958.
5. F. Helfferich, *Ionenaustauscher*, Band I, Verlag Chemie GMBH, Weinheim/ Bergstr. (1959), *Ion Exchange* (English translation and revision), McGraw-Hill, New York, 1962.
6. C. L. Mantell, *Adsorption*, McGraw-Hill, 2nd ed., New York, 1951.
7. R. L. Moison and H. A. O'Hern, Jr., in *Adsorption, Dialysis, and Ion Exchange,* *Chem. Eng. Progr. Symp. Series*, **55**, no. 24, 71–86 (1959).

8. G. P. Monet in Reference 1.
9. Howe and Putter, U. S. Pat. 2,511,420.
10. N. Lengborn, *Teknisk Tidskrift*, **1955**, 107–112 (1955).
11. W. C. Baumann, R. M. Wheaton, and D. R. Simpson in Reference 1.
12. F. H. Spedding and J. E. Powell in Reference 1.
13. L. J. Snyder and W. E. Stewart, work in progress.
14. R. B. Bird, W. E. Stewart, and E. N. Lightfoot, *Transport Phenomena*, Wiley, New York, 1960.
15. J. J. Carberry and R. H. Bretton, *A.I.Ch.E. J.*, **4**, no. 3, 367–375 (1958).
16. E. A. Ebach and R. R. White, *A.I.Ch.E. J.*, **4**, no. 2, 161–169 (1958).
17. K. W. McHenry and R. H. Wilhelm, *A.I.Ch.E. J.*, **3**, 83 (1957).
18. R. Aris, *Proc. Roy. Soc. (London)*, **252A**, 538 (1959).
19. O. A. Hougen, K. M. Watson, and R. A. Ragatz, *Chemical Process Principles, Part I*, 2nd ed., Wiley, New York, 1954.
20. D. Graham, "Adsorption Equilibria," *Adsorption, Dialysis, and Ion Exchange, Chem. Eng. Prog. Symp. Series*, **55**, no. 24 (1959).
21. S. Brunauer, *The Adsorption of Gases and Vapors*, Princeton University Press, Princeton, N. J., 1945.
22. V. Rothmund and K. Drucker, *Z. Physik. Chem.*, **46**, 827 (1903).
23. I. B. Chacham, *J. Gen. Chem. (USSR)*, **18**, no. 7, 1215, 1222 (1948).
24. W. M. Ramm, *Absorptionsprozesse in der Chemischen Industrie*, Verlag Technik, (East) Berlin (1952).
25. T. K. Sherwood and R. L. Pigford, *Absorption and Extraction*, McGraw-Hill, New York, 1952.
26. E. Høgfeldt, *Acta. Chem. Scand.*, **9**, 151–165 (1955).
27. H. P. Gregor, *J. Am. Chem. Soc.*, **70**, 1293 (1948).
28. H. P. Gregor, *J. Am. Chem. Soc.*, **73**, 642 (1951).
29. D. de Vault, *J. Am. Chem. Soc.*, **65**, 532 (1943).
30. E. Glueckauf, *Nature (London)*, **156**, 748 (1945).
31. E. Glueckauf, *J. Chem. Soc. (London)*, **1949**, 3280.
32. C. N. Merriam and H. C. Thomas, *J. Chem. Phys.*, **24**, 993 (1956).
33. E. Glueckauf, *Trans. Faraday Soc.*, **51**, 1540 (1955).
34. O. A. Hougen, K. M. Watson, and R. A. Ragatz, *CPP Charts*, Wiley, New York, 1960.
35. B. Gamson, *Chem. Eng. Prog.*, **27**, 19–28 (1951).
36. R. M. Barrer, *Diffusion in and through Solids*, Macmillan, New York, 1941.
37. O. A. Hougen and K. M. Watson, *Chemical Process Principles, Part III*, Wiley, New York, 1947.
38. W. Jost, *Diffusion in Solids, Liquids, and Gases*, Academic Press, New York, 1952.
39. T. Vermeulen, "Kinetic Relationships for Ion-exchange Processes," *Adsorption, Dialysis, and Ion Exchange, Chem. Eng. Prog. Symp. Series*, **55**, no. 24 (1959).
40. A. Klinkenberg and F. Sjenitzer, *Chem. Eng. Sci.*, **6**, 258 (1956).
41. H. C. Thomas, *Annals N.Y. Academy of Sciences*, **49**, 161 (1948).
42. T. Vermeulen and N. K. Hiester, *J. Chem. Phys.*, **22**, 96 (1954).
43. N. K. Hiester and T. Vermeulen, *A.I.Ch.E. J.*, **2**, no. 3, 404 (1956).
44. J. B. Rosen, *J. Chem. Phys.*, **20**, 387 (1952).
45. J. B. Rosen, *Ind. Eng. Chem.*, **46**, 1590 (1954).

46. M. J. Hatch, J. A. Dillon, and H. B. Smith, *Ind. Eng. Chem.*, **29**, 1812 (1957).
47. E. N. Lightfoot, unpublished calculations.
48. E. L. Shurts and R. R. White, *A.I.Ch.E. J.*, **3**, no. 2, 183 (1957).
49. E. N. Lightfoot, *J. Phys. Chem.*, **61**, 1686 (1957).
50. F. B. Hildebrand, *Advanced Calculus for Engineers*, Prentice-Hall, Englewood Cliffs, N. J. 1948, pp. 444–446.
51. W. C. Bastian and L. Lapidus, *J. Phys. Chem.*, **40**, 816 (1956).
52. L. Lapidus and N. R. Amundson, *J. Phys. Chem.*, **56**, 984 (1950).
53. D. H. Harris and E. R. Tompkins, *J. Am. Chem. Soc.*, **69**, 2792 (1947).
54. S. W. Mayer and E. R. Tompkins, *J. Am. Chem. Soc.*, **69**, 2792 (1947).
55. A. Anzelius, *Z. angew. Math u. Mech.*, **6**, 291–294 (1926).
56. A. Acrivos, unpublished analysis.
57. E. N. Lightfoot and D. C. MacMurray, unpublished analysis.
58. A. S. Michaels, *Ind. Eng. Chem.*, **44**, 1922 (1952).
59. R. F. Baddour, D. J. Goldstein, and P. Epstein, *Ind. Eng. Chem.*, **46**, 2192 (1954).
60. N. K. Hiester and T. Vermeulen, *Chem. Eng. Prog.*, **48**, no. 10, 505 (1952).
61. Chi Tien and G. Thodos, *A.I.Ch.E. J.*, **5**, 373 (1959); **6**, 364 (1960).
62. E. Glueckauf, *Trans. Faraday Soc.*, **51**, 34–44 (1955).

# 3

# ZONE MELTING

## W. D. Lawson and S. Nielsen

## Contents

## I. Introduction

In 1952 W. G. Pfann (1) discovered a new process for the purification of materials for which he coined the term "zone melting." The process was simple in conception but has proved to be an extremely powerful and versatile technique, not only for the purification, but also for the preparation and fabrication of solids. In its simplest form the process involves the movement of a small molten region—a zone—through a solid ingot of material. In Figure 1, for example, movement of the heater causes a molten zone to move through the ingot. Material melts in front of the zone and solidifies at the rear. The material is therefore melted and recrystallized, and the purification effected by the passage of a single zone is comparable to that effected by any other recrys-

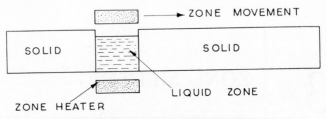

Fig. 1. Zone melting.

tallization process. A great advantage of Pfann's process, however is that by passing further zones through the ingot a repeated recrystallization can be obtained with no intermediate handling of the material.

Pfann first applied the process to the purification of germanium. The result was dramatic. Passage of six zones produced germanium containing only 1 in $10^{10}$ electronically active impurities, a purity hitherto not obtained by any other method. The significance of this result was at once apparent, and laboratories throughout the world applied the zone melting process first to the technologically important semiconductors and later to many other materials and systems.

The process is most conveniently applied to those materials which form a stable melt, with low vapor pressure, at reasonable temperatures. Such materials include the low melting elements some inorganic, and many organic compounds. It also includes water and organic liquids which can be easily solidified. However neither the melting temperature, nor the vapor pressure, nor the stability of the melt are absolute limitations. The high melting refractory metals, e.g., Mo, W, V, Ti, materials with high vapor pressure, e.g., Mg, Fe, PbSe, HgTe, have all been successfully purified. Further, those materials which decompose at the melting point can be zone melted in the form of solutions or eutectic.

It must be mentioned here that not all impurities are swept along by the moving zone, although most often, the majority are. Certain impurities may move in the opposite direction, and some may not move at all. General considerations suggest that the process is most efficient when the structure of the liquid and solid phases is most different. Purification of glassy materials, for example, may not be possible.

Zone melting has perhaps been of greatest value in removing trace impurities from materials already very pure, but other separations may prove no less useful. For example, it has been possible to separate materials with similar boiling points, azeotropic mixtures, and mixtures of isomers, which are difficult to separate by other means. Some separation of heavy water has also been achieved. The technique has also been used to concentrate solutions: brine from sea water; dyes, vitamins, and salts from solutions; enzymes, bacteria, and plankton from aqueous media; and colloidal solutions of gold, are examples. Some fractionation of a polymer solution has been reported, and the technique has been used to concentrate impurities as a preliminary stage in their analysis.

Zone melting has been used as a preparative technique for the preparation of intermetallic compounds, alloys, eutectics, and peritectics. Single crystals of pure materials and alloys have been grown by starting the zone at a single crystal seed. Crystals with a predetermined, uniform or nonuniform distribution of impurities have been produced. The technique, as used for the hitherto difficult task of producing a uniform distribution of impurity throughout a crystal or ingot, is known as zone levelling. In another variation of zone melting the movement of the zone is effected by a temperature gradient across the ingot—temperature gradient zone melting. The term zone freezing has also been used to describe the passage of a solid zone through a liquid, a process which may have application in particular cases, although it is essentially the same as zone melting.

Zone melting, then, embraces that family of techniques which has developed from the concept of moving a zone of one phase through another. Here we shall be mainly concerned with zone refining, i.e., the zone melting process as used for the purification and separation of materials and in particular with the movement of molten zones through the solid. However, the use of solid–solid or vapor–solid zone melting may have useful applications.

At the present time zone melting is a very useful but mainly a research technique. This, because it is still relatively new, because there are problems in increasing the size, throughput, and efficiency of the apparatus, and because the demand for ultra-pure materials is relatively small. However, there are indications of a steady increase in the commercial use of zone melting. The principal use has been in the field of semiconductors, in particular silicon and germanium. These materials are being zone refined in kilogram batches with a total annual production running into tons. Several zone refined metals and antimony and tellurium are now available commercially, although as yet on a comparatively small scale for research use. The zone refining of certain inorganic materials for research projects, and where high purity is a priority, e.g., optical materials, scintillation counters, is being actively considered, but has not to the authors' knowledge been extensively applied.

The largest industrial use of zone refining may be in the separation, concentration, and purification of organic materials. Many pharmaceutical and fine chemical firms are already preparing small batches of ultra-pure materials in this way, mainly for use as standards, but perhaps larger scale application may be found in the separation of chemicals from petroleum, bituminous, and coal by-products. This may be especially so when techniques designed for continuous zone refining are completely worked out. Some further possible applications are discussed later (Section VII-C).

This article is principally concerned with the application and apparatus used in zone refining various materials. It is necessary however, before describing individual cases, to discuss the process in more general terms, and this can perhaps be best done by considering the relationship between zone melting and the equilibrium diagrams (Section II) and some of the factors affecting the rate of removal of impurities (Sections III and IV). Then in Section V we describe particular applications, attempting to include as much variety of apparatus and technique as possible, and summarizing the results which have been obtained. Two final sections discuss large scale and continuous processes (VI) and the limitations and future possibilities (VII).

At the time of writing, March 1960, several hundred references and patents on this subject have appeared in the literature, and to help readers interested in particular aspects we have included the titles of papers in our references.

Much of our understanding of zone melting and many of the ingenious applications of the process originate from the work of W. G. Pfann. Since his first papers in 1952, he has contributed many papers and patents on this technique to the literature. Many have enjoyed his lectures and a personal contact with him, and his book

(2) published in 1958 has been widely acclaimed. His inspiration
and perseverance have been rewarded by the presentation of the
Mathewson medal of the A.I.M.E. and the Clamer medal of the
Franklin Institute.

Other reviews of zone melting applied to particular fields are listed
in references 3–11.

## II. Zone Melting and the Equilibrium Diagrams

**A.** As mentioned above, zone melting is a recrystallization process and can, therefore, be usefully described in terms of the phase
or equilibrium diagrams. Figure 2, for example, illustrates the case
of a complete range of solid solutions between materials A and B.

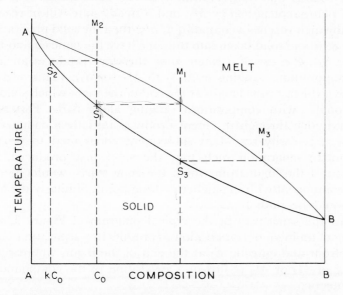

Fig. 2. Equilibrium or phase diagram for materials A and B which form a complete range of solid solutions.

This indicates that, when a melt of composition $M_1$ solidifies under
equilibrium conditions, the first solid to form would have a composition $S_1$. Precipitation of $S_1$ leaves the melt richer in B, and subsequent solidifications gives a range of compositions defined by the
solidus line $S_1B$—assuming complete mixing in the melt but no

mixing in the solid and that equilibrium conditions are obtained. Such conditions could apply for example in the case of a crystal being withdrawn from a well stirred melt or a horizontal ingot solidifying from one end. This process has been termed "directional" or "normal" freezing. Further separation of A and B can be obtained by repeating the process on the first parts of the ingot to solidify. This has been known for many years, and has been used recently, but is wasteful in terms of material.

Passage of a molten zone as in Figure 1 through an ingot of composition $M_1$ produces a slightly different result. Again the first solid to form has composition $S_1$, the melt becomes richer in B, and solid subsequently deposited has a composition indicated by the solidus line $S_1S_3$. However, as the zone moves it is constantly being replenished by $M_1$, and a steady state will be reached when the melt reaches a composition $M_3$; then the solid precipitated by the zone and solid taken into the zone have the same composition $M_1$ (or $S_3$). Passage of a single zone therefore produces an ingot with compositions ranging from $S_1$ to $M_1$ (or $S_3$). (This neglects, of course, the last zone length at the end of the ingot which solidifies directionally with compositions ranging along $S_3B$.) Passage of a second zone through the ingot produces initially a composition $S_2$ and it is easily seen that subsequent zones tend to produce a complete separation such that the solid first produced, i.e., that end of the ingot from which the zone starts, would be pure A the component with the higher melting point. Similarly the other end would be pure B.

**B.** In the same way in the typical diagram of Figure 3, zone melting of an ingot of composition $M_1$ results in a separation into A at the front and eutectic $E_1$ at the end of the ingot, whereas zone melting of $M_2$ or $M_3$ results in a separation of the compound AB and eutectic.

Figure 3 indicates that zone melting would be particularly useful in the preparation of intermetallic compounds, these often being difficult to prepare by other methods. This has certainly proved to be the case. It is however worthwhile to point out that the compound prepared in this way is that which has a maximum melting point (or minimum free energy), and this may or may not be precisely the stoichiometric composition. Thus the composition having a maximum melting point in the In–Sb diagram is InSb,

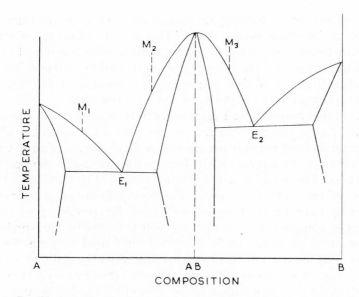

TEMPERATURE

A                AB                      B

COMPOSITION

Fig. 3. Equilibrium diagram for materials A and B which form a compound AB and eutectics $E_1$ and $E_2$.

stoichiometric to at least 1 in $10^{11}$, whereas that in the Pb–Te diagram is PbTe containing 1 in $10^6$ excess Te.

These considerations show that, in zone refining, impurities which decrease the melting point of the material being refined tend to move with the zone and concentrate at the end of the ingot to which the zone travels, whereas impurities which increase the melting point move in the opposite direction. The equilibrium diagrams of metals and inorganic systems, where these are known, show the former case is the more common. It is also well known experimentally in organic chemistry that impurities tend to lower the melting point of a material; the melting point is in fact a much used criterion of purity. There is therefore a wide range of materials which can be purified by zone refining. This of course includes many materials which are liquids at normal temperatures; these can be zone refined at ambient temperatures below their melting point. Water, benzene, and pyridine are typical examples. Materials which have an excessively high vapor pressure at the melting point can be zone refined using an external pressure to reduce evaporation or by holding the whole ingot at a temperature just below the melting point, thus reducing the difference of vapor pressure between melt and ingot and reducing the transfer of material from the zone. Mercury selenide and telluride, lead selenide and telluride (Section V-E-3) are examples, but no success has yet been reported for any of the salt hydrates, alums, etc.

C. Ternary equilibrium diagrams can be considered in the same way. Thus a binary eutectic can be purified, impurities which lower its melting point being moved in the direction of zone travel and those which increase its melting point moving in the opposite direction. The KCl/ice eutectic containing 0.1% NaCl is an example of this (Section V-D-4). The zone refining of eutectic compositions may prove a useful technique for purifying materials which decompose at the melting point, in particular, perhaps, various organic compounds. The "solvent" used to form the eutectic must of course be easily removable when the refining is complete, e.g., by vaporization or differential solubility. However zone refining of eutectics may be less efficient, for in this case crystals of two materials precipitate in the solid and entrapment of impurity seems more likely.

D. Zone refining in the solid state has been proposed by Pfann (2) and may have a limited application. In this case there must be a difference in solubility of impurity between two coexisting solid phases. Also for effective separation, diffusion of impurity in one of the phases, the "zone" phase, must be considerably more rapid than in the other. Since diffusion is the only process by which rejected impurity may become redistributed in the zone, the rate of zoning must be very slow, otherwise the increased impurity concentration at the interface limits the effective segregation (Section IV-C). This is probably the greatest disadvantage of solid zone refining.

E. Zone refining involving crystallization from solutions has also been considered. (The distinction between a melt and a solution is of course not well defined, but we use the terms in their familiar notation.) For example, solvent could be added to an impure solute to form a zone and, if the solute is more soluble in the solvent at higher temperatures, movement of a heater should effect transfer of solute across the zone, with a resulting purification similar to that obtained by direct recrystallization in the usual way. One ıherent difficulty with this type of process may be the slow rate of oning required, because of the slower rate of formation of crystals ʾom solutions and the possible entrapment of solvent.

**F.** A particular case of this "solution" technique is the "temˌerature gradient zone melting" process (35). Here a temperature ˌradient across the ingot rather than a moving heater causes the ˌsolution" zone to move. For example, aluminum may be added to ˌlicon to form a zone of lower melting alloy. When a temperature ˌradient is impressed across the zone, silicon dissolves at the hotter ˌde, diffuses through the zone, and precipitates at the colder side. ʾhe zone thus moves through the ingot to the hotter end at a rate ˌependent on the applied temperature gradient. An advantage of ˌis technique is that very thin zones in the form of plates, wires, ˌr other shapes can be moved through a material, which may be ˌseful, for example, in the fabrication of semiconductor devices. ˌn the other hand traces of "solvent" may remain in the purified ˌlid.

The use of a vapor zone moving through a solid has also been ˌuggested and may be a promising alternative for volatile materials ˌSection V-E-10).

### III. Distribution of Impurity during Zone Refining

**A.** The equilibrium diagrams are sufficient, as we have seen, to ˌhow whether an impurity can be removed from a material by zone ˌefining. The ease with which a second component may be reˌnoved can be expressed in terms of a distribution or segregation ˌoefficient, $k$, defined as the ratio of the amount of impurity in the ˌolid phase to that in the coexisting liquid phase. This is similar in ˌonception to other distribution coefficients, for example, the disˌribution of a solute between two immiscible solvents.

The equilibrium coefficient, $k_0$, not necessarily equal to $k$, can ˌe derived from the solidus and liquidus lines of equilibrium diaˌrams. Thus in Figure 2, melt $M_2$ of composition $C_0$ is in equilibrium ˌvith $S_2$ of composition $k_0C_0$, $k_0$ being less than one. Impurity B in A ˌvould concentrate at the end of the ingot to which the zone moves. ˌ\ considered as an impurity in B would have a $k_0$ greater than 1 and ˌoncentrate at the opposite end.

Consideration of typical equilibrium diagrams indicates that ˌ$_0$ is not constant, but depends on impurity concentration. How-

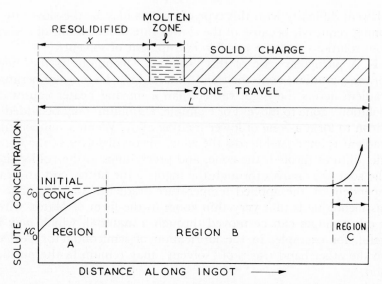

Fig. 4. Distribution of impurity with $k < 1$ after one zone pass.   (From W. G. Pfa
(1).   Courtesy of Metallurgical Society of A.I.M.E.).

ever, at sufficiently low impurity concentrations, $k_0$ becomes in
dependent of impurity concentration, and quoted values of $k_0$ refe
to this condition.

In practice the experimental conditions during refining may b
different from those required for equilibrium solidification. Th
observed or effective segregation coefficient $k$ would then have a
value $k_0$ (ideal separation) and unity (zero separation). This i
discussed later. Here we wish to show how the distribution of im
purity along an ingot depends on the value of $k$, on the width of th
zone, and on the number of zone passes, the segregation coefficien
referred to being either the ideal $k_0$ or an effective $k$ as appropriat
to the particular conditions.

**B**. The distribution of an impurity with segregation coefficien
$k$ ($<1$) after a single pass is illustrated in Figure 4. The first solid t
form from the zone has composition $kC_0$ (by definition); the im
purity concentration in the zone therefore increases above $C_0$, an
solid forming subsequently has a higher impurity concentratior
This continues (region A) until the impurity concentration in th
molten zone reaches a value $C_0/k$. At this point solid entering an

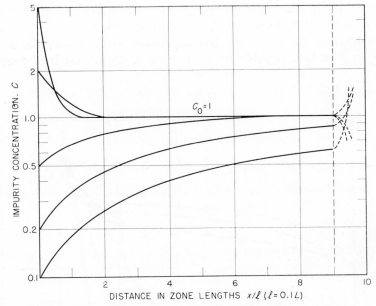

Fig. 5. Distribution of impurity after one zone pass for values of $k$ from 5 to 0.1 and $l = 0.1L$ ($k = C$ at $x = 0$).

leaving the zone has the same composition $C_0$ (region B). Finally the last zone length (region C) solidifies normally. The equation governing the distribution of impurity in regions A and B has been neatly and simply derived by Read (see Pfann(1)) and is

$$C/C_0 = 1 - (1 - k) \exp (-kx/l) \qquad (1)$$

where $C$ is the impurity concentration at a point $x$ from the starting end, $C_0$ the initial impurity concentration, $l$ the zone length, and $k$ the appropriate distribution coefficient.

The assumptions made in this derivation are: (1) there is no diffusion of solute in the solid; (2) the composition of the molten zone is always uniform; and (3) $k$ is constant. These assumptions are often valid experimentally but need not be so. These, and derivations involving other assumptions are discussed later.

Figure 5 illustrates the distribution according to equation 1 along an ingot for impurities with values of $k$ ranging from 5 to 0.1, the zone length $l$ being one-tenth of the ingot length.

Equation 1 notes that the distribution of impurity is affected by the zone length $l$. This is illustrated in Figure 6.

Separation for one zone pass improves with increase in zone length. The best possible separation for a single pass is of course

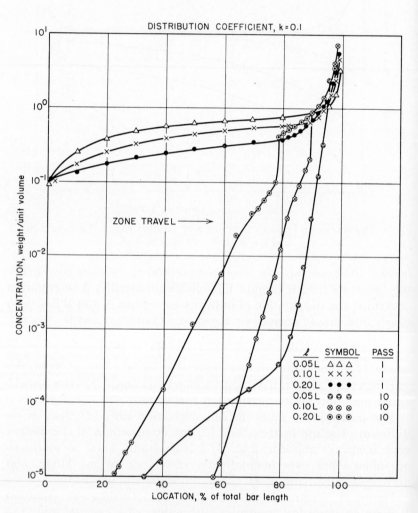

Fig. 6. Effect of zone length on distribution of impurity. ($k = 0.1$). (From L. Burris et al. (12). Courtesy of Metallurgical Society of A.I.M.E.)

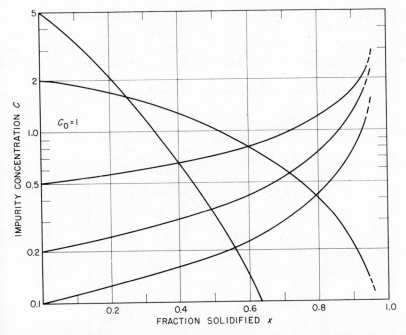

FRACTION SOLIDIFIED $x$

Fig. 7. Distribution of impurity after normal freezing for values of $k$ from 5 to 0.6.

that "for normal" freezing, i.e., when a melt solidifies directionally from one end. The equation describing normal freezing is

$$C = kC_0(1 - x)^{k-1} \qquad (2)$$

where in this case $x$ is the fraction of the ingot solidified. (Equation 2 is also derived using the assumptions stated above.) Curves showing the separation for $k$ values from 5 to 0.1 after normal freezing are given in Figure 7 for comparison.

C. However, as may be expected, the ultimate distribution, i.e., that distribution which does not alter by passage of a further zone, is less good the wider the zone. The computed curves of Burris et al. (12) (Fig. 8) show this effect for the case of an impurity with $k$'s of 5 and 0.1 and zone lengths of 5, 10, and 20% of the ingot length.

Davies (13) has investigated theoretically the efficiency of the zone refining process particularly in terms of optimum zone length.

Making the usual assumptions of negligible diffusion in the solid, complete mixing in the liquid, and $k$ independent of concentration, he shows as expected that maximum separation with the first zone is achieved when the zone length $l_1$ is equal to $L$, the length of the

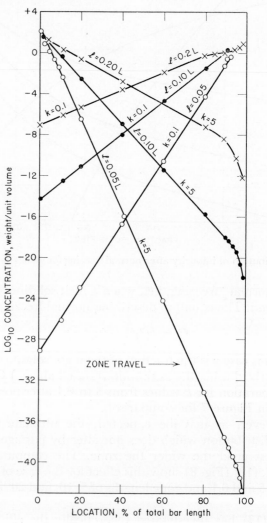

Fig. 8. Effect of zone length on ultimate distribution for $k = 0.1$ and 5. (From L. Burris *et al.* (12). Courtesy of Metallurgical Society of A.I.M.E.)

ingot, i.e., normal freezing for all values of $k$. He then shows that following a normal freeze the most effective length for the second zone depends on $k$, but an optimum value is $l_2 = 0.3L$. The analysis for further zones is not given, but after the second zone the use of a

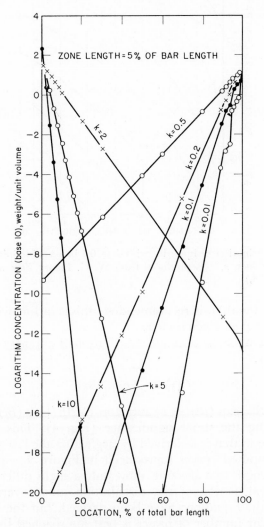

Fig. 9.  Ultimate distribution for different values of $k$.    (From L. Burris *et al.* (12). Courtesy of Metallurgical Society of A.I.M.E.)

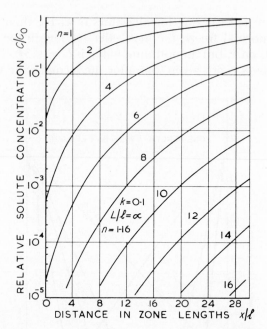

Fig. 10. Distribution of impurity with $k = 0.1$ in a semi-infinite charge after several zone passes, $n$. (Reproduced from W. G. Pfann, *Zone Melting*, Wiley, New York, 1958.)

zone length $l = 0.1L$ is recommended; this is in line with the findings of Burris *et al.* given earlier.

An equation for the ultimate distribution of impurity was derived by Pfann (1).

$$C(x) = A \exp (Bx) \qquad (3)$$

where $k = Bl/[\exp (Bl) - 1]$ and $A = C_0 BL/[\exp (Bl) - 1]$, $L,l,k$, and $x$ having the usual significance (Fig. 4). This equation is approximate in that it is derived by neglecting the last zone length, but the computed curves reproduced in Figure 9, which take the final zone length into account, show only a slight difference.

**D.** The calculation of the distribution after several passes is more difficult. Equations have been derived, but the solution for any particular number of passes is best approached by numerical computation. Numerous curves representing distributions after specific numbers of passes have been prepared and many are included in the appendix to Pfann's book. He also describes various simple and ingenious mechanical devices which can be used to make the computations. Such curves follow an expected course. We reproduce in Figures 10, 11, and 12, curves for distribution after several passes of impurities with $k = 0.1$, $0.9$, and $1.5$. Other theoretical papers are listed in references 15–27.

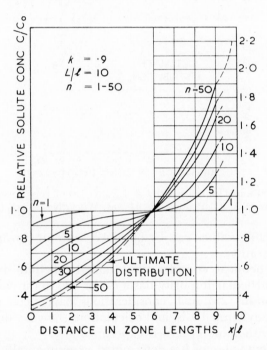

Fig. 11. Distribution of impurity with $k = 0.9$ after several zone passes, $n$ (Reproduced from W. G. Pfann, *Zone Melting*, Wiley, New York, 1958).

**E.** We are left then with the problem of calculating or estimating $k$. As we have seen, $k_0$ can be derived from the equilibrium diagrams, and we show in the following section how experimental conditions affect $k_0$ to produce some effective segregation coefficient, $k$. Unfortunately the usually available equilibrium diagrams are not sufficiently detailed in the region of very low impurity concentration for an accurate estimate of $k_0$ to be made, although in some

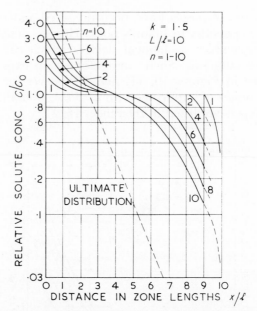

Fig. 12. Distribution of impurity with $k = 1.5$ after several zone passes, $n$ (Reproduced from W. G. Pfann, *Zone Melting*, Wiley, New York, 1958).

cases reasonable values can be obtained from an extrapolation to zero concentration.

General chemical considerations may be helpful in deciding whether a particular impurity has a $k >$ or $< 1$. In the case of silicon and germanium (28) such considerations have been put on an exact thermodynamic basis, and calculations show $k$ values in good agreement with those obtained experimentally.

In practice a value of $k$ is determined experimentally. This can be done by direct comparison of the distribution of impurities (determined analytically) with the equations or curves illustrated above. Many values have been determined for the case of normal freezing this being particularly useful for crystals pulled from the melt. The values of $k$ thus obtained are also more easily correlated with values of $k_0$. However, the computed curves for any number of zone passes and any zone length may be used.

One useful procedure is to determine the distribution of impurity after one pass. It will be seen that equation 1 reduces to $C_1(0) =$

$kC_0$ for the position $x = 0$ at the head of the ingot. $C_1$ (0), the impurity concentration at the head of the ingot may be obtained by extrapolation, and $k$ is then the ratio of $C_1(0)$ to $C_0$, the initial concentration.

Values of $k$ can also be obtained from experiments where impurity is introduced only into the first zone length of the ingot. It can be shown that the appropriate equation for the distribution after one pass is

$$C_1/C_0 = k \exp (-kx/l)$$

or

$$\log kC_0 - \log C_1 = kx/l$$

This indicates that the slope of the curve of $\log C_1$ versus $x$ is proportional to $k$, and that at $x = 0$, $\log C_1 = \log kC_0$. Thus if two impurities are introduced into the first zone length, the ratio of the slopes of the appropriate curves is also the ratio of their $k$ values.

In certain cases the purification effected by the passage of molten zones is not wholly due to the segregation between liquid and solid phases. The vapor phase for example, may play an important part. In such cases it is usual to describe the results obtained by zone refining in terms of a purification factor. This can be defined to suit the particular case; usually it is defined as the ratio of the initial impurity concentration to that after a stated number of zones.

Radiotracers are particularly useful for determining impurity distribution, and hence the value of $k$. They have the great advantage that extremely small impurity concentrations can be easily determined.

## IV. Other Factors Affecting the Impurity Distribution

**A.** Several factors not previously discussed may influence the observed distribution of impurities during zone refining, with the result that the observed effective segregation coefficient $k$ is nearer unity than the ideal $k_0$ obtained from the equilibrium diagrams or from theoretical considerations. Such factors are the interaction of impurities, diffusion in the solid, lack of uniformity in the melt, temperature gradient at the solid/melt interface, impurity vapor pressure, and mass transfer of material; these are discussed briefly in this section.

The segregation coefficient of an impurity may be altered by the presence of other impurities. This is to be expected, for example, if the impurities interact with each other in the host material; in this case some association or "compound" of the impurities is being removed rather than the individual impurities. Such effects have been observed in several systems and most thoroughly investigated in the ingenious experiments at the Bell Laboratories using Si and Ge as host materials (5).

Impurities also interact with "physical" defects such as grain boundaries, dislocations, and vacancies in the solid, indicating that ideality is most nearly approached during the growth of near perfect crystals.

A particular case is an impurity interaction leading to the precipitation of a second phase in the zone. Typical examples may be found with impurities such as oxides, sulfides, silicates, etc. in metals. The solubility of an oxide in a molten metal may be only a few parts per million, any excess forming a scum or slag on the surface. The scum may not be swept along by the molten zone but may remain on the surface of the solid to be remelted into subsequent zones. Then, even if the segregation coefficient of oxide in the melt is very low, many zone passes will be required to remove the total amount. The removal of a lighter slag phase may of course be facilitated by vertical zone refining with the molten zone moving from bottom to top. Alternatively such "slag" impurities may be removed by etching the surface of the ingot or by previously melting and filtering.

**B.** The assumption that there is no diffusion of impurity in the solid is usually true. The diffusion coefficients of impurities in the solid state are usually of the order of $10^{-9}$ cm$^2$/sec. Exceptions may perhaps be expected for materials with a particularly "open" or "defect" structure, on in those cases where the whole ingot has to be maintained at a temperature near the melting point. The high effective diffusion coefficient, $10^{-5}$ cm$^2$/sec of Cu in Ge appears to be due to the interaction of Cu with defects.

**C.** The assumption that the impurity distribution is uniform in the molten zone is less likely to be true and has been considered in some detail. The solid surface advances into the molten zone

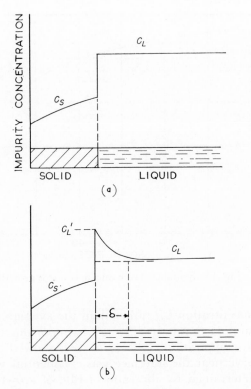

Fig. 13. Concentration of impurity with $k < 1$ in front of a freezing interface. (a) Uniform distribution in melt. (b) Build-up in boundary layer.

rejecting impurities. These impurities may concentrate in a boundary layer immediately in front of the growing surface or may be distributed uniformly throughout the melt. This latter case, Figure 13a is most likely when the rate of advance is very slow, allowing time for diffusion and convective processes, or when the liquid zone is stirred or agitated in some way. The improved efficiency obtained using a slower zone rate, certain shapes and sizes of container (to give improved thermal stirring), and by physical stirring of the zone has been commented on by various workers (Section V-A-5).

The build-up of rejected impurities in a boundary layer in front of the growing surface is illustrated in Figure 13b. The impurity concentration in the solid is now determined by the bound-

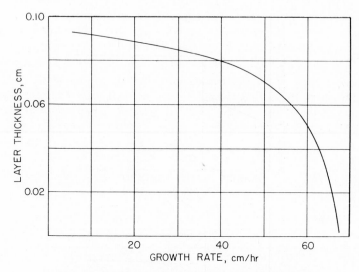

Fig. 14. Boundary layer thickness versus growth rate.

ary layer concentration $C_L'$ rather than the average melt composition $C_L$. Assuming that only diffusion is important in obtaining a uniform melt composition, Tiller *et al.* (29) showed that the shape of the $C_L$ curve near the interface was exponential with a "decay constant" determined by the ratio of rate of growth of the solid to the diffusion coefficient. The thickness δ of the boundary layer, i.e., the distance from the interface to that region of the melt where there is little excess concentration of impurity, can be calculated, and Figure 14 gives an approximate relation between the thickness of this layer and the growth rate, or speed of zoning, for an average diffusion coefficient in liquids. This shows that for high zone rates the layer may become extremely thin, implying that $C_L$ rapidly reaches a value of $C_0/k$, with no further segregation.

Assuming that homogeneity in the melt is achieved only by diffusion, Tiller *et al.* derive equations to describe the distribution of impurity during zone melting, but because of the largely unknown effect of thermal stirring their expressions have limited application.

A more useful approach due to Burton, Prim, and Slichter (30) considers the case of a well-stirred melt. Here the boundary layer is that region unaffected by the stirring, impurity transfer in the

ayer being controlled only by diffusion. The more effective the
tirring, the thinner the diffusion-controlled boundary layer and
he more effective the separation of impurities. (In the previous
:ase a thicker boundary layer produced a better separation, but
)nly diffusion was responsible for dispersing the rejected impurities
.nto the melt.) The expression correlating the growth rate $R$,
)oundary layer thickness $\delta$, diffusion coefficient $D$, and the equilib-
:ium $k_0$ was derived for the case of pulling single crystals from
:he melt

$$k = k_0/[\, k_0 + (1 - k_0)\exp\,(\, - R\delta/D)\,]\qquad(4)$$

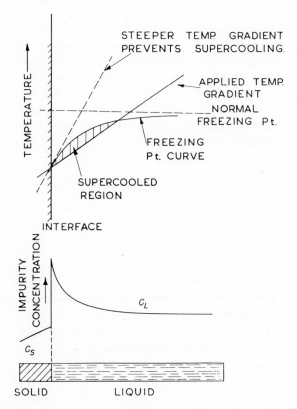

Fig. 15. "Constitutional supercooling" due to build-up of impurities in boundary
layer.

**D.** A further consequence of the high impurity concentration in the boundary layer is that the freezing point of the layer may be less than that in the rest of the melt. Then a temperature low enough to freeze material from the layer may mean that other regions of the melt are supercooled. This would result in an irregular solidification with the inclusion of bands of impurity, an effect observed by many workers, and can be easily seen in the zone refining of colorless inorganic materials containing colored impurities. This effect has been studied especially by Chalmers and co-workers who called it "constitutional supercooling." This is shown diagramatically in Figure 15, which shows that the effect can be reduced if a steeper temperature gradient is applied across the solid/melt interface.

**E.** The distribution of impurities is also complicated if the impurity or host material has a high vapor pressure at the temperature of the molten zone. Movement of both impurity and host material via the vapor phase is possible. Indeed the removal of volatile impurities may be facilitated by suitable design of apparatus (Section V-A-2). A good deal of the purification of the refractory metals by zone refining appears to be due to the vaporization of impurities.

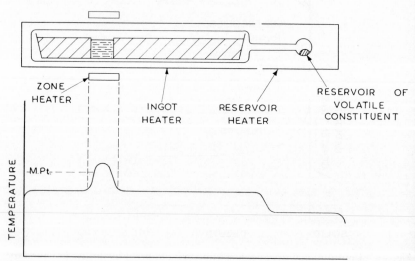

Fig. 16. Control of composition during zone refining.

The vapor phase may also be used to control the composition of the material being zone refined (Fig. 16), this being especially important in certain intermetallic semiconductors. Van den Boomgaard (31) and with Kröger and Vink (32) considered this problem in some detail. The composition of the melt (and hence the solid) at any time is determined by the rate of reaction of vapor with the melt in addition to those other factors previously discussed. If the rate of reaction is very rapid, equilibrium between vapor and liquid is reached at once, and if a constant vapor pressure is maintained the composition of the melt and solid will be uniform. If the rate of reaction is extremely slow, distribution is determined only by the solid/melt reaction as has been considered above. In the intermediate cases, the composition depends on the value of the rate constant of the vapor/liquid reaction and on the time the melt remains in contact with the vapor (zone rate).

In two further papers (33, 34) van den Boomgaard deals with the zone melting of a pure compound AB and treats in particular

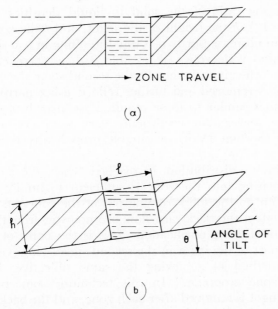

Fig. 17. (a) Matter transport due to density difference.    (b) Prevention by tilting charge.

the problem of deviation from stoichiometry, a point of considerable importance in semiconductor work.

**F.** It has been shown recently by Hulme and Mullin (36) that the crystal axis can affect the value of $k$. Thus in the case of InSb, the segregation coefficient of tellurium was $\sim$3 when the solid/melt interface coincided with a (111) face but was $\sim$0.5 elsewhere.

**G.** If the density of the solid and melt are different, movement of the zone results in a movement of material. This effect arises because the level of the solid just frozen tends to be the same as that of the liquid, as shown in Figure 17. If the density of the solid is less than the melt, matter is moved in the direction of zone movement, and vice versa. In vertical zone refining this causes the material to "walk" up or down the tube depending on the density ratio and the direction of zoning. Movement of material can be compensated in horizontal zone refining by suitably tilting the ingot as shown in Figure 17. The angle of tilt for zero transport is given by

$$\tan \theta = 2h(1 - \alpha)/l$$

where $\alpha$ is the ratio of the solid to liquid densities (less than 1 in Figure 17), $h$ the height of the ingot, and $l$ the zone length.

**H.** For an ultimate purity it is usual to refine in two stages. The first stage uses wide zones, if possible with a steep temperature gradient and effective stirring. In the second stage the center part of the ingot is removed and further refined using narrower zones and conditions similar to those required for growth of good crystals. If the segregation coefficients vary with crystallographic orientation (Section IV-F), a suitable growth direction must be chosen.

The ultimate distribution is reached when the amounts of impurity melting into the zone is sufficient to nullify the effect of segregation on the solid freezing out of the zone, all along the ingot, i.e., when the backward flow of impurities from the impure ends prevents further purification. This is the point of removing the center part of the ingot in the second stage. However, there is a neater method of achieving the same objective, known as "terminal zone cropping." In this technique some part of the end of the ingot is removed after each zone, and the backward flow of impurity reduced. Johnson and Zimmerman (37) have used it with advantage in the purification of germanium and the group

III–V compounds. They took advantage of matter transport (Section IV-G), and allowed a small fraction of the last zone length to overflow into a separate trap in the crucible. An overflow trap holding 10% of the initial charge was filled in 10–15 passes, and the average purity obtained by this means was equivalent to that which would otherwise have taken 30–40 passes.

## V. Apparatus and Applications

### A. GENERAL REQUIREMENTS

*1.* In general the requirements for zone refining are simple. The material must be contained in some way, a heater arranged to produce a molten zone in the material, and either the heater or container moved in such a way that the molten zone traverses the material. For optimum results some degree of control must be exercised on the heating conditions, rate of motion, etc., and some form of stirring or agitation of the zone is desirable.

Figure 18 illustrates a simple form of zone melting apparatus using a gas burner mounted on a trolley on guide rails to melt the zone and a small clockwork or electric motor and gearbox to pull the trolley. If the charge is long enough, several burners can be used and narrower zones at closer spacing can be formed by cooling between with jets of cold air. Using single zones in apparatus like this, Reynolds (38) of the National Chemical Laboratory,

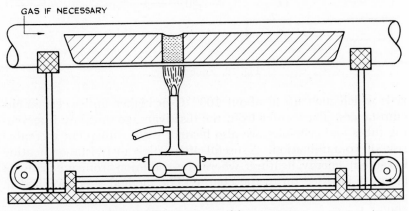

Fig. 18. Simple zone melting apparatus.

Teddington, has obtained considerable purification of some lower melting metals. For instance, he found with bismuth that initial concentrations of 300 ppm of Zn, Pb, Cu, and Ag were reduced to the order of 1 ppm after only three passes at about 5 cm/hr.

2. Electrical heaters are more commonly used. These have been described by Lawson and Nielsen (39), shown in Figure 19, and by Spialter and Riley (40). Resistance heaters can be used for mate-

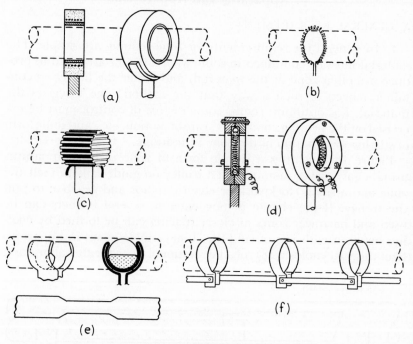

Fig. 19. Zone heaters.

rials which melt up to about 1000 °C or higher under certain circumstances. They suffer from the disadvantage that any intervening tubes and crucibles are also heated, with consequent increased risk of contamination. A useful alternative to resistance heating is radiant energy heating, where the radiation from an array of lamps is focussed on to the charge. The method is economical in power, for instance Weisberg and Gunther-Mohr (41) used three 500-w. lamps to zone-melt germanium in a graphite crucible, and

Baum (42) zone-melted intermetallic systems up to 900 °C with an array of six 150-w. projection lamps.

3. Induction heating is particularly suitable for metals and semiconductors since the heat can be induced directly into the charge and narrow zones can be formed. Also the interaction of induced currents with the primary field sets up a stirring action in the zone. Induction heating can also be used for materials with poor electrical conductivity by using a graphite crucible or by inducing the power into a ring-shaped susceptor of graphite or metal which then heats the zone. The authors have used this method successfully on a number of semiconductors.

Dielectric heating is a possibility for electrical insulators but has not been widely used. The power is absorbed directly in the charge, but the frequency of the heater must correspond to an absorption frequency of the material and this factor restricts the application of the method.

4. An alternative to moving the heater or charge has been described by Fohl and Christy (43). They arranged a series of closely spaced stationary heater coils along the entire length of the charge and, by supplying adjacent coils in turn with current via a motor driven rotary switch, a molten zone could be moved along. Their system can be used for any number of zones with a number of rotating contacts equal to the number of zones, and operation can easily be made fully automatic.

5. The importance of stirring to maintain uniform impurity distribution in the zone and permit higher zoning rates has already been emphasized. Convection stirring can be encouraged by suitable design of container and heater arrangement, but it is unlikely that convection currents alone can establish complete mixing and some form of forced stirring is desirable. Figure 20 shows possible methods. To date, little has been reported on forced stirring techniques other than for metals and semiconductors where advantage is taken of their electrical conductivity to apply a magnetomotive force.

Pfann and Dorsi (44) suggested passing a direct current along the charge and siting a magnet so that the zone was in a nonuniform magnetic field. The force acting on different regions of the melt which is proportional to $H \times I$, would then be different, and stirring would ensue. They stirred lead by this means.

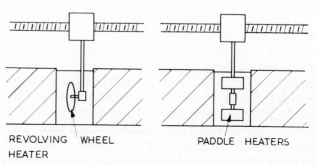

REVOLVING WHEEL          PADDLE HEATERS
HEATER

Fig. 20. Zone stirrers.

Mullin and Hulme (45) used the rotating field from the stator of a three phase induction motor to stir InSb and In. The stator surrounded the charge and was made to move along with the zone. Considerable improvement was obtained over unstirred melts in the separation of Te from InSb and Sn from In, systems in which $k$ is close to unity. Their method has the advantage that only the the molten zone need be conducting; it can be applied to materials which are insulators in the solid state. Braun et al. (46) have also used electromagnetic stirring.

For many organic and inorganic materials, mechanical stirring with paddles or pumps may be the most suitable arrangement.

## B. ORGANIC CHEMICALS

1. Zone melting techniques should have wide application both in research and industry for the purification, separation, and concentration of organic materials. This because many materials melt at convenient temperatures without decomposition and are difficult to obtain in a high state of purity by other means.

The efficacy of purification from the melt was demonstrated by Schwab and Wickers (47) as early as 1940. They showed that the purity of benzoic acid after two recrystallizations from the melt was comparable to that achieved by 11 recrystallizations from benzene and 25 from water. More recently Glasgow and Ross (48), Dickinson and Eaborn (49), and Matthews and Coggeshall (50) have used similar methods to purify other materials.

The application of zone refining techniques has shown that large numbers of compounds can be purified to an exceptional degree. Some idea of the separations which have been achieved is obtained, for example, in the removal of anthracene from naphthalene in seven passes, the separation of the azeotropic mixtures ben-

Fig. 21. Commercial apparatus for zone melting organic compounds. (Courtesy of Baird and Tatlock Ltd., London.)

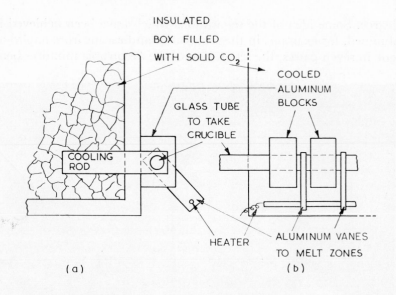

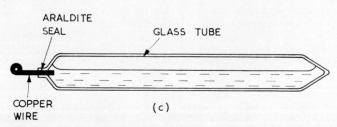

Fig. 22. (a) and (b) Zone melting apparatus for low melting point materials (c) Crucible with copper wire insert to prevent supercooling. (After Sue, Pauly and Nouaille (60).)

zene/acetic acid and water/propionic acid, the separation of $p$- from $o$-bromotoluene, and the separation of ordinary from heavy water. We include a list of materials which have been refined (see Section V-B-5).

2. Early attempts to refine organic materials—especially at the N.C.L., England—suggested that refining in horizontal boats was not satisfactory. Organic materials contract on solidification and

tend to pull away from the containing glass vessels, allowing the liquid zone to run underneath the contracting solid. It was also difficult to maintain a suitable zone shape. Handley and Herington (51) therefore developed vertical refiners of the type illustrated in Figure 21. Their procedure was as follows. Material to be refined was poured into a thick-walled, hard-glass tube and allowed to solidify. The glass stopper at the bottom of the tube was then replaced by a straining tube. The column was then mounted in the apparatus and zones arranged to move from the top of the column to a point at the bottom such that a plug of solid material always remains in the tube. In operation it was found that liquid occasionally percolated through this plug and was caught in the draining tube. A convenient apparatus for 1 kg quantities used a 4-foot column with a maximum diameter of 1.5 inches. The resistance heater maintained a zone width between 2 and 5 inches, and a zone velocity of 1.5 inches/hour proved suitable for most materials. Handley (52) has described some of their results.

Using a similar technique, Ball, Helm, and Ferrin (53) devised an apparatus in which five tubes could be processed simultaneously. Stainless steel tubes were used in preference to glass which often cracked in operation, and compounds melting below room temperature were refined in a refrigerated container.

Two other variations of this type of apparatus have been described by Wolf and Deutsch (54) and Rock (55), the latter, for low melting materials, enclosed in a vacuum flask. Other useful apparatus has been described by Beynon and Saunders (56).

Handley and Herington (57) also developed a semimicro zone-melting apparatus (for about 150 mg) using focussed radiation from a parabolic mirror. Tubes less than 0.1 inch diameter could not be used, since occasional formation of air bubbles prevented the zone moving from end to end. Ronald (58) describes a slightly different apparatus, and Hesse and Schildknecht (59) described an apparatus for even smaller quantities.

Other workers have successfully used horizontal systems. The apparatus due to Sue, Pauly, and Nouaille (60), including the container used to prevent supercooling in the first zone, is shown in Figure 22. A very neat circular refiner with four zone heaters has also been described (61).

3. Vertical refining—as used by Handley and Herington has

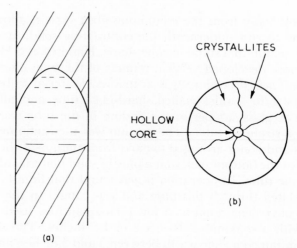

Fig. 23. (a)  Zone shape.  (b)  Cross section of solid.

two inherent advantages, at least for small scale (1 kg) operation: Convection currents are effective in stirring the zone, and gravitational effects aid the removal of dust and other insoluble matter. There is a tendency for vertical tubes to crack, owing possibly to the large pure crystals keying or sticking to the walls, but thick-walled glass tubes have proved satisfactory. Copper and steel tubes have also been used.

The poor thermal conductivity of organic materials limits the diameter of the tube to about 1.5 inches. Even at this diameter, the contour of the solid/liquid interface is not ideal (Fig. 23) and probably accounts for the hollow central core often found in vertically refined material. Larger diameter specimens could probably be zone melted using dielectric heating at suitable frequency. Attempts have also been made to utilize concentric tubes to increase the volume of material being refined, but care must be taken over the design of the heater.

The upper limit for the zone rate is probably determined by the low speed of crystallization of organic materials and may be about 2–3 inches/hour. Stirring of the zone would of course increase the efficiency of separation.

*4.* Dickinson and Eaborn (49) found progressive freezing more convenient to use than zone refining for the purification of liquids and low melting solids. For example benzene (300 ml) in a 3-cm diameter glass tube, was lowered at 4 cm/hour into an ice/water mixture. In six passages, in which the top tenth was left unfrozen and removed, the melting point rose from 0.34 to 5.54 °C. For materials with higher melting points, the material passed from a heated copper tube into water, whereas dry ice/methanol was used to freeze materials with lower melting points. An overflow system was used to keep the level constant. Purification of $p$-bromotoluene, in which the melting point was increased from 15–25 to 23.5–27 °C, nitromethane, and pyridine was obtained in this way.

Matthews and Coggelshall (50) used a similar system for concentrating impurities from reagent grade benzene. They used a stirrer motor in the liquid with marked improvement in efficiency of the separation. Slower rates of lowering also increased efficiency in the 4–16 cm/hour range, but a 10 °C variation in cooling temperature had little effect.

5. The following organic compounds have been purified by zone melting:

Benzoic acid (47); 2,5-dichlorostyrene (48); benzene, $p$-bromotoluene, nitromethane (49); 3-methylpyridine, indole, 9-methylcarbazole (53); benzene (55); naphthalene (54); cetyl alcohol, stearyl alcohol, 3-methyl-1,2-cyclopentanophenanthrene (59); $p$-bromotoluene from $o$-isomer, $p$-xylene from $o$-isomer, benzene from thiophene, benzene from acetic acid, water from propionic acid (60); naphthalene, anthracene, pyrene, chrysene, benzoic acid, phenol, $o$-, $m$-, and $p$-cresols, 6-isomeric xylenols, pyridine, quinoline, isoquinoline, alkyl phenols, dihydric phenols, $\beta$-naphthol, bisphenol, benzene hexachloride ($\gamma$-isomer), $p$-xylene (Handley and Herington).

Benzoic acid; 1,4,5-trichloroanthraquinone; 4-chloro-2-nitro-aniline; 2-nitro-4-methylaniline; 3-methylindole; naphthalene; anthracene; 1-amino-2-methylanthraquinone; 3-methoxybenz-anthrone; acetamide; diphenylacetic acid; phenoxyacetic acid; aldrin; aniline; 2-methyl-4-nitroaniline; antipyrene; $N,N$-dimethyl-$p$-nitroaniline; methyleneaniline; $p$-nitroaniline; $p$-anisidine; anthranilic acid; anthraquinone; 1-amino-2-cyanoanthraquinone; 1-chloro-2-methylanthraquinone; 1,5-dihydroxyanthraquinone; 1,8-dihydroxyanthraquinone; 1-hydroxyanthraquinone; 1-methyl-aminoanthraquinone; azobenzene; 1-,2-benzanthracene; benzamide; benzene; dibenzyl; cetyl alcohol; 4-chloro-2-methyl-phenol; 2,5-dimethylphenol; 2-cyanocyclopentylideniene; fluore-none; 2,3-dimethylindole; 1,3,5,7-tetramethylindole; 1,2,3,-5,7-pentamethylindole; maleic anhydride; dichloromaleic anhy-dride; phenanthrene; 2-methycyclohexyl-4-methylphenol; *p-tert*-butylphenol; pyrazolone, 1-*p*-tolyl-3-methyl-5-pyrazolone; pyrene; resorcinol; succinic acid; sulfur; dimethyl terephthalate; urea; δ-cyanovaleramide (56).

## C. WATER AND SOLUTIONS

*1.* The use of zone refining for the purification of water, for con-verting sea water to fresh water, and for the separation of heavy water have been considered.

The apparatus used by Smith and Thomas (62) for the separation of heavy water consisted of a spiral of Tygon tubing wound on a 1.5-inch cylinder of wire mesh. In the experiment the tubing was filled with a mixture of $D_2O$ and $H_2O$ and plugged with a pyrex stopper. The spiral was arranged so that the lower half of each turn was submerged in refrigerated brine, and zones were produced in the upper half by a strip heater. By turning the spiral at 0.75 rev-olution/hour, 40 evenly spaced zones traveling at 4.1 inches/hour traversed the material. Under these conditions the effective segregation was appreciably less than the theoretical and the sep-aration of $D_2O$ extremely slow, but nevertheless the result is note-worthy in that separation of isotopes was achieved. Using the ap-paratus of Figure 22, Sue *et al.* (60) came to a similar conclusion.

*2.* Zone refining has been successful in concentrating solutions. Schildknecht and Mannl (63) describe a horizontal apparatus en-closed in a refrigerated box for concentrating aqueous solutions. They showed that methylene blue, rhodamine, $KMnO_4$, ascorbic acid, the enzymes catalase and arylamine acetylase, bacteria and bacteriophage, and plankton, could be concentrated efficiently in this way; some 15% loss in activity of the enzymes was observed. Sue *et al.* showed that colloidal solutions of gold could be concen-trated in a similar way. The concentration of NaCl solution from 3 to 12 Be has also been reported (64).

The use of zone refining for concentrating impurities may of course be a valuable preliminary step in analytical procedures.

*3.* The preliminary results of Peaker and Robb (65) suggest that a zone refining process could be used to fractionate polymer solutions. They used a solution of polystyrene in naphthalene and refined this in a vertical tube. It is not clear at the present time whether the fractionation obtained is due to a diffusion phenomenon rather than a solid/melt segregation.

## D. INORGANIC CHEMICALS

*1.* Comparatively few inorganic chemicals have been purified by zone refining, because the melting points of inorganic materials are in general appreciably higher than the organic materials discussed above and some form of decomposition or dissociation frequently occurs before the melting point. Also molten inorganic materials tend to react more readily with glass and quartz containers and necessitate somewhat more complicated apparatus. However, in those cases reported, zone refining has proved capable of producing extremely pure material, and it appears that, despite the above limitations, would be capable of much further development. Also preliminary investigations have shown that it is possible to refine inorganic materials in the form of eutectic solutions of other salts or water, although this does not seem likely to supersede conventional crystallization procedures.

*2.* $GaCl_3$ (m.p. 75 °C) was zone refined by Richards (66) in quartz boats in a conventional horizontal apparatus. After 20 passes the front end of the ingot became transparent and practically single crystal—certainly visible indication of purification. After 20 passes through the chloride Richards recovered gallium metal by electrodeposition and found that the elements Cu, Fe, Ca, Mg, Si, Al, and Ag were reduced from 20–70 ppm to below 1 ppm, the limit of detection (electrodeposition alone was not effective in removing impurities). Zone melting gallium alone was relatively ineffective in removing these impurities even after 40 passes.

In a similar way Rubin, Moates, and Weiner (67) examined the possibility of obtaining very pure silicon by zone refining $SiI_4$ (m.p. 121.5–122.5 °C). The $SiI_4$ was contained in sealed pyrex ampules and zones about 2.5 cm wide passed vertically downwards at 5 cm/hour. Estimation of segregation coefficients from an observed distribution of impurity showed for boron, $k = 0.16$; aluminum, $k = 0.88$; sodium, $k = 0.07$; magnesium, $k = 0.58$; and copper,

TABLE I
Melting Points of Halides, °C

| Metal | F | Cl | Br | I |
|-------|-----|-----|-----|-----|
| Al | 1040 | 190[(2.5)] | 97.5 | 191 |
| Sb | 292 | 73.4 | 96.6 | 167 |
| As | −8.5 | 18 | 32.8 | d 136 |
| Ba | 1280 | 962 | 847 | 740 |
| Be | 800 | 440 | 490[(5)] | 510 |
| Bi | — | 230 | 218 | 439 |
| B | −127 | −107. | −46 | 43 |
| Cd | 1100 | 568 | 567 | 3.88 |
| Ca | 1360 | 772 | 765 | 575 |
| Ce | 1324 | 848 | | |
| Cs | 684 | 646 | 636 | 621 |
| Cr | 1100 | | | |
| Cu$^I$ | 908 | 422 | 504 | 605 |
| Cu$^{II}$ | | 498 | 498 | |
| Eu | | 623 | | |
| Gd | | 628 | | |
| Ga$^{II}$ | | 170.5 | | |
| Ga$^{III}$ | >1000 | 77.9 | 121 | 212 |
| Ge$^{II}$ | d | d | 122 | 5d |
| Ge$^{IV}$ | s | −49.5 | 26.1 | 144.0 |
| Au | | d | d | d |
| In$^I$ | | 225 | 220 | 351 |
| In$^{II}$ | | 235 | 235 | 212 |
| In$^{III}$ | 1170 | 586(s) | 436 | 210 |
| Ir | 444 | | | |
| Fe$^{II}$ | 1000 | 670 | d | 177 |
| Fe$^{III}$ | | 282 | (s) (d) | |
| La | | 872 | | 761 |
| Pb | 855 | 501 | 373 | 402 |
| Li | 870 | 613 | 547 | 446 |
| Mg | 1396 | 708 | 700 | 700  d |
| Mn | 856 | ds | d | d |
| Hg$^I$ | 570 | s | s | s |
| Hg$^{II}$ | d | 276 | 236 | d |
| Mo | | 194 | d | |

[a] d = decompose, s = sublime.

$k = 0.63$. McCarty (68) has also studied this method for obtaining pure silicon.

Some success in zone refining lithium fluoride (m.p. 870°C) has been achieved by Stevenson (69) using a circular rotating charge in a graphite crucible. A circular channel with a 2-cm in-

TABLE I (continued)

| Metal | F | Cl | Br | I |
|---|---|---|---|---|
| Ni | | s | d | d |
| Nb | | 194 | 150 | |
| Pd | s | d | d | d |
| P | −160 | −91 | −40 | 61 |
| Pt | | 435 | | |
| K | 880 | 776 | 730 | 723 |
| Re$^{IV}$ | 124.5 | | | |
| Re$^{VI}$ | 25.6 | | | |
| | d | | | |
| Rh | | d | | |
| Rb | 760 | 715 | 682 | 642 |
| Ru | 101 | | | |
| Sm$^{II}$ | | 740 | | |
| Sm$^{III}$ | | 678 | | 816 |
| Sc | | 939 | | |
| Si | −77 | 75 | 93 | 120.5 |
| Ag | 435 | 455 | 434 | d |
| Na | 997 | 801 | 755 | 651 |
| Sr | 1190 | 873 | 643 | 402 |
| Ta | 96.8 | 221 | 240 | |
| Te | | 209 | 210 | s |
| Tb | | 588 | | |
| Tl | | 430 | 460 | 440 |
| Th | d | s | | |
| Sn$^{II}$ | | 246 | 215.5 | 320 |
| Sn$^{IV}$ | | −33 | 31 | 143.5 |
| Ti$^{II}$ | | s | d | |
| Ti$^{IV}$ | | −30 | 39 | 150 |
| W$^{V}$ | | 248 | 276 | |
| W$^{VI}$ | 2.5 | 275 | | |
| U | 1000 | s | | 500 |
| V$^{III}$ | 800 | d | d | |
| V$^{IV}$ | d | −28 | | |
| Y | | 680 | | |
| Zn | 872 | 262 | 394 | 446 |

terruption was milled in a graphite ring to contain the charge, and the section of the channel had its inner surface sloping to prevent fracture on cooling. Two strip heaters 1 inch wide provided two diametrically opposite zones through which the charge was rotated. A very marked and obvious separation of deliberately added impurities was obtained with a zoning rate of 6 cm/hour. Transfer of material to the front of the charge was considerable but could be countered by gradually altering the depth of the milled channel. The method should be applicable to other stable high melting point fluorides such as those used for optical components.

3. Table I shows that it may be possible to refine some other halides. However, the low thermal conductivity, reactivity, and high vapor pressure of some of these do raise difficult problems, which vapor zone refining (Section V-E-10) may help to solve.

4. In several interesting papers, Sue, Pauly, and Nouaille (60, 70) discuss the application of zone refining to inorganic compounds, especially $KNO_3$ and to eutectic mixtures. In one series of experiments $KNO_3$ (m.p. 334 °C) containing 0.1% impurity with radioactive tracer, was refined in horizontal glass boats. The boats were 15 cm long, 1 cm wide, zone width 1 cm, and zone rate 5.6 mm/hour.

They showed for $Na^*NO_3$, 10, 1250; $Na^*NO_3$, 20, 4000; $Sr^*$-$(NO_3)_2$, 40, 12,500; $KS^*O_4$, 10, 1,000; $K_3P^*O_4$, 10, 500; $K_3P^*$-$O_4$, 30, 5,000; the asterisk denoting the tracer, the first figure the number of zones and the second the purification factor obtained. The variation of $k$ with zone rate was also studied; a $k$ of 0.25 increased to 0.55 for an increase in rate from 2.8 to 40 cm/hour.

From other experiments they estimated the values of $k$ for Ca-$(NO_3)_2$ and $Sr(NO_3)_2$ in $NaNO_3$ to be 0.01 and 0.05, and for $K_2SO_4$ and $Cs_2SO_4$ they found $k$ to be 0.6 and 0.1. $CaSO_4$ in $Na_2SO_4$ moved against the zone in agreement with the phase diagram, and in experiments on $Na_2B_4O_7$ zone refining failed to effect purification because this salt solidifies as a glass.

In other interesting experiments they showed that it was possible to purify lead nitrate, which decomposes on melting, by forming a eutectic of lower melting point with potassium nitrate. They obtained purification factors as follows after four zone passes: $Na^*NO_3$, 4; $Cs^*NO_3$, 5; $Sr^*(NO_3)_2$, 1.4; $La^*(NO_3)_2$, 1.05.

They showed that purification of KC1/ice eutectic was possible. Purification factors for NaCl of 15 and 28 after 8 and 10 zones, and for $SrCl_2$ of 65 after 20 zones were obtained. Coefficients of purification, $p$, analogous to the usually defined segregation coefficient were obtained, viz: for NaCl, 0.32; CaCl, 0.18; $CaCl_2$, 0.44; $SrCl_2$, 0.36; $K_2SO_4$, 0.34; $K_3PO_4$, 0.43.

5. Ammonium nitrate has been zone refined by Shirai and Ishiboshi (71) and some useful purifications obtained. Experiments to determine the segregation of radium and thorium X in various nitrate mixtures (72) and of radium in the binary systems $PbCl_2/$ NaCl, $PbCl_2/CdCl_2$, $PbCl_2/ZnCl_2$ have also been reported (73).

## E. METALS AND SEMICONDUCTORS

1. It is with metals and semiconductors that zone melting techniques have been most widely used, and so are especially successful. The diverse properties of these materials—such as melting points, vapor pressure, reactivity to containers and atmosphere—have resulted in a great diversity of apparatus and techniques. Here we discuss the apparatus used for various materials and summarize the results which have been obtained.

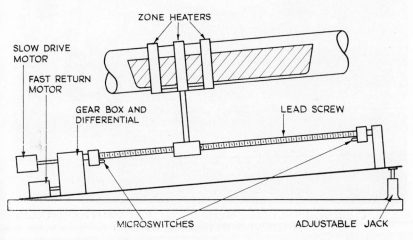

Fig. 24. Zone melting apparatus with automatic fast return of heaters.

Many metals and semiconductors, e.g., Zn, Cd, In, Sn, Pb, Sb, Bi, Te, InSb, $Bi_2Se_3$, InTe etc. may be refined in apparatus of the type illustrated in Figure 24. In this typical research apparatus the motion of heaters is via a lead screw and block arrangement. The lead screw may be driven by a slow variable speed motor, and it is convenient to arrange the drive through a differential gear so that a fast return motor can return the heaters to their original position.

Heaters may be insulated turns of resistance tape or wire and the apparatus can be tilted away from the horizontal to prevent matter transport (Section IV-G).

By suitable positioning of microswitches a "reciprocal" zone motion may be obtained. In this system the zone heaters move only an interzone distance before automatically returning and restarting, this arrangement enabling maximum number of zones to pass through the material.

Fig. 25. Commercial zone refining of germanium.    (Courtesy of Société Générale Metallurgique de Hoboken, Belgium.)

Such materials may be refined in sealed quartz or glass tubes or in open boats protected by an atmosphere of inert gas. Difficulty has been experienced with certain metals which stick to or wet the crucible and may crack the container. This can be much reduced if the boats or tubes are filled to only one-third of their volume, or if the boat is coated with a layer of carbon before use (74). Cracking is also reduced if the metal is free from traces of oxide, e.g., by refining in an atmosphere of hydrogen.

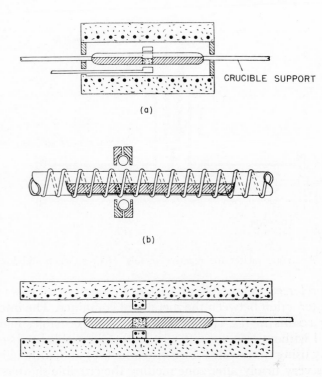

(a)

(b)

(c)

Fig. 26. Zone melting apparatus for materials with high vapor pressure at the melting point. (a) and (b) Zone heater moves. (c) Crucible or furnace arrangement moves.

An apparatus using the underslung heaters of Figure 19(e) proved successful for refining of InSb (75). Jets of cold air along the top of the refining tube encouraged the condensation of volatile impurities, and the heater shape avoids their re-evaporation on passage of a zone.

2. Materials such as Ge, Au, Ag, and Cu are usually refined in graphite containers using induction heating to melt the zone. Figure 25 shows the type of apparatus commonly used for the refining of germanium.

Aluminum, iron, and silicon have been refined in similar apparatus, alumina, lime (sintered CaO), and quartz, respectively.

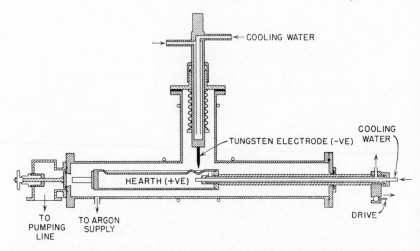

Fig. 27. Arc zone melter for reactive metals.    (After Geach and Jones (80).)

being preferred as crucible materials, although in all cases there is
some interaction between the metal and container. The interaction
usually results in the charge sticking to the crucible, making its
removal without fracture difficult. With silicon this has been overcome by using thin-walled silica crucibles (76) and, although silicon
adheres very firmly after zone melting the crucible shatters during
cooling, not the ingot.

3. Where the material has a high vapor pressure at the melting
point, as happens with many compound semiconductors, e.g., PbS,
PbSe, PbTe, HgSe, HgTe, GaAs, InP, etc., apparatus of the type
illustrated in Figure 26 is required. The high ambient temperature
reduces evaporation from the zone. In general, one component has
a higher vapor pressure, but a close control of the composition of
of the compound can be obtained using an auxiliary furnace as in
Figure 16 to control the vapor pressure over the ingot of the more
volatile component. An extremely close control of auxiliary furnace temperature, to better than a hundredth of a degree centigrade
throughout the process, may however be necessary to maintain
exact stoichiometry in the compound.

Yue and Clark (77) were able to prevent evaporation of magnesium during zone refining in an open crucible inside a tube by
forming a thin coherent surface skin of $MgSO_4$ on the charge. They

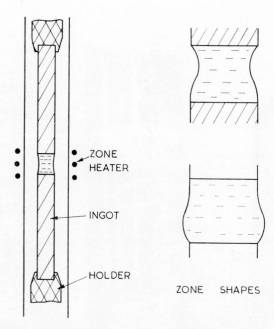

Fig. 28. Floating zone melting.

did this by passing an atmosphere of $SO_2$ along the tube. Prevention of evaporation enabled them to use a vycor tube to view the zones.

4. Materials such as Re, W, V, and Mo, which are highly reactive to the container have been refined in an apparatus shown in Figure 27 (79,80). In this apparatus zones were produced by an electric arc maintained between a tungsten electrode and the material contained in a U groove in a water-cooled copper hearth. A Ti getter in a separate dimple in the hearth could be fired before zoning commenced. One difficulty with this apparatus and arc melting in general is the tendency of the arc to wander. This can be reduced by setting the tungsten electrode as near the work as possible or by the use of magnetic fields to concentrate the arc. A further difficulty may be the pick up of trace impurity from the electrode and hearth.

Using a similar apparatus, Burch and Young (81) attempted to separate fission products from alloys of thorium with 3–16% uranium. There was no segregation of U at 2 inches/hour but a

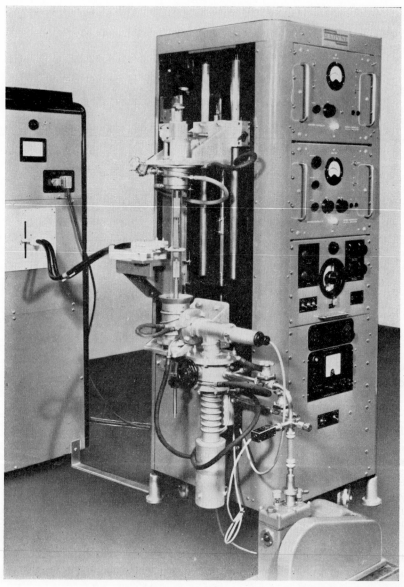

Fig. 29. Commercial apparatus for floating zone refining of silicon using induction heating. (Courtesy of Radio Heaters Ltd., Workingham, England.)

noticeable redistribution at 0.5 inch/hour. Te and Ru were easily removed, Co and Sr completely volatilized, and Ce, Y, and various rare earths partially volatilized.

5. Undoubtedly the most convenient and safest method for refining reactive materials, at least in research quantities is the floating zone technique (82). This technique, first described by Keck and Golay (83), was originally developed for zone refining silicon, which reacts when molten with all known crucible materials, but the method has since been used for many other reactive materials. No retaining crucible is used the zone instead being held in place by surface tension as shown in Figure 28.

The zone can be moved either up or down the rod. Experience varies and both methods have been found satisfactory for maintaining a stable zone and uniform diameter rod. Rotation of one or both ends of the rod ensures complete melting through and stirs the zone. G. W. Green (84) has used contrarotation with advantage to straighten initially distorted rods.

Commercial equipment is available, designed particularly for silicon but suitable for many other materials. Figure 29 illustrates one version. Beuhler (86) has described an automatic floating zone apparatus with which he prepared silicon rods of very uniform diameter containing less than 1 ppm of active impurities. Boron, an acceptor impurity in silicon, has a $k$ very close to unity but can be removed by refining in an atmosphere of wet hydrogen (85).

If the zone is too long it becomes pear-shaped and may become unstable. Heywang's analysis (87) indicates that for any given material there is a limit to the zone length, e.g., for silicon 1.5 cm, and this may restrict the diameter of the rod. At present, rods of silicon up to an inch diameter have been processed.

In an effort to overcome the limitation on rod diameter and process larger quantities, Pfann, Benson, and Hagelberger (89) have been experimenting with zones in ingots of different cross-sectional shapes, e.g., disk zones and wide zones in flat sheets and annular zones in cylindrical ingots. Cage zone refining, utilizing vertical fins which do not melt to support the zone, has been reported for titanium (88).

6. Electron bombardment heating, first suggested by Calverley, Davis, and Lever (90,91) has been used for floating zone refining and is particularly suitable for refractory metals. Electrons emitted

from a ring cathode of tungsten are accelerated and focused on to the rod, as shown in Figure 30, and melt the zone. A good vacuum is necessary and it is likely that purification is assisted by evaporation of volatile impurities. Power requirements are modest, half a kilowatt being adequate for rods up to a centimeter diameter of the refractory metals. W, Ta, Mo, Rh, Ni, Ru, Co, Re, Pt, and Ir have been zone melted with this type of heating. In the design of heater shown, tungsten evaporating from the cathode can contaminate the charge, and vice versa. Gusa, Krzhizh, and Ladnar (92) overcame this difficulty by suitable design of cathode and focusing assembly which enabled then to increase greatly the cathode–anode distance and deflect contaminating ions away from the charge or cathode.

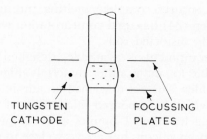

TUNGSTEN                    FOCUSSING
CATHODE                     PLATES

Fig. 30. Production of a floating zone by electron bombardment heating.

Electron bombardment has also been used to melt zones in materials contained in crucibles. For instance, le Couteur (93) has purified germanium in horizontal graphite boats by a multizone process and was able to space zones closer and use less power per zone than with conventional heating methods.

Electron bombardment heating is difficult to apply directly to insulators since there is no conducting path for electrons to escape, but secondary electron emission can be used for this purpose. Strnad (94) has attempted to zone refine alumina using this principle and, although he succeeded in forming and maintaining a zone, loss of material by evaporation was too great for the process to be continued for any length of time.

7. Pfann and Hagelberger (95) have suggested supporting a horizontal zone by the force acting on a conductor carrying a current

in a magnetic field, but the method does not appear to have been widely used.

The floating zone method suffers the disadvantage that only one zone at a time can be passed, and the diameter of the rod may be limited. Its main advantage is the absence of a crucible which eliminates the risk of contamination from that source. It is thus a slow process, to be used only when absolutely necessary, but eminently suited to the production of small quantities of ultra-pure materials.

8. Mention should be made in this section of two applications of zone melting which, though not concerned with purification, nevertheless emphasize the usefulness of the technique. They are crystal growth and zone levelling.

Crystals of semiconductors and metals are now commonly grown by zone melting. The process consists simply of a normal zone melting apparatus with a seed crystal inserted at the start of the charge. The molten zone starts at the end of the ingot, near the seed crystal, is traversed back to melt a part of the seed, and is then moved along the charge in the normal way so that the seed crystal grows as the melt solidifies. The conditions for growth of crystals in this way have been discussed by Lawson and Nielsen (96). Bennett and Sawyer (97) and others have developed this technique to a very high degree for producing very high quality crystals of germanium.

9. The normally difficult process of preparing crystals and ingots with very uniform composition has been solved very neatly by zone melting. When used in this way the process is known as zone levelling. Reference to Figure 4 shows that the middle region of a charge will tend to have uniform composition after one zone pass, and the closer $k$ is to unity the longer the uniform region will be. Passing a zone to and fro along a charge also tends to produce a uniform distribution of solute in all but the last zone to freeze.

If $k$ is known and the first zone length is arranged to have a solute concentration $C_0/k$ and the remainder $C_0$, then after passage of a single zone concentration in the bar is uniformly $C_0$ except in the last zone. Pfann and Olsen (98) showed that if $k$ is very small ($<0.1$), a desired uniform concentration of solute could be injected into a pure charge by adding the requisite amount of solute to the first zone. On passage of a zone, since $k$ is very small, the zone composition and hence the solid tends to remain uniform.

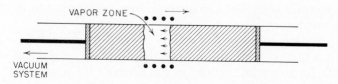

Fig. 31. Vapor-zone refining.    Schematic.

Zone leveling is important in semiconductor device manufacture for the production of uniformly doped crystals, particularly of germanium (97) and silicon (99).

It will be evident from consideration of the above and the phase diagrams of Figures 2 and 3, that zone melting can be a useful and relatively easy method of preparing uniform alloys (100), intermetallic compounds, eutectics, peritectics, etc. (101), which may sometimes be difficult to prepare in other ways.

*10.* Recently Weisberg and Rosi (102) have shown how a high vapor pressure at the melting point, normally a disadvantage in zone melting, could be used with advantage to pass vapor zones through a solid. They termed the process "vapor-zone refining." Purification occurs by relative sublimation, and the process bears the same relation to fractional sublimation that zone melting does to fractional crystallization.

Using this technique, Weisberg and Rosi purified arsenic in a precision bore pyrex tube with graphite plungers. After six passes in nonoptimum conditions they found Si, Fe, Al, and Cu increased by a factor of about three at the front end of the charge. Pb and Bi increased about the same at the other end, while Mg and Ag remained uniformly distributed. The method, shown in outline in Figure 31, should be applicable to other volatile elements, e.g., S, P, Sb, I, and many volatile compounds.

## F. ELEMENTS

### 1. Group IB: Cu, Ag, Au

Copper, silver, and gold have been refined in graphite crucibles. Values of resistivity ratio $(R_{298°K}/R_{4.2°K})$ for Cu indicated that refining was effective, but impurities were being picked up from the apparatus (103). Experiments on copper containing added impurity elements (0.01 weight %) showed that, for a zone rate of 11 mm/

our, Sb, Cr, Mn, Si, As, and Sn had $k$'s <1, and Co, Fe, and Ni had
's >1 (104). For the alloy Cu–Sn (Sn 5.4–13.2%), $k$ varied from
.09 to 0.2 and for Cu–Ni (Ni 5.8–15.5%) $k$ varied from 2.1 to
.7; the zone rate greatly influenced degree of purification (105).
'reliminary experiments suggested that the refining of Ag (106)
.nd Au (107) was effective.

### ?. Group IIB: Be, Mg, Zn, Cd, Hg

Several attempts to purify and fabricate Be have been made
ecently, particularly for atomic energy applications. Zone melting
.nd single crystal growth have been reported (163).

Mg has been zone refined as described previously (108). Six
.asses at 0.3 inch/hour gave effective separation from Al, Cu, Ni,
.n, Pb, Zn, Si, and Mn; all except Mn ($k = 6.1$) had $k$'s <1 through
.omewhat greater than the values estimated from equilibrium
liagrams.

Zn has been refined in quartz boats and tubes. A particularly
horough investigation has been made with the removal of Pb from
.lectrolytic Zn with a view to using the method on an industrial
.cale (109). A value of $k_0 \sim 0.02$, and $\delta = 10^{-2}$ cm, for Pb in Zn were
·eported, and the effect on $k$ of zone rate, zone width, zone stirring,
hermal gradient at the interface, and Pb concentration were in-
.estigated. Other results have shown that six passes at 2 inches/
.our reduced the Pb content from 12 to 1 ppm and the Cd content
·rom 2 to 1 ppm. Tl and Bi had $k$'s <1 and were easily removed, but
·'e and Cu had $k$'s slightly greater than 1 (110,111).

Cd may be refined in the same way; early results suggested Pb,
.u, and Tl could be easily removed (111). Hg can of course be
.nore easily purified in other ways (112).

### 3. Group IIIA: B, Al, Sc, Y, La and the Bare Earths

Boron has been refined in boats made from boron nitride (113);
.uch boats are relatively inert to the molten metal but tend to
.crack after a few zone passes. Qualitative results indicated $k$ >1
for Al and Cu, $k \geq 1$ for Ti, $k \leq 1$ for Si and Cu, and $k << 1$ for
Fe, Ni, and Cr. Coarsely crystalline boron has also been obtained
from a rod of compressed powder, using $B_2O_3$ as a binder, in a
floating zone apparatus (114). The rod was supported by graphite

holders, and zones, formed using a 3.5 Mc/sec induction heater were passed downwards at 0.044 inch/hour.

Aluminum has been refined in many laboratories, particularly in those under the direction of Professor Chaudron (116,117,118) and the unusual properties of the refined metal have been the subject of several publications (119–124). Alumina crucibles have been used to contain the metal. Using a zone rate of 0.5 cm/hour, impurities such as Cu, Na, Fe, Si, and the rare earths were shown to move with the zone. The resistivity ratio and temperature of spontaneous recrystallization have also been used to estimate the purity of the refined metal; values of 7000 have been reported for the former and about $-50°C$ for the latter (116,117,118), Tongas (115) reports purification factors after nine zone passes for Cu, 6–7; Mg, 6–7; Si, 5.0; Fe, 7.5; for Cu, $k(\text{eff}) = 0.66$ (cf. $k(\text{theory}) = 0.32$); and for Mg, $k(\text{eff}) = 0.65$ (cf. $k(\text{theory}) = 0.13$).

No results for other metals in this group are available, although some consideration has been given to the separation of the rare earth metals by zone refining one of their compounds.

### 4. Group IIIB: Ga, In, Tl

Ga has been refined in a quartz boat using a reciprocating refiner and refrigerated coils to cool the interface region. Cooling is most necessary as gallium supercools to a considerable extent. No impurities were detected in the refined material and lead was shown to move with the zone (125). A more satisfactory process involves refining $GaCl_3$ (66) as described earlier (Section V-D-2).

In has been refined in a quartz boat or a carbon-lined quartz boat (126,127). InCl or $InCl_3$ may be useful intermediates (128).

### 5. Group IVA: C, Si, Ge, Sn, Pb

The further purification of C, especially as a crucible material, is an urgent problem. Zone refining is, however, impracticable, and recourse may have to be made to the cracking of some carbonaceous compound.

Si and Ge have been the subject of considerable research, and were among the first materials to be zone refined. Silicon has been refined in thin-walled quartz boats (129), although there is considerable interaction between the molten Si and the quartz boat.

The floating zone techniques described previously (Section V-E-5) produce a purer product and are widely used. A detailed list of distribution coefficients is available (130), B ($k \simeq 1$) being difficult to remove by direct zone refining (85).

Ge is usually refined in graphite containers (131). Distribution coefficients for impurities have been estimated with precision and fully reported (130).

Tin has usually been refined in pyrex container. The purity of the refined tin has been estimated as 99.999% (132). The resistivity ratio of such material, $10^5$, is the highest of any yet measured. Experiments on Sn containing added impurity elements showed that after 50 passes at 4 cm/hour, Pb, Cu, Zn, and Ni were removed to less than $10^{-4}\%$ in 60–70% of the total bar, Bi only over 20% and Sb moved in the opposite direction. Ag, Cd, Zn, Hg, Bi, Te, and In also moved with the zone, the last four elements more slowly (135).

Lead has also been refined in pyrex. Several papers have been concerned with the effect of rate and temperature gradient at the interface on the removal of Sn (133). Preliminary results suggested Cu, Ag, and Zn moved rapidly and Bi, Cd, Fe, Te, and Sb moved slowly with the zone (135).

### 5. Group IVB: Ti, Zr, Hf, Th

Ti has been refined by the floating zone method (136,137) and also using the "cage" effect (88). Results showed that impurities such as Ni, Mn, Hg, Fe, Si, Cu, Ca, Al, and Mg were removed largely by evaporation. Au and Zr move with the zone.

Zr has also been refined by the floating zone method; ten zones at 6 cm/hour reduced the Fe and Ni content from 880 ppm and 9 ppm to 8 ppm and 1 ppm respectively (139). In addition the absence of hardness suggested the C, O, N content was small (138).

### 7. Group VA: P, As, Sb, Bi

It may be possible to zone refine phosphorus in pyrex containers provided interzone cooling is arranged, and to refine arsenic if the vapor pressure could be artificially lowered, although no attempts have been reported (see also Section V-E-10).

Sb has been refined in quartz. Seven zones reduced Ni, As, Pb, Ag, and Cu by a factor of 10 or more. After ten zone passes only As ($k = 1$) and Zn were detected by mass spectroscopy (132).

Bi has been refined in a sealed evacuated pyrex tube using a reciprocal refiner. Twelve passes at 1.8 inches/hour produced material having a total impurity of less than 10 ppm. Ag, Cu, Pb, Sn, and Ni moved with the zone, and Mg and Ca also moved with the zone, but less readily. Fe moved in the opposite direction to the zone (140). Using a circular refiner and a zone rate of 1.1 cm/hour, radiotrace amounts of Zn, Cu, Ag were shown to move with the zone and Sb in the opposite direction (141). Preliminary results suggested Cd, In, Tl, Cr, As, Sn, Hg, and Mg, and Te moved with the zone, the last four more slowly and Ga in the opposite direction (135).

## 8. Group VB: V, Nb, Ta

V has been refined by the floating zone method. Results showed the content of Co, Cr, Cu, Fe, and Mn was reduced mainly by evaporation, that of Si and W not appreciably effected, and that Al, Ca, and Ti moved in the opposite direction to the zone (137).

## 9. Group VIA: S, Se, Te

Se forms an amorphous phase on cooling from the melt, and zone refining in the ordinary way is not successful (135). Refining is possible if carried out under pressure, when a hexagonal crystalline form is obtained (142). Successful refining has also been claimed using a d.c. current between two electrodes to form the zone.

Te has been refined in quartz containers to produce material with 1 in $10^7$ electronically active impurities (143,144). Preliminary results have shown Mn, Cd, Ge, Al, Fe, Cu, Pb, Bi, Sn, Zn, In, and Sb move with the zone, As moved in the opposite direction and Hg did not move at all (135).

## 10. Group VIB: Cr, Mo, W, U

Mo and W have been refined by the floating zone method using electron bombardment (90,91,145,146) or by arc melting (79). It is probable that many impurities are removed by evaporation.

U has been refined in BeO, $UO_2$, $U_3O_8$, and thoria coated $Al_2O_3$ containers (147,148). A slow zone rate 1 inch/hour appears to be essential. Using a vertical system and moving the zone upwards has the advantage that less dense impurity atoms and slag phases are more easily removed (78). "Self-slagging" has also been used to improve separations.

*11. Group VIII: Fe, Co, Ni, Ru, Rh, Pd, Os, Ir, Pt*

Fe has been refined by a floating zone method (136) and in CaO containers (149). Co (150) and Ni (90,137) have also been refined by floating zone methods. The properties of the refined iron suggest considerable improvement in purity (151–153); the material obtained by the floating zone method appeared to be more pure.

### G. COMPOUND SEMICONDUCTORS

Articles dealing mainly with the properties of semiconducting compounds but giving some information on their zone melting, and not already mentioned, are as follows: $Zn_3As_2$ (154); InP (155); AlSb (156); $Mg_2Sn$ (157); CdTe (158,161); GaAs (155,159); $Bi_2Te_3$, $Sb_2Te_3$ (160); HgTe (161); InSb (162).

## VI. Large Scale and Continuous Operation

**A.** In Section IV, we noted that there are many interconnected variables to be considered during zone refining. These included specimen shape and size, zone and ingot length, number of zones and interzone distance, zone rate, temperature gradient at the interface, and stirring in the zone. A steep temperature gradient at the interface, stirring of the zone, and slower zone rate improve the separation per zone pass. The optimum zone lengths for a minimum number of zone passes should be: first zone = ingot length $L$, second zone = $0.3L$, subsequent zones = $0.1L$ (see Section II-C). Also obviously separation is more rapid with a minimum interzone distance. However, for commercial applications, the costs of apparatus, maintenance, heating, time of operation, amounts of material and purity required, must be taken into account. At the present time there is insufficient data available to relate these factors in mathematical form and thus optimize the apparatus and conditions for any particular separation.

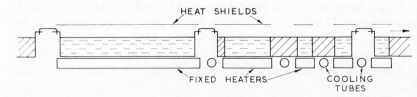

Fig. 32. Zone melting on a larger scale. A succession of charges moving over fixed heaters.

In many cases the cost of heating is of over-riding importance. For example, Scacciati and Gondi (109) considered the large scale purification of electrolytic zinc. In a pilot experiment, they pulled an ingot 5 × 15 × 200 cm at 0.5 mm/minute from a melt, reducing the lead content from 50–70 kg to 20–30 kg per long ton with the expenditure of 860 kcal/kg of zinc purified. They hoped to reduce heat expenditure to 220 kcal/kg but point out, that even at this figure, heat consumption during zone refining would be very high.

To reduce heating costs, particular attention must be paid to the insulation of the charge and molten zone. This ensures that heat loss is small and that the maximum latent heat is transferred from the freezing to the melting interface. Also a rapid zone rate is required. However, the separation per zone pass is lowered by increased zone rate. Equation 4 (Section IV-C) shows that the effective $k$ is determined by $R\delta/D$ where $R$ is the zone rate, $D$ the diffusivity in the zone, and $\delta$ the thickness of the diffusion controlled boundary layer. Experiments with germanium (30) indicated that a practical possibility for $\delta$ is 0.001 cm, which allows a maximum zone rate of 0.01 cm/sec or 36 cm/hour. In other cases, e.g., zoning solutions or organic compounds, the maximum zone rate may be limited by the "velocity of crystallization," i.e., the rate at which atoms or molecules can organize themselves from the liquid to the solid phases and 10–15 cm/hour may be a maximum.

B. Batch zone refining can be made largely automatic and one operator can attend to the loading and unloading of several refiners. Charges can move through the refiner coupled together trainwise, with loading and unloading and any other necessary operations, carried out at intervals along the track. Figure 32 shows a simple arrangement where charges pass over fixed heaters pro-

lucing a prescribed pattern of zone lengths (Section III-C). An
alternative arrangement is shown in Figure 33. The limit to the
ross section of the batch is a practical one, namely that of being
ble to induce a reasonably shaped zone throughout the cross
ection. This may be more difficult for materials with low thermal
conductivity and in such cases some form of internal heater for
producing the zones would be advantageous. As separation is improved by stirring the molten zone a design which incorporated
tirring and internal heating would be most suitable. Two possibil-
ties have been shown in Figure 20.

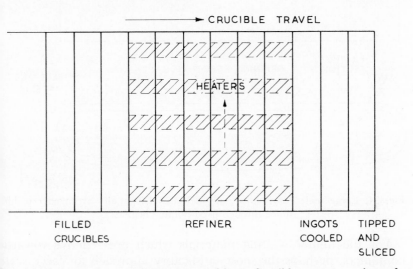

Fig. 33. Large scale continuous zone melting. Crucibles move continuously
through the refining section.

For nonreactive, low melting point materials, some form of
pseudo-continuous process of the type illustrated in Figure 34 may
be feasible. Here material contained in a ribbed or moving belt
moves through fixed heaters such that zones move diagonally across
the belt. Waste and product are tapped off as shown in the required
proportions. Alternatively the ribs may be dispensed with and a
series of short heaters arranged to move across the charge at right
angles to the belt drive. This again results in a diagonal movement
of zones.

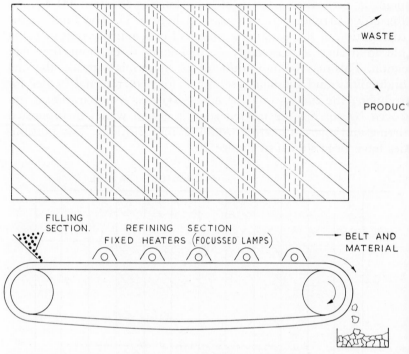

Fig. 34. Large scale continuous zone melting. Diagonally arranged crucible move through fixed refining heaters.

For the higher melting materials which are reactive towards containers, perhaps the most satisfactory approach for large scale production will be to use the material itself as a container or to develop the cooled hearth arc-melting technique or magnetic levitation described previously (Section V-E-5).

C. The throughput of material in a refiner can be increased by increasing the area of solid/melt interface with respect to the volume of material. This can be achieved by decreasing the interzone distance, but there is a practical limitation to this. One possibility is to solidify a thin layer of melt on a cooled moving surface. Thus if a cooled surface is brought into contact with a melt, solid precipitates on the surface and can be separated. If the solidification on the moving surface proceeds in a similar way to that normally occurring at the solid/melt interface, then the composition of ꞁe solid separated will be $k$ times that in the liquid. For any ꞁoving surface solidification, some degree of temperature control ꞁould seem to be essential, otherwise the initial solidification would ꞁe so rapid that $k$ would be approximately unity.

Pfann describes various possibilities, the most promising of which ꞁay be the use of circular rotating drums of the type shown dia-ꞁrammatically in Figure 35. Such arrangements may have advan-ꞁges over conventional zone refiners. Stirring from rotation of the ꞁrum is more effective the smaller the interdrum distance and with ꞁaned interleaving drums. The heating efficiency could be high if ꞁeat of fusion can be transferred directly from freezing liquid to melt-

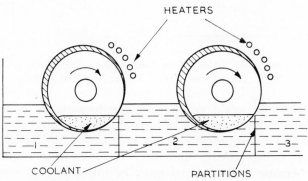

HEATERS

COOLANT      PARTITIONS

ꞁig. 35. Rotating drum crystallisers. Drum axes horizontal. (Reproduced from W. G. Pfann, *Zone Melting*, Wiley, New York, 1958.)

ꞁng surface. The pure and impure products can be trapped off at ꞁppropriate places and feed liquid introduced at points where the ꞁeed composition equals that in the tank. The apparatus is suitable ꞁor refining solutions and is capable of high throughput of material.

Pfann gives the following example to show the order of magnitude ꞁf quantities involved. Assuming a drum 1 in wide and 1 in diameter ꞁotating at 6 rpm with freezing and melting over a quarter of the ꞁircumference, freezing rate 0.01 cm/sec consistent with favorable ꞁffective $k$ and taking off about a fifth of the freeze as purified ꞁaterial (50 liters/hour); then if the latent heat of fusion is 25 ꞁal/g and the density 4 g/cc the heat supplied to and extracted from ꞁhe material is about 1 cal/sec/cm², or a total of 7500 cal/sec for ꞁhe freezing area of the drum.

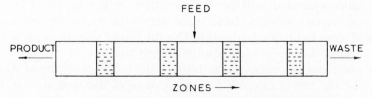

Fig. 36. Schematic of continuous one refining process.

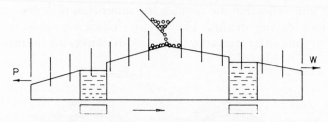

Fig. 37. Zone transport method of continuous zone refining. (Reproduced from W. G. Pfann, *Zone Melting*, Wiley, New York, 1958).

This example again emphasizes the importance of design, in particular for direct transfer of heat of fusion.

**D.** It will be appreciated that any truly continuous zone refiner must bring a third dimension into the conventional refiner. This is because feed material must be introduced at some point preferably where impurity concentration in the zone refined charge equals the initial concentration, and product and waste removed continuously. Figure 36 shows the generalized scheme. Perhaps the most obvious way of achieving this is by the zone transport method due to Pfann and shown in Figure 37. In this method fresh material is fed in as shown near the center of the charge, at the equal concentration point, and is transported to the ends by the zones, not by matter transport (Section IV-G) but simply by the difference in levels. Vertical panelling prevents overflow of liquid.

Some purified product escapes through the port every time a zone starts, and some impure waste is removed similarly when the zone reaches the end of the charge.

**E.** The "cross-flow" zone refiner, another suggestion discussed by Pfann, utilizes a wide container separated by partitions into sections along which the zones move simultaneously. These sections are independent except at either end where a small hole allows

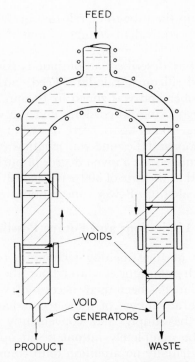

Fig. 38. "Zone-Void" continuous zone refiner.   (From W. G. Pfann (4).   Courtesy of the Institute of Metals, London.)

cross-flow of material. Feed is injected into the system at both ends but into one side zone only at each end when all the initial or final zones are molten, and forces product and waste out of the end zone at the other side.   Again details of possible operation are given but no practical results are available.

F. Finally we refer to another of Pfann's ingenious suggestions, the "zone-void" refiner. The principle of operation is the same as in Figure 36, but the container is bent into an inverted U as shown in Figure 38 with a feed tube at the top and the material at the junction of feed tube with purifying tube maintained in the molten state. Some purified material is released by the generation of a void at the start of each zone, and similarly impure waste escapes when the zone reaches the other end. The two arms of the inverted U-tube can in fact be treated separately with separate heaters.

The voids travel up the tube to be released in the molten region at the top, so that an equivalent volume of material is passing in the other direction.

Moates (164) has described a continuous zone-void refiner in which he purified silicon tetraiodide. Feed came directly from a sublimation chamber and was zoned in 10 mm bore pyrex tubes, the "product" arm being 50 cm long and the waste arm 30 cm. Zones 1.6 cm long, 10 cm apart, were passed at 5 cm/hour with a reciprocating action, and the zone-void length was 0.3 cm, these conditions being calculated for a given degree of purification. Material could be processed at the rate of 300 g per month in this apparatus, which could be scaled up. Power consumption was not given.

## VII. Limitations and Future Possibilities

**A**. The family of zone melting techniques is now well established in research laboratories throughout the world. Zone refining, in particular, has been used successfully with a wide variety of materials. The advantage of these techniques is considerable Apparatus may be simply and conveniently assembled. Such apparatus may be completely automatic in operation and once started requires virtually no attention until complete. Contamination during refining may be limited to interaction with the crucible and ambient atmosphere. The product is obtained in a compact often largely monocrystalline, form, which is convenient for handling and transference and also for a variety of electrical, mechanical, physical, and often chemical tests.

**B**. The limitations of zone refining are in many cases not absolute but must be considered when any competitive process is possible. A first limitation is on materials which can be refined, these should be crystalline and melt to a stable liquid phase without decomposition or excessive vapor pressure. However, apparatus can be designed for materials with high vapor pressure (Section V-E-3), and refining of solutions and eutectics is possible (Section V-D-4).

A second limitation is that not all impurities have segregation coefficients sufficiently different from unity. However, a very small difference of $k$ from unity is sufficient to make a separation possible as is instanced in the separation of heavy water (Section V-C-1).

Also it is often possible to refine an intermediate, e.g., $GaCl_3$ in the refining of Ga (Section V-D-2).

A third limitation concerns crucible materials. Ideally the crucible or container material should be inert to the charge and be of very high purity. The lack of such materials—especially for the high melting metals is a problem to which increasing attention is being paid. There are, in addition—as has been described—several techniques for refining without a crucible (Section V-E-3) or without contact with the crucible (Sections V-E-5 and V-E-8), but these are designed mainly for small scale and batch operation.

C. The use of zone refining on a larger scale can be considered from two points of view: (1) as a method of producing extremely high purity material and (2) as a competitive process for the production and separation of materials of ordinary or above ordinary purity.

For the production of extremely high-purity material, zone refining offers considerable promise. The increased cost of materials refined in this way need not be excessive, especially for lower melting point and unreactive materials and especially if larger and more efficient apparatus can be designed. For the higher melting and more reactive materials zone refining would seem to be at least competitive, for small scale operation, and may be a most useful final stage in a large scale operation. For example, a reactive metal may be refined to a considerable extent, say by fractional distillation of the chloride, and as a final stage a single zone passed through the material to remove traces of chloride and other impurities.

The use of zone refining for the production and separation of materials of ordinary and above ordinary purity must depend on the relative merits of other processes and the individual properties of the material. In the remaining part of this chapter we discuss some of the present day uses of zone refined material as a guide to future requirements and speculate on some other possible applications.

Certainly in the field of semiconductors, where purity and control of composition are of paramount importance, zone melting has proved invaluable. The use of such techniques seems certain to increase as newer uses are found for those materials which have already been investigated and as the properties of other materials become better understood.

The preparation of highly pure metals has proved and is proving of great value in the understanding of their intrinsic properties. Many impurities profoundly affect the mechanical, electrical, magnetic, and even chemical properties. Zone refined aluminum has been the subject of much research. Such material when severely strained by cold rolling, shows an ability to recrystallize to large grain size at temperatures as low as $-40\,^{\circ}$C, indicating an abnormally low resistance to the motion of dislocations. Zone refined iron exhibits higher values of magnetic permeability, reduced corrosion and a lower solubility for oxygen.

Several firms are interested in zone refining small quantities of pure metals for research use, but whether a large scale use exists for highly pure metals or alloys, for example, as specific structural items, depends on further research and, of course, on the cost of production.

Zone refining techniques would appear to be of value in various branches of atomic energy research. Apart from the ever pressing requirements for pure materials for reactor design, the technique has been considered for the refining of uranium and the removal of fission products from uranium and its alloys.

The inorganic compounds which have been zone refined are in the main restricted to intermediates in the preparation of a pure element, e.g., Ga and Si. There seem, as we have suggested, to be other possibilities in this field, e.g., optical, photographic, or scintillation counter materials. Zone refining of inorganic materials may offer a new starting point for the preparation of a whole range of ultra-pure reagents, for analytical, semiconductor, and preparative purposes, and for the fluxes used in the solution growth of certain crystals, e.g., ferrites, garnets, piezo- and ferroelectric, and even semiconductors. It is also possible that some chemical compounds could be obtained in a purer state or more efficiently in this way; zone melting could perhaps be used to separate the chemical from its solvent. For example, metal fluorides precipitated from aqueous solutions usually contain absorbed water around each crystallite which is difficult to remove. A possible solution would be to form the fluoride in an inorganic solvent and concentrate the product by a zone refining technique, e.g., KF/LiF eutectic (m.p. $500\,^{\circ}$C) $+$ $MgCl_2$ $\rightarrow$ $MgF_2$.

Many organic compounds have been purified by zone refining

and there is every evidence that the technique will prove increasingly useful. The low melting points and thermal conductivity suggest that the process would be economical in terms of power consumption. The main requirement is for an efficient apparatus of a larger throughput than those in use at the present time.

Present research is concentrated on the production of small quantities of highly pure material, particularly for use as standards. Such standards are especially useful for biochemical work. To take only one example, 2-methyl-4-chlorophenoxyacetic acid, the active principle of Verdone weed killer, was produced in a highly pure state by zone refining to act as a reference standard for the commercial product.

Purer materials and solvents must also be required as starting materials in organic synthesis. Separation of a purer product with higher yield is particularly advantageous, for example, in the preparation of biochemical materials or materials which have been labelled with radiotracers. Purer solvents must also find application. The separation and analysis of trace impurities from such materials must also be of value.

Separations of mixtures which are otherwise difficult or impossible, constant boiling mixtures, isomers, etc., have been achieved, and there are many possibilities. Separations of the complex mixtures obtained as by-products of the coal and petrochemical industries may be possible by zone techniques.

As with inorganic materials, the purification of compounds as solutions or eutectics offers some possibilities, particularly for materials which decompose at their melting points or are insoluble in the usual solvents.

Again zone refining techniques may be used with advantage for the concentration of materials from solutions, or as a preliminary step in the concentration. This would seem to offer an alternative to the freeze drying of large volumes of liquid, at present necessary for example in the production of pure proteins and enzymes. Perhaps the concentration of natural products such as milk may be a possibility.

We wonder, too, if zone refining could be used in combination with chromatography. Separations would depend on partition of impurities between column material and the liquid zone in the usual way, and impurities would be carried down the column by usual segregation phenomenon. The advantage, if any, lies in the increased range of solvents which could be used and the fact that only small volumes of solvent are required.

Perhaps finally one could speculate on the use of a zone technique for certain chemical reactions. Suppose, for example, molten material A reacts with gaseous atmosphere C to form AC, and possibly $AC_2$. It may be possible to arrange that as the reacting molten zone moves along, AC is precipitated from the zone preferentially and at such a rate that little $AC_2$ is formed. Similarly the use of a zone technique may be of advantage in an equilibrium reaction $AB + CD \rightleftharpoons AC + BD$. It may be possible to remove product AC preferentially by its precipitation on the advancing solid/melt interface.

Much more data are required before an accurate assessment of the future potential of zone melting can be made. Many more materials and mixtures must be investigated, and more quantitative information is required on the factors influencing the segregation coefficient, $k$, and on the mathematics and economics of heat consumption.

# References

*General Review Articles*

1. W. G. Pfann, Principle of zone melting, *Trans. A.I.M.E.*, **194**, 747 (1952).
2. W. G. Pfann, *Zone Melting*, Wiley, New York, 1956.
3. W. G. Pfann, Zone melting, *Met. Revs.*, **2**, 29 (1957).
4. W. G. Pfann, Techniques of zone melting and crystal growing, *Solid State Physics*, Vol. 4, Academic Press, New York, 1957, p. 423.
5. W. D. Lawson and S. Nielsen, *Preparation of Single Crystals. A Semiconductor Monograph*, Butterworths, London, and Academic Press, New York, 1958, Chap. IV.
6. S. Bhattacharya, Zone refining technique, *Sci. & Culture (Calcutta)*, **22**, 362 (1957).
7. N. L. Parr, Zone refining, *Roy. Inst. Chem. (London) Monographs*, **1957**, No. 3, 1.
8. Zone melting opens new horizons in metallurgy, *Metal. Progr.*, **73**, No. 4, 97 (1958).
9. T. Federighi, The zone melting method for the purification of metals, *Allumino*, **26**, 361 (1957).
10. R. A. King, High purity metals in commercial quantities, *Metal Progr.*, **75**, 127 (1959).

11. E. F. G. Herington, Zone melting, with some comments on its analytical potentialities, *The Analyst*, **84,** 680 (1959).

*Theoretical*

12. L. Burris, C. H. Stockham, and I. G. Dillon, Contribution to mathematics of zone melting, *Trans. A.I.M.E.*, **203,** 1017 (1955).
13. L. W. Davies, Efficiency of zone refining processes, *Trans. A.I.M.E.*, **215,** 672 (1959).
14. L. Gold, Terminal zone cropping and ultimate zone purification, *J. Phys. Soc. Japan*, **14,** 386 (1959).
15. I. Braun and S. Marshall, On the mathematical theory of zone melting, *Brit. J. Appl. Phys.*, **8,** 157 (1957).
16. N. W. Lord, Analysis of molten zone refining, *Trans. A.I.M.E.*, **197,** 1531 (1953).
17. K. S. Milliken, Simplification of a molten zone refining formula, *J. Metals*, **7,** 838 (1955).
18. H. Reiss, Mathematical methods for zone melting processes, *Trans. A.I.M.E.*, **200,** 1053 (1954).
19. J. L. Birman, On zone refining, *J. Appl. Phys.*, **26,** 1195 (1955).
20. I. Braun, Ultimate concentration distribution in zone melting, *Brit. J. Appl. Phys.*, **8,** 457 (1957).
21. L. W. Davies, The Ultimate distribution of impurity in the zone melting process, *Phil. Mag.*, **3,** 159 (1958).
22. L. W. Davies, Determination of limiting segregation of gallium in germanium, *Trans. A.I.M.E.*, **212,** 719 (1958).
23. F. Bertein, Simple analogue apparatus for study of treatment of an ingot by zone melting, *J. phys. radium*, **19,** 121A (1958).
24. F. Bertein, Electrical analogue for the study of treatment of an ingot by zone melting, *J. Phys. radium*, **19,** 182A (1958).
25. W. A. Tiller, Use of controlled solidification in equilibrium studies, *Trans. A.I.M.E.*, **215,** 555 (1959).
26. J. Krempashy, Concentration of admixture in a crystal prepared by zone melting when the impurity is introduced into the first zone only, *Chem. Abstr.*, **52,** 5918 (1958).
27. G. Schreiber and R. Schubert, Purification of substances by growing monocrystals from the melt and distribution of admixtures in the crystal, *Z. physik. Chem.*, **206,** 102 (1956).
28. K. Weisser, Theoretical calculation of distribution coefficients on impurities in germanium and silicon, heats of solid solution, *J. Phys. Chem. Solids*, **7,** 118 (1958).
29. W. A. Tiller, K. A. Jackson, J. W. Rutter, and B. Chalmers, The redistribution of solute atoms during the solidification of metals, *Acta Met.*, **1,** 428 (1953).
30. J. A. Burton, R. C. Prim, and W. P. Slichter, Distribution of solute in crystals grown from the melt. I. Theoretical, *J. Chem. Phys.*, **21,** 1987 (1953); II. Experimental, J. A. Burton, E. D. Kolb, W. P. Slichter, and J. D. Struthers, *J. Chem. Phys.*, **21,** 1991 (1953).

31. J. van den Boomgaard, Zone melting process under influence of the atmosphere, *Philips Research Repts.*, **10**, 319 (1955).
32. J. van den Boomgaard, Zone melting of decomposing solids, F. A. Kroger, and H. J. Vink, *J. Electronics*, **1**, 212 (1955).
33. J. van den Boomgaard, Zone melting processes for compounds AB with a measurable vapor pressure under influence of the atmosphere, *Philips Research Repts.*, **11**, 91 (1956).
34. J. van den Boomgaard, Zone melting processes for pure compounds AB with a negligible vapor pressure, *Philips Research Repts.*, **11**, 27 (1956).

*Apparatus and Techniques*

35. W. G. Pfann, Temperature gradient zone melting, *Trans. A.I.M.E.*, **203**, 961 (1955).
36. K. F. Hulme and J. B. Mullin, Facets and anomolous solute distribution in InSb, *Phil. Mag.*, **4**, 1286 (1959).
37. L. R. Johnson and W. Zimmerman, Modified boat design for rapid purification, *Rev. Sci. Instr.*, **31**, 203 (1960).
38. F. M. Reynolds, private communication.
39. W. D. Lawson and S. Nielsen, *Preparation of Single Crystals*, Butterworth, London, and Academic Press, New York, 1958, p. 62.
40. L. Spialter and J. Riley, Toroidal heaters for zone melting, *Rev. Sci. Instr.*, **30**, 139 (1959).
41. L. R. Weisberg and G. R. Gunther-Mohr, Radiant energy heater, *Rev. Sci. Instr.*, **26**, 896 (1955).
42. F. J. Baum, Radiant energy zone heating unit, *Rev. Sci. Instr.*, **30**, 1064 (1959).
43. T. Fohl and R. W. Christy, Zone refiner for laboratory use, *J. Sci. Instr.*, **36**, 98 (1959).
44. W. G. Pfann and D. Dorsi, Magnetic stirring technique, *Rev. Sci. Instr.*, **28**, 720 (1957).
45. J. B. Mullin and K. F. Hulme, Electromagnetic stirring in zone refining, *J. Electronics & Control*, **4**, 170 (1958).
46. I. Braun, F. C. Frank, S. Marshall, and G. Mayrick, Electromagnetic stirring in zone refining, *Phil. Mag.*, **3**, No. 8, 208 (1958).

*Organic Compounds*

47. F. W. Schwab and E. Wichers, Preparation of benzoic acid of high purity, *J. Research Natl. Bur. Standards*, **25**, 747 (1940).
48. A. R. Glasgow and G. Ross, Purification of substances by a process of freezing and fractional melting under equilibrium conditions, *J. Research Natl. Bur. Standards*, **57**, 137 (1956).
49. J. D. Dickinson and C. Eaborn, Purification of liquids and low melting solids by progressive freezing, *Chem. & Ind.* (*London*), **1956**, 959.
50. J. S. Matthews and N. D. Coggeshall, Concentration of impurities from organic compounds by progressive freezing, *Anal. Chem.*, **31**, 1124, (1959).
51. R. Handley and E. F. Herington, Apparatus for the purification of organic compounds by zone melting, *Chem. & Ind.* (*London*), **1956**, 292; **1957**, 1184.

52. R. Handley, Purification of chemicals by zone melting, *Manufacturing Chemist*, **27**, 451 (1956).
53. J. S. Ball, R. V. Helm, and C. R. Ferrin, Zone melting—new purification tool, *Petrol. Engr.*, **30**, No 13, C36–C39 (1958).
54. H. C. Wolf and H. P. Deutsch, Preparation of pure naphthalene crystals by zone melting, *Naturwissenschaften*, **41**, 225 (1954).
55. H. Rock, Zone melter for purification of organic substances with melting points under room temperature, *Naturwissenschaften*, **43**, 81 (1956).
56. J. H. Beynon and R. A. Saunders, Purification of organic materials by zone refining, *Brit. J. Appl. Phys.*, **11**, 128 (1960).
57. R. Handley and E. F. G. Herington, Semimicro zone melting apparatus, *Chem. & Ind. (London)*, **1956**, 304,
58. A. P. Ronald, Automatic multistage semimicro zone-melting apparatus, *Anal. Chem.*, **31**, 964, (1959).
59. G. Hesse and H. Schildknecht, Microzone melter for purification of organic substances, *Angew. Chem.*, **68**, 641 (1958).
60. P. Sue, J. Pauly, and A. Nouaille, Application of the zone melting process to inorganic and organic compounds, *Bull. soc. chim. France*, **5**, 593 (1958).
61. H. Schildknecht, Ring zone melter for organic substances, *Z. Naturforsch.*, **12B**, 23 (1957).
62. H. A. Smith and C. O. Thomas, Separation of mixtures of ordinary and heavy water by zone refining, *J. Phys. Chem.*, **63**, 445 (1959).
63. H. Schildknecht and A. Menal, Ice zone melting, *Angew. Chem.*, **69**, 634 (1957).
64. T. Okabe, Concentration of NaCl solution by freezing, *Chem. Abstr.*, **53**, 18557 (1959); *Netsu-Kanri*, **11**, 20, (1959).
65. F. W. Peaker and J. C. Robb, A new method of fractionating high polymers, *Nature*, **182**, 1591 (1958).

*Inorganic Compounds*

66. J. L. Richards, Purification of a metal by zone-refining one of its salts, *Nature*, **177**, 182 (1956).
67. B. Rubin, G. H. Moates, and J. R. Weiner, Transistor grade silicon. I. Preparation of ultra-pure $SiI_4$, *J. Electrochem. Soc.*, **104**, 656, (1957).
68. L. V. McCarty, Electrical properties of high purity silicon made from silicon tetraiodide, *J. Electrochem. Soc.*, **106**, 1036, (1959).
69. R. W. H. Stevenson. Private communication.
70. P. Sue, J. Pauly, and A. Nouaille, Purification of a salt by the fusion zone method, with the aid of radioactive indicators, *Compt. rend.*, **244**, 1212, 1505 (1957).
71. T. Shirai and T. Ishiboshi, Segregation of some cations in ammonium nitrate melt by zone melting, *Sci. Papers Coll. Gen. Educ. Univ. Tokyo*, **8**, 139 (1958); *Chem. Abstr.*, **53**, 16631 (1958).
72. V. R. Klokman and Y. H. Garmesher, Crystallization coefficients of radium in nitrate systems, *Radiokhimiya*, **1**, 26 (1958); *Chem. Abstr.*, **53**, 19547 (1959).
73. V. R. Klokman, Relation between the crystallization coefficient, $D$, and the distribution constant, $k$, in melts. *Radiokhimiya*, **1**, 32 (1959); *Chem. Abstr.*, **53**, 19547 (1959). See also *Chem. Abstr.*, **53**, 19549 (1959).

*Metals and Semiconductors*

74. W. D. Lawson and S. Nielsen, *Preparation of Single Crystals*, Butterworth, London, and Academic Press, New York, 1958, p. 127.
75. K. F. Hulme and J. B. Mullin, Role of evaporation in zone refining InSb, *J. Electronics & Control*, 3, 160 (1957).
76. E. A. Taft and F. H. Horn, Zone purification of silicon, *J. Electrochem. Soc.*, 105, 81, (1958).
77. A. S. Yue and J. B. Clark, Zone melting of magnesium, *Trans. A.I.M.E.*, 212, 881 (1958).
78. J. E. Antil, Zone melting of uranium, *Nuclear Power*, 1, 155 (1956).
79. G. A. Geach and F. O. Jones, Zone melting of refractory metals including rhenium and tungsten, *J. Less Common Metals*, 1, 56 (1959).
80. G. A. Geach and F. O. Jones, Arc furnace for zone refining metals, *Metallurgia*, 58, 209 (1958).
81. R. D. Burch and C. T. Young, Fission product separation from the Th-V alloy by arc-zone melting, *U.S. Atomic Energy Comm. NAA-SR 1735*, 1957.
82. W. Bardsley, The floating zone process, *Research*, 12, 183 (1959).
83. P. H. Keck and M. J. E. Golay, Crystallization of silican from a floating liquid zone, *Phys. Rev.*, 89, 1297 (1953).
84. G. W. Green. Private communication.
85. H. C. Theurer, Removal of boron from silicon by hydrogen-water vapor treatment, *Trans. A.I.M.E.*, 206, 1316 (1956).
86. E. Beuhler, Contribution to the floating zone refining of silicon, *Rev. Sci. Instr.*, 28, 453 (1957).
87. W. Heywang, The stability of vertical melting zones, *Z. Naturforsch.*, 11A, 238 (1956).
88. P. H. Brace, A. Cochardt and G. Comenetz, Cage zone refining, *Rev. Sci. Instr.*, 26, 303 (1955).
89. W. G. Pfann, K. E. Benson, and D. W. Hagelberger, Improvement in the floating zone technique, *J. Appl. Phys.*, 30, 454 (1959).
90. A. Calverley, M. Davis, and R. F. Lever, The floating zone melting of refractory metals by electron bombardment, *J. Sci. Instr.*, 34, 142 (1957); *J. Appl. Phys.*, 27, 195 (1956).
91. F. E. Birbeck and A. Calverley, Improved apparatus for floating zone melting by electron bombardment, *J. Sci. Instr.*, 36, 460 (1959).
92. V. Gusa, I. Krzhizh, and I. Ladnar, Zone melting of silicon with an electron beam, *Soviet Phys. Solid State*, 1, 261 (1959).
93. A. Calverley, Heating by electron bombardment, *Nature*, 184, 690 (1959) (Report of a symposium at S.E.R.L., March 1959).
94. A. R. Strnad, An attempt to zone melt sapphire by electron bombardment techniques, *Proc. 1st Symposium Electron-Beam Melting, March 1959*, p. 82. (Alloyd Research Corporation.)
95. W. G. Pfann and D. W. Hagelberger, Electromagnetic suspension of a molten zone, *J. Appl. Phys.*, 27, 12 (1956).
96. W. D. Lawson and S. Nielsen, *Preparation of Single Crystals*, Butterworth, London, and Academic Press, New York, 1958, Chap. 2.

97. D. C. Bennett and B. Sawyer, Preparation of single crystals of germanium of exceptional uniformity and perfection by zone melting, *Bell System Tech. J.,* **35,** 637 (1956).

98. W. G. Pfann and K. M. Olsen, Purification and prevention of segregation in single crystals of germanium, *Phys. Rev.,* **89,** 323 (1953).

99. E. D. Kalb and M. Tanenbaum, Uniform resistivity p-type silicon by zone levelling, *J. Electrochem. Soc.,* **106,** 597 (1959).

100. P. Levesque, New technique for preparing homogeneous alloys, *J. Metals,* **6,** 772 (1954).

101. G. E. C. Ltd and C. H. L. Goodman, Preparing specimens of incongruently melting phases, Brit. Pat. 767, 016, March, 1955.

102. L. R. Weisberg and F. D. Rosi, Vapor-zone refining, *Rev. Sci. Instr.,* **31,** 206 (1960).

*Zone Melting of Elements (References Classified According to Periodic Table)*

*Group IB:* Cu, Ag, Au

103. W. G. Pfann, *Zone Melting,* Wiley, New York, 1956, p. 105.

104. E. D. Tolmie and D. A. Robins, The zone refining of impure copper, *J. Inst. Metals,* **85,** 171 (1957).

105. Refining of metals by the zone melting method. I. Normal segregation in copper-tin and copper-nickel alloys, *Chem. Abstr.,* **53,** 17851 (1959).

106. W. G. Pfann, *Zone Melting,* Wiley, New York, 1956, p. 107.

107. J. H. Wernick, D. Dorsi, and J. J. Byrnes, Techniques and results of zone refining some metals, *J. Electrochem. Soc.,* **106,** 245 (1959).

*Group IIB:* Be, Mg, Zn, Cd, Hg

108. A. S. Yue and J. B. Clark, Zone melting of magnesium, *Trans. A.I.M.E.,* **212,** 881 (1958).

109. G. Scacciati and P. Gondi, The industrial purification of zinc by aid of zone melting, *Metallurgik ital.,* **49,** 774 (1957).

110. High purity metals in commercial quantities, *Metal Progr.,* **75,** 127 (1959).

111. W. G. Pfann, *Zone Melting,* Wiley, New York, 1956, p. 109.

112. W. D. Lawson, S. Nielsen, E. H. Putley, and A. S. Young, Preparation and properties of HgTe and mixed crystals of HgTe–CdTe, *J. Phys. Chem. Solids,* **9,** 325 (1959).

*Group IIIA:* B, Al, Sc, La, and R.E.

113. F. H. Horne, Zone refining of boron, *J. Appl. Phys.,* **30,** 1612 (1959).

114. E. S. Greiner, Zone melting of boron, *J. Appl. Phys.,* **30,** 598 (1959).

115. R. Tongas, Ultra-purification of Al by the zone melting method, *L'Ingenieur,* **43,** 12 (1957).

116. F. Montaroil, R. Reich, P. Albert, and G. Chaudron, Application of zone melting for obtaining extreme purification of Al, *Compt. rend.,* **238,** 815 (1954).

117. G. Chaudron, Application of zone melting to the extreme purification of aluminum and the extension of the method to other materials, *Congr. intern. aluminum, Paris*, **1**, 179 (1954) (Publ. 1955).

118. F. Montariol, Preparation and new properties of pure Al, *Publ. sci. et tech. ministere air (France)*, **344**, 70 (1955); *Chem. Abstr.*, **53**, 507 (1959).

119. O. Dimitrov, Influence of impurities on the elimination of reticular defects from cold worked zone refined Al by low temperature annealing, *Compt. rend.*, **247**, 2355 (1958).

120. O. Dimitrov and P. Albert, Recrystallization of zone melted Al, *Rev. mét.*, **56**, 267 (1959).

121. J. C. Blade, Effect of Cu, Zn, and Ag additions on the recrystallization of pure Al, *Rev. mét.*, **56**, 229 (1959).

122. J. C. Blade, J. W. H. Clare and H. J. Lamb, Recrystallization of zone refined Al, *Acta Met.*, **1**, 136 (1959).

123. O. Dimitrov and P. Albert, Recrystallization in zone refined Al, *Rev. mét.*, **56**, 267 (1959).

124. F. Montariol, The intergranular corrosion of Al purified by zone melting by HCl, *Compt. rend.*, **244**, 2163 (1957).

125. D. P. Detwiler and W. M. Fox, Zone refining of gallium, *Trans. A.I.M.E.*, **203**, 205 (1955).

126. T. C. Harman, Effect of zone refining variables on the separation of impurities in InSb, *J. Electrochem. Soc.*, **103**, 128 (1956).

127. J. B. Mullin and K. F. Hulme, Use of electromagnetic stirring in zone refining, *J. Electronics and Control*, **4**, 170, 1958.

128. Dr. F. M. Reynolds. Private communication.

*Group IVA:* C, Si, Ge, Sn, Pb

129. E. A. Taft and F. H. Horn, Zone purification of silicon, *J. Electrochem. Soc.*, **105**, 81 (1958).

130. J. A. Burton, Impurity centers in Ge and Si, *Physica*, **20**, 845 (1954).

131. W. G. Pfann and K. M. Olsen, Purification and prevention of segregation in single crystals of Ge, *Phys. Rev.*, **89**, 323 (1953).

132. M. Tanenbaum, A. J. Goss, and W. G. Pfann, Purification of antimony and tin by zone refining, *Trans. A.I.M.E.*, **200**, 762 (1954).

133. W. A. Tiller and J. W. Rutter, Effect of growth conditions on solidification of a binary alloy, *Can. J. Phys.*, **34**, 96 (1956).

134. A. Yu. Baimakov, B. F. Verner, H. G. Larikova and N. K. Dmitrieva, Purification of tin by zone melting, *Tsvetnaya Met.*, **29**, 51 (1956).

135. R. J. Heritage and S. Nielsen, Unpublished preliminary results.

136. R. L. Smith and J. L. Rutherford, Zone purification of reactive metals, *Trans. A.I.M.E.*, **209**, 478 (1959).

137. J. H. Wernick, D. Dorsi, and J. J. Byrnes, Techniques and results of zone refining some metals (Ni, Ti, V, Al, An), *J. Electrochem. Soc.*, **106**, 245 (1959).

138. G. D. Kneip Jr. and J. O. Betterton Jr., Floating zone purification of zirconium, *J. Electrochem. Soc.*, **103**, 684 (1956).

139. J. P. Langeron, P. Lehr, P. Albert, and G. Chaudron, On the purification of Zr by the method of vertical zone refining, *Compt. rend.*, **248**, 35 (1959).

140. J. H. Wernick, K. E. Benson, and D. Dorsi, *Trans. A.I.M.E.*, **209**, 996 (1957).

141. N. P. Sazin and P. Y. Dulkina in *Intern. Conf. Peaceful Uses Atomic Energy*, Vol. 9, United Nations, New York, 1956, p. 265.

142. P. T. Kozynev, Growing monocrystals of hexagonal selenium, *Soviet Physics— Tech. Phys.*, **3**, 470 (1958).

143. A. P. de Carvalho, The recombination process in Te, *Compt. rend.*, **244**, 461 (1957).

144. W. G. Pfann, *Zone Melting*, Wiley, New York, 1956, p. 102.

145. E. Buehler, The growth of molybdenum, tungsten, and niobium crystals by floating zone melting in vacuum, *Trans. A.I.M.E.*, **212**, 694 (1958).

146. R. G. Carlson, Tungsten zone melting by electron bombardment, *J. Electrochem. Soc.*, **106**, 49 (1959).

147. C. I. Whitman, V. Compton, and R. B. Holden, Zone melting of uranium, *J. Electrochem. Soc.*, **104**, 240 (1957).

148. P. Albert, D. Dimitrov, J. le Heriez, and G. Chaudron, Extended refining of uranium by the zone melting method, *Compt. rend.*, **244**, 965 (1957).

149. J. Talbot, P. Albert, and G. Chaudron, Extended zone purification of iron, *Compt. rend.*, **244**, 1577 (1957).

150. F. G. Morral, Pure cobalt—its properties, *J. Metals*, **10**, 662 (1958).

151. S. Besnard and J. Talbot, Influence of the purity of iron on the brittleness at low temperatures, *Compt. rend.*, **247**, 1612 (1958).

152. R. Sifferlin, Insolubility of $O_2$ in $\alpha$-iron purified by zone melting, *Compt. rend.*, **247**, 1608 (1958).

153. S. Besnard and J. Talbot, Influence of the purity and structure of iron and its capacity for cathodic hydrogen pick-up, *Rev. mét.*, **56**, 163 (1959).

154. G. A. Silvey, $Zn_3As_2$ a semiconducting compound, *J. Appl. Phys.*, **29**, 226 (1958).

155. D. G. Folberth and H. Weiss, Preparation and electrical properties of InP and GaAs, *Z. Naturforsch.* **10a**, 615 (1955).

156. W. P. Allred, B. Paris, and M. Genser, Zone melting and crystal pulling experiments with AlSb, *J. Electrochem. Soc.*, **105**, 93 (1958).

157. W. D. Lawson, S. Nielsen, E. H. Putley, and V. Roberts, The preparation, electrical, and optical properties of $Mg_2Sn$, *J. Electronics*, **1**, 203 (1955).

158. F. A. Kroger and D. de Nobel, Preparation and electrical properties of CdTe, *J. Electronics*, **1**, 290 (1955).

159. J. M. Whelan and G. H. Wheatley, Preparation and properties of GaAs, *J. Phys. Chem. Solids*, **6**, 169 (1958).

160. T. C. Harman, B. Paris, S. E. Miller, and H. L. Goering, Preparation and some properties of $Bi_2Te_3$, $Sb_2Te_3$, and $As_2Te_3$. *J. Phys. Chem. Solids*, **2**, 181 (1957).

161. W. D. Lawson, S. Nielsen, E. H. Putley, and A. S. Young, Preparation and properties of HgTe and mixed crystals of HgTe–CdTe, *J. Phys. Chem. Solids*, **9**, 325 (1959).

162. K. F. Hulme, A reliable method for the preparation of high purity InSb, *J. Electronics and Control*, **6**, 397 (1959).

163. V. D. Scott, Twinning caused by abrasion on single crystals of beryllium, *Acta Cryst.*, **13**, 313 (1960).

164. G. H. Moates, Continuous multistage purification of silicon tetraiodide by zone melting, in *Solid State Physics in Electronics and Communications*, Vol 1, Academic Press, New York, 1960, p. 1.

# 4

# ADDUCTIVE CRYSTALLIZATION

## R. A. Findlay

### Contents

# I. Introduction

The technology of separation processes has advanced rapidly during the past 25 years. A whole spectrum of the so-called "diffusional operations" is now available from which a selection can be made suited to the difficulty of the problem. However, one separation which offers more than the usual challenge is that of resolving mixtures of isomers which have similar chemical properties and nearly the same volatility.

A typical example is a mixture of $m$- and $p$-cresols the constituents of which boil at 396.3 and 395.6 °F, respectively. Ordinary distillation is impractical. Vapor–liquid equilibrium studies with 14 different solvents (1) failed to disclose even one "entrainer" which would make it possible to separate these isomers by either extractive or azeotropic distillation. Similar reasons rule out liquid–liquid extraction. Failure of the more usual diffusional operations led to consideration of more extreme measures and many chemical methods have been proposed (2). For example, it is possible to sulfonate the mixture, then steam distill the cresol sulfonic acids. The meta acid hydrolyzes at about 240–250 °F and the para acid is stable until a temperature of about 272 °F is reached. Obviously a chemical method of this type is expensive in reagent consumption, and other costs.

However, there is one diffusional operation which can be appl ed to the separation of isomers and other separations which are difficult if attempted by the more ordinary methods. This method is crystallization. Ordinary crystallization will not usually give complete separation of two isomers because of the formation of a eutectic. It is thus possible to prepare one pure compound and a eutectic mixture. Mixtures of $m$- and $p$-cresol are even less separable because these two components form a molecular addition compound, $m\text{-}CH_3C_6H_4OH \cdot p\text{-}CH_3C_6H_4OH$ and, of course, two eutectics. Thus, if the original mixture is in a certain composition range, no pure material at all can be made by ordinary crystallization. The two products would be (a) the addition compound and (b) a eutectic between the addition compound and one of the pure components.

It is common practice in other diffusional separation methods to use extraneous agents to make separation easier. Similar techniques have recently been applied to crystallization. Extraneous agents can be either: (a) such as to cause a lighter phase to form or (b) those which induce formation of a heavier phase. Table I makes this distinction clear.

The first grouping is generally called "extractive crystallization" and comprises the use of solvents to influence the course of crystallization operations. Extractive crystallization may be considered

TABLE I

Diffusional Separation Methods

| | Means of creating separate phases | | |
| --- | --- | --- | --- |
| Phases used in method | Removal or addition of heat | Material added to help create lighter phase | Material added to help create heavier phase |
| Solid–solid | — | — | — |
| Solid–liquid | | | |
|   Solid is crystalline | Crystallization from the melt | Extractive crystallization | Adductive crystallization |
|   Solid is amorphous | — | Leaching | Adsorption |
| Liquid–liquid | Thermal diffusion[a] | Extraction[b] | Extraction[c] |
| Gas–liquid | Distillation | Stripping, etc. | Absorption |
| Gas–solid | | | |
|   Solid is crystalline | Sublimation | — | Adductive crystallization |
|   Solid is amorphous | — | — | Adsorption |
| Gas–gas | Diffusion[a] | — | Sweep diffusion,[a] Atmolysis[a] |

[a] Diffusion utilizes only one phase in the strictest sense of the word.
[b] With a lighter solvent.
[c] With a heavier solvent.

analogous to those operations of a vapor–liquid nature which are classified as "stripping." Solvent dewaxing of lubricating oils is an extractive crystallization. Perhaps the most common example is the widespread use of crystallization from water solutions in the inorganic chemial industry. Chivate and Shah (3) studied the use of acetic acid as a solvent for the extractive crystallization of mixtures of *m*- and *p*-cresol. They presented a ternary diagram showing how the eutectic may be "by-passed" using a solvent. As Chivate and Shah point out, the term "extractive crystallization" has occasionally been misapplied to other types of crystallization, leading to an unfortunate confusion of terminology. The problem has been discussed in detail by Findlay and Weedman (4).

The second method which uses an extraneous agent is called "adductive crystallization." In this type of operation, the material added to the feed causes formation of a crystalline solid phase. Various types of extraneous agents can be used with varying degrees of selectivity as regards which components of a mixture are taken nto the solid phase. It is also proposed to include under the head-ng "adductive crystallization" processes in which a crystalline ,olid phase is caused to be deposited from a gas phase. However, t should be noted that adsorption processes are specifically ·uled out by use of the term "crystalline solid phase." The field )f adsorption covers an entirely different area of technology. Adductive crystallization is analogous to absorption among the ✓apor–liquid processes (see Table I). Technological advances ✓ithin the past 10 to 15 years have opened new vistas in the field of adductive crystallization. Possibilities exist for sorting out the con-:tituents of a mixture according to molecular shape rather than according to size or chemical type. The field is so new that its pos-:ibilities are just beginning to be realized.

## II. Fundamentals of Adductive Crystallization

The various possible extraneous agents for adductive crystalliza-tion may be classified into four groups: (a) solid-solution formers, (b) those which form molecular addition compounds, (c) clathrate "hosts," and (d) adduct formers. An essential feature in an agent for adductive crystallization is the capability of forming a single-phase solid containing the extraneous compound and one or more of the components of the mixture to be separated. Table II dis-tinguishes between the four known systems of this type on the basis of their physical nature and the range of compositions possible with each. Phenomena involving gross imperfections in the solid state such as misfitting monolayers and oriented overgrowths have been excluded from consideration.

Solid solutions are the analog in the solid state of ordinary solutions in liquid solvents. Physically speaking, molecules of the solute fit themselves into the crystal lattice of the solvent. Thus solid solutions are most commonly formed between "isomorphous" substances. Solid–liquid phase diagrams for systems forming solid solutions are essentially similar to the well-known types of vapor–liquid diagrams for liquid solutions. Since detailed quantitative explanations of the relations involved in solid solutions are available in numerous texts on physical chemistry and on the phase rule, they will not be repeated here. Suffice it to say that, in the majority of cases of interest, the two components are completely miscible in the solid phase. In these cases all compositions from 0 to 100%

TABLE II

Possible Agents for Adductive Crystallization

(Two or more components form a homogeneous (single-phase) solid)

| Type | Physical nature | Compositions possible | Typical example |
|---|---|---|---|
| A. Solid solutions | Formed by isomorphous compounds or those of similar molecular size and crystal habit. Molecules of one substitute in the lattice of the other. | All compositions from 0–100% solute except where limited by phenomenon of partial miscibility. | Silver–gold alloys |
| B. Molecular compounds | Components form loose addition compound which crystallizes as a single-phase molecular crystal. | Definite composition corresponding to a simple ratio of whole numbers. | $CuSO_4 \cdot 5H_2O$ |
| C. Clathrate compounds | One component crystallizes in a cage-like structure. Molecules of second are entrapped in "cells" of crystal lattice of first. | All compositions up to a maximum amount of guest component. | Gas hydrates; e.g., $C_3H_6 \cdot 17H_2O$ or lesser proportions of $C_3H_6$ |
| D. Adducts | One component crystallizes in a structure having tunnels. Molecules of second are held in tunnel by attractive forces. | Definite composition but not normally expressible as ratio of small integers. | Urea–$n$ - paraffin adducts; e.g., $(n\text{-}C_8H_{18})6 \cdot 7(\text{urea})$ |

solute are possible. Cases of partial solubility are known but are of less importance for our purpose.

Likewise, the quantitative relations regarding molecular compounds in the solid state are well known and need no detailed discussion in this chapter. Molecular compounds crystallize as if they were a single component in the form of a homogeneous molecular crystal. Such a single-phase solid has a definite composition which can be expressed in terms of its components as ratios of small integers.

Clathrate compounds are formed by molecules of a crooked shape which can crystallize in the form of a cage, trapping foreign molecules in the cells of the lattice. Clathrate compounds are characterized by variable composition up to a maximum amount of the "guest" component. In this respect clathrates are more like solid solutions of limited miscibility.

Adducts crystallize in a lattice with tunnels or channels in which molecules of foreign components are held by attraction. Adducts have definite compositions as do molecular compounds. However, the composition of an adduct cannot usually be expressed in terms of small integers.

These four types of extraneous agents can be used in essentially the same manner to cause the formation of a solid phase in equilibrium with a liquid or vapor phase. Both the resulting phases will usually have a different composition than the original feed. The manner in which this can be done will be described first in terms of solid solutions.

## A. SOLID SOLUTIONS

Much as an oil is used in an absorber to effect separation of a normally gaseous mixture, it would be possible to use a solid to form solid solutions with one of the components of a liquid feed in order to carry out separations. For example, methylcyclopentane freezes at $-224.4\,°F$. Separation of methylcyclopentane by direct crystallization would be virtually impossible because of the very low temperatures involved. However, methylcyclopentane forms solid solutions with cyclohexane which freezes at $+43.8\,°F$. Cyclohexane could be added to a liquid mixture containing methylcyclopentane and then crystallized. If solid cyclohexane were passed countercurrently with respect to the liquid feed through a number of equilibrating and phase-separating steps, the process would be directly analogous to an oil absorber operating on natural gas.

Figure 1 is a solid–liquid diagram, representing the data for mixtures of cyclohexane and methylcyclopentane over the range in which solid solutions are formed. Composition of the solid phase is plotted as the ordinate versus composition of the equilibrium liquid phase as the abscissa. This method of plotting the data is analogous to the so-called "$x$–$y$ plot" used in simple distillation calculations for binary systems. If certain simplifying assumptions are made, multistage crystallization calculations can be conducted by stepping off equilibrium stages in a manner similar to the well-

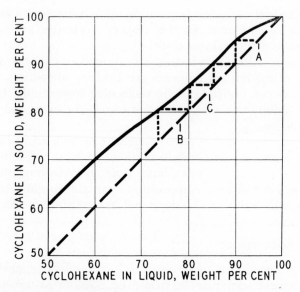

Fig. 1. Solid–liquid equilibrium for cyclohexane–methylcyclopentane system over region in which solid solutions are formed, showing method of calculating equilibrium stages of crystallization graphically.

known McCabe-Thiele method for distillation. The steps shown in Figure 1 depict operations under conditions of total reflux where the liquid in the "overhead" product contains only 5% methylcyclopentane and the liquid in the fourth stage contains 26% methylcyclopentane. Stage-by-stage calculations (5) in which heat and material balances were made on each stage checked the graphical method closely.

Of course the data of Figure 1 apply only to a two-component system. More complex methods would be necessary for calculation of an adductive crystallization process. For example, assume it were desired to separate a mixture of methylcyclopentane and normal hexane (respective boiling points 161.3 and 155.7°F) by adductive crystallization using cyclohexane. It would be necessary first to determine solid–liquid equilibrium data on the three-component system. The equilibrium data could then be expressed in terms similar to the $K$ values used in multicomponent distillation calculations. The proposed process could then be evaluated by calculation

nethods analogous to the Kremser-Brown method of computing
·il absorbers. Karl Hachmuth (6) has demonstrated that this
alculation method is widely applicable to calculation of separation
·rocesses such as azeotropic distillation, extractive distillation, and
iquid–liquid extraction. Application to solid solutions would be
imilar. However, the author has seen no reference in the literature
·o the possibility of using the phenomenon of solid solutions in this
nanner.

*. Possible Extraneous Agents*

Table III contains a list of some of the compounds which form
·olid solutions. There are several types of equilibrium diagrams.
·igure 2 depicts the following types for ready reference:

1. Components completely miscible in the solid state.
    a. Uninterrupted curve.
    b. Minimum freezing mixture (analogous to azeotrope).
    c. Maximum freezing mixture (analogous to azeotrope).
2. Components only partially miscible in the solid state.
    a. Peritectic or transition point.
    b. Eutectic.
3. Complex systems.

t will be observed from Table III that the normal paraffins of
imilar molecular weights form solid solutions with one another.
This phenomenon explains why it is possible to crystallize paraffin
vax (which contains all the normal paraffins present), out of the
·omplex mixture of countless different hydrocarbons which are
·resent in a lubricating oil. An identical phenomenon pertains to
·ydrocarbons of lower molecular weight and it has been demon-
trated (7) that a mixture of $C_{12}$ to $C_{16}$ normal paraffins can be
·rystallized from a kerosene. Likewise many condensed-ring aro-
natics form solid solutions.

In addition to the systems in Table III, many pairs of inorganic
·alts, other organic compounds, and of course, many metals form
·olid solutions. In general solid solutions are formed by compounds
·hose molecules are of similar sizes and shapes so that they can fit
nto the same crystal without undue distortion of the lattice. It

TABLE III
Solid-Solution Forming Systems

| Type of compound | Solid solutions formed | Type of diagram | Reference |
|---|---|---|---|
| Normal paraffins | | | |
| $C_8$–$C_9$ | Yes | Complex | 9 |
| $C_{16}$–$C_{18}$ | Yes | Complex | 10 |
| $C_{20}$–$C_{30}$ | No | — | 11 |
| $C_{30}$–$C_{32}$ | Yes | Complex | 11 |
| $C_{30}$–$C_{34}$ | Yes | Complex | 12 |
| $C_{34}$–$C_{36}$ | Yes | Complex | 12 |
| Aromatic hydrocarbons | | | |
| Indene–naphthalene | Yes | Uninterrupted | 13 |
| Isoquinoline–naphthalene | Yes | Uninterrupted | 13 |
| Indene–isoquinoline | Yes | Uninterrupted | 13 |
| Indene–benzene | No | — | 13 |
| Isoquinoline–benzene | No | — | 13 |
| Naphthalene–benzene | No | — | 13 |
| Anthracene–phenanthrene | Yes | Uninterrupted | 14 |
| Fluorene–phenanthrene | Yes | — | 14 |
| Fluorene–anthracene | Yes | Peritectic | 14 |
| Anthracene–carbazole | Yes | Uninterrupted | 14 |
| Phenanthrene–carbazole | Yes | Peritectic | 14 |
| Fluorene–$m$-xylene | No | — | 15 |
| Fluorene–ethylbenzene | No | — | 15 |
| Fluorene–durene | No | — | 15 |
| Fluorene–naphthalene | No | — | 15 |
| Fluorene–2-methylnaphthalene | Yes | Minimum point | 15 |
| Fluorene–2,7-dimethylnaphthalene | No | — | 15 |

has been observed (8) that hydrocarbons having low heats of fusion tend to form solid solutions with other close-boiling hydrocarbons. It follows that highly branched isoparaffins, whose molecules are nearly spherical and have low heats of fusion, are among those which form solid solutions. Similar considerations apply to cyclopentane and cyclohexane.

## 2. Hypothetical Adductive Crystallization Process Using Solid Solutions

A true adductive crystallization process could be visualized, based on normal paraffins, as follows: Normal tetradecane (freezing point +42.5 °F) could serve as a solid absorbent to remove unwanted low

TABLE III (*continued*)

| Type of compound | Solid solution formed | Type of diagram | Reference |
|---|---|---|---|
| soparaffins, etc. | | | |
| 2,2,3,3-Tetramethylbutane–2,2,3-trimethylbutane | Yes | Uninterrupted | 9 |
| 2,2-Dimethylbutane–2,3-dimethyl butane | Yes | Complex (compound) formed) | 16 |
| 2,3-Dimethylbutane–cyclopentane | Yes | Complex (compound formed) | 16 |
| n-Hexadecane–n-hexadecene | Yes | Uninterrupted | 17 |
| Cyclohexane–methylcyclopentane | Yes | Complex | 18 |
| Miscellaneous | | | |
| Silver–gold | Yes | Unbroken | — |
| Silver–zinc | Yes | Peritectic | — |
| Mercuric bromide–mercuric iodide | Yes | Minimum point | — |
| d-Carvoxime–l-carvoxime | Yes | Maximum point | — |
| Potassium nitrate–sodium nitrate | Yes | Minimum point | — |
| Naphthalene–β-naphthol | Yes | Unbroken | — |
| Naphthalene–monochloroacetic acid | Yes | Eutectic | — |

octane-number normal paraffins from gasoline. Solid n-tetradecane would be fed into the top of a suitable contactor as shown in Figure 3 where it would flow countercurrently with respect to a heavy gasoline (containing normal paraffins from nonane to undecane) which enters near the bottom of the column. Treated gasoline leaves the top of the contactor denuded of the lower normal paraffins ($C_9$ to $C_{11}$) but saturated with tetradecane. Since tetradecane boils at 488.4 °F (88.4 °F higher than the heaviest portion of the gasoline) it is easily recovered by distillation and recycled. Solid tetradecane leaves the bottom of the contactor in the form of a solid solution with $C_9$ to $C_{11}$ normal paraffins. The tetradecane would be recovered by distillation and recycled. The "raffinate" product (or mother liquor, to use crystallization terminology) would be an improved

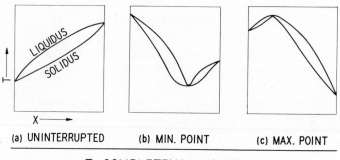

(a) UNINTERRUPTED          (b) MIN. POINT          (c) MAX. POINT

I COMPLETELY MISCIBLE

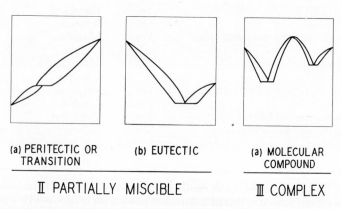

(a) PERITECTIC OR          (b) EUTECTIC          (a) MOLECULAR
    TRANSITION                                       COMPOUND

II PARTIALLY MISCIBLE          III COMPLEX

Fig. 2. Types of solid–liquid phase equilibrium diagrams encountered for solid-solution-forming systems illustrating their similarity to vapor–liquid diagrams for liquid solutions.

gasoline of higher octane number. The "crystallizate" would be a mixture of normal paraffins which could be further separated by distillation to produce chemical intermediates.

The above process has not been developed so far as the author knows. It would be anticipated that the quantity of tetradecane used to accomplish the separation would be large. A substantial refrigeration load would also be required because the process would have o operate at low temperatures. Mass transfer rates in the solid phase would be low. Special equipment would have to be developed. It does not appear likely that, in this case, the process would be competitive with other means of making the same separation (e.g., molecular sieves).

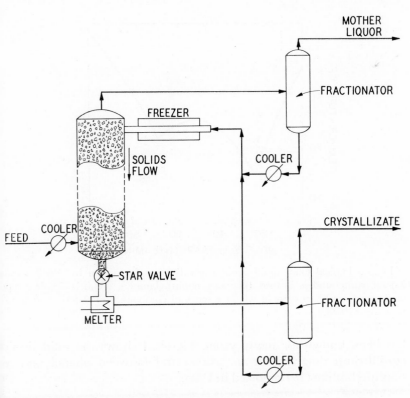

Fig. 3. Process flow diagram illustrating hypothetical adductive crystallization of n-paraffins from gasoline using solid n-tetradecane as extraneous agent.

However, similar processes can be conceived in other fields. Many aromatic compounds form solid solutions with other aromatics not too dissimilar in molecular weight. Thus one aromatic with a high freezing point could, in certain cases, be used as a solid absorbent to recover others from solution. It is possible that a process using solid solutions in this manner will be developed in the future.

## B. MOLECULAR ADDITION COMPOUNDS

The formation of loose compounds and the crystallization of these from the liquid phase is a common phenomenon. Probably the best known examples are hydrates of inorganic salts. However formation of compounds between molecules of organic compounds

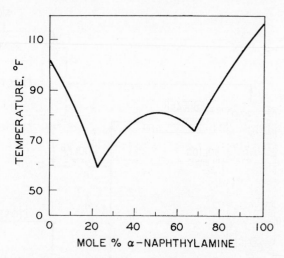

Fig. 4. Typical solid–liquid equilibrium diagram for system in which a molecular compound is formed (phenol-α-naphthylamine). This is simplest type of diagram. Others exist in which a series of compounds of different compositions are formed.

has been known for many years. Figure 4 shows the solid–liquid equilibrium diagram for the compound between phenol and α-naphthylamine (19) reported in 1903.

### 1. Compound Formation to Eliminate Refrigeration

In the simplest application, an extraneous agent can be added to a mixture to cause formation of a solid compound and to permit crystallization to be conducted at higher temperatures. Fenske (20) suggested making use of the compound formed between antimony trichloride and the xylenes for such as purpose. Recovery of p-xylene from mixed xylenes by crystallization is a well-developed commercial process. The yield of p-xylene is limited by the eutectic hich, in the case of $p$-xylene–$m$-xylene mixtures, for example, ontains 13% $p$-xylene and is reached at a temperature of $-70.6\,°F$. hus, deep refrigeration is required.

Antimony trichloride forms compounds with both $p$-xylene and $_$-xylene; namely $(SbCl_3)_2 \cdot p\text{-}C_6H_4(CH_3)_2$ and $(SbCl_3)_2 \cdot mC_6H_4\text{-}CH_3)_2$. The composition of the eutectic between these two com-ounds, expressed in terms of xylenes only, is not greatly different om the composition of the eutectic in the absence of antimony ichloride. However, the temperature of operation is raised since e eutectic temperature between the compounds is about $+102\,°F$ nd the process could be carried out at ordinary temperatures using ooling water instead of refrigeration. Of course, savings in re-igeration would be offset by the cost of antimony trichloride make-p and circulation. The compounds with antimony trichloride are nstable and are readily decomposed by raising the temperature. he hydrocarbons are then separated by distillation.

*. Compound Formation to Increase Yield Past Eutectic Limit*

Nixon and Deal (21) provide more detailed equilibrium diagrams f various antimony trichloride–aromatic systems. They found dditional metastable compounds formed in which one mole of ntimony trichloride combines with one mole of xylene. Using the netastable equilibria it is possible to "by-pass" the eutectic and btain complete separation of $m$- and $p$-xylenes. Antimony tri-romide (22) appears preferable for this purpose, considering only he phase diagram and not such other matters as cost of agent, tability, corrosiveness, etc.

It is in this latter regard that molecular compounds should prove nost useful in adductive crystallization; i.e., in eliminating the 'eutectic barrier" to the complete separation of two components ny crystallization. Egan and Luthy (23) describe how this technique nay be applied. They studied systems in which compounds are ormed between various aromatics and the tetrahalogenated nethanes. An ideal situation is exemplified by the series of carbon etrachloride–xylene systems. Carbon tetrachloride forms a com-pound with $p$-xylene; i.e., $CCl_4 \cdot p\text{-}C_6H_4(CH_3)_2$. However, it does not form compounds with $o$-xylene or $m$-xylene. As a result it may be used to permit nearly complete crystallization of $p$-xylene from solution. The ternary eutectic between $m$-xylene, $CCl_4$, and

$CCl_4 \cdot p\text{-}C_6H_4(CH_3)_2$ is at $-105\,°F$. The mother liquor at this poin contains only about 1% $p$-xylene.

### 3. Adductive Crystallization Agents

Table IV lists some of the adductive crystallization processe which have been proposed to take advantage of the phenomenor of solid compound formation. The range of applicability of sucl

TABLE IV

Molecular Addition Compounds for Adductive Crystallization

| Separation | Extraneous agent | Composition of compound | Refer-ence |
|---|---|---|---|
| m-Cresol, p-cresol | Nitrous acid | — | 24 |
| m-Cresol, p-cresol | Urea | m-Cresol · urea | 25 |
| m-Cresol, p-cresol | 2,6-Lutidine | m-Cresol · 2,6-lutidine | 26 |
| m-Cresol, p-cresol | 4-Picoline | p-Cresol · 4-picoline | 27 |
| m-Cresol, p-cresol | 2,4-Dimethyl-quinoline | p-Cresol · 2,4-dimethyl-quinoline | 27 |
| m-Cresol, p-cresol | Phenol | | 28 |
| Quinaldine, isoquinoline | Phenol | Phenol · quinaldine | 29 |
| Quinaldine, isoquinoline | 1,2,4-Xylenol | 1,2,4-Xylenol · quinaldine | 29 |
| Durene | Sym. tetrachloro-ethane | $C_2H_2Cl_4 \cdot C_6H_2(CH_3)_4$ | 30 |
| p-Xylene | Chloral | — | 31 |
| Mesitylene, pseudocumene | SbCl₃ | SbCl₃ · pseudocumene | 21 |
| 2,4- and 2,5-Lutidines | SbCl₃ | — | 21 |
| β- and γ-Picolines | SbCl. | — | 21 |
| p-Xylene | CCl₄ | $CCl_4 \cdot p\text{-}C_6H_4(CH_3)_2$ | 23 |

processes is limited by the availability of suitable extraneous agents which will form a molecular compound with the component which it is desired to separate. Additionally, the extraneous agent must satisfy certain stringent requirements. It must have the classical characteristics of suitable selective solvents for liquid–liquid extraction processes as well as certain special ones necessary for crystallization techniques. Thus the discovery and development of such processes is unusually difficult. In recent years new approaches to this problem have become possible using clathrate compounds and adducts rather than true molecular compounds. This widens the field of possibilities very considerably.

## 2. CLATHRATE COMPOUNDS

Unusual complexes, not explained by ordinary valence theory, have been known for a long time. For example, the "gas hydrates" were observed as early as the 1880's. However, it has been less than 5 years since Powell (32) used X-ray studies to elucidate the structure of these nonstoichiometric compounds and introduced the term "clathrate compound." Powell observed that minerals, metals, and many complex ionic substances crystallize so that their atoms are in positions corresponding to the closest, or nearly the closest, possible packing of a group of spheres. Similarly many molecular crystals are formed in such a manner that the projections of one molecule fit into the indentations of another. Attractive forces are such that the lowest state of potential energy is achieved when the atoms are packed together as closely as possible. Large vacant spaces are avoided. However, some molecular forces are stronger than the van der Waals attractions, particularly where polar groups are involved. These forces may cause a more open structure containing voids in which other molecules may be encaged.

### A. Clathrate Hosts

Thus, a clathrate compound is a single-phase solid formed when a "host" substance crystallizes in a form resembling a cage, having small uniform cavities, in which the molecules of the "guest" are entrapped. Clathrates are not compounds in the normal chemical sense. They have no fixed composition but can be prepared with varying amounts of the "guest" compound up to a definite maximum value. The composition of this maximum value is frequently expressed in terms such as:

$$x(\text{Host}) \cdot y(\text{Guest})$$

where $x$ is the number of molecules of the host compound making up a unit cell of the cage lattice and $y$ is the number of molecules of the guest which can fit into a single cavity in the host crystal. Table V lists a number of typical clathrate compounds with their maximum-composition formulas. If the reader is interested in more detail, Mandelcorn (33) has published an excellent review of the chemistry of clathrate compounds. Figure 5 is a representation of a clathrate compound of monoamminenickel cyanide and benzene.

## TABLE V
### Typical Clathrate Compounds

| Host | Maximum composition | Guests | Reference |
|------|---------------------|--------|-----------|
| Hydroquinone | $3C_6H_4(OH)_2 \cdot G$ | $SO_2$, HCl, HBr, HCN, $H_2S$, HCOOH CO, $CH_3OH$, A, Kr, X, $N_2$, $O_2$ | 33 |
| Water | 46 $H_2O \cdot 8G$ | $CH_4$, $H_2S$, argon | 33 |
| | 46 $H_2O \cdot 6G$ | $C_2H_4$, $Br_2$, $SO_2$, $Cl_2$ | |
| | 136 $H_2O \cdot 8G$ | $C_3H_6$ $CH_4I$, $C_2H_5Cl$ | |
| | 136 $H_2O \cdot 24G$ | $H_2S$, etc. | |
| Phenol | 12 $C_6H_5OH \cdot 5G$ | HCl, HBr | 33 |
| | 12 $C_6H_5OH \cdot 4G$ | $SO_2$ | |
| | 12 $C_6H_5OH$ 2G | $CS_2$ | |
| Monoamminenickel cyanide | $Ni(NH_3)(CN)_2 \cdot G$ | Benzene, thiophene, furan, pyrrole, aniline, or phenol | 33 |
| Tetra-(4-methylpyridine) nickel dithiocyanate | $Ni(4\text{-me-py})_4(SCN)_2 \cdot G$ | (see Table VI) | 34 |
| Hexamethylisocyanido- ferrous chloride | $Fe(CNCH_3)_6Cl_2 \cdot 3G$ | $H_2O$ | 33 |
| Tri-$o$-thymotide | 2 $C_{33}H_{36}O_6 \cdot G$ | Benzene, chloroform | 33 |
| Dianin's compound (polymer of phenol and mesityl oxide) | 6 $C_{18}H_{20}O_2 \cdot 3G$ 6 $Cl_{18}H_{20}O_2 \cdot 2G$ 6 $C_{18}H_{20}O_2 \cdot G$ | Methanol, etc. $CCl_4$, etc. Ethylene dichloride, etc. | 33 |
| $p$-Cresol novolac tetramer (polymer of cresol and formaldehyde) | 1 : 1 | Ethylene dichloride | 33 |
| Methylnaphthalene | 8 : 1 8 : 3 1 : 1 | Branched and straight chain hydrocarbons up to $n$-$C_{16}$. Also toluene, phenylcyclohexane, decalin, etc. | 35 |

The structure of clathrates in some cases becomes rather complex
For example, in the so-called "gas hydrates," the host (water
crystallizes in one form having 46 molecules of water per unit cell
a cube of approximately 12 A sides. This cell contains eight ap
proximately spherical cages, two being 5.2 A diameter and si₃
5.9 A diameter. Hence, different amounts of guests can be retained

lepending on the size of the guest molecule. A second crystalline
orm has a unit cell with 136 molecules of water (a 17.3-A cube)
laving 16 holes 4.8 A in diameter and 8 voids 6.9 A in size. Double
·lathrates have been observed in which each of the small cells

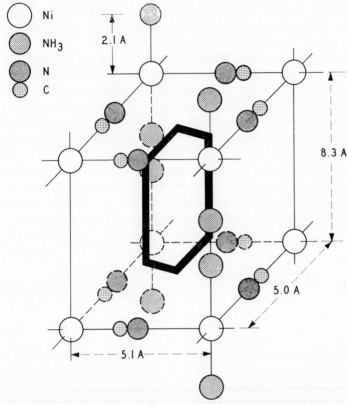

Fig. 5. Structure of clathrate formed between monoaminenickel cyanide and
benzene showing the benzene molecule trapped inside a cage formed by the
crystal lattice of the former.

·contain a small molecule and the large cells a larger molecule
(e.g., $CHCl_3 \cdot 2H_2S \cdot 17H_2O$). On the other hand, if chloroform
alone is present, the maximum formula for the hydrate is $CHCl_3 \cdot$
$17H_2O$ since chloroform molecules will not fit into the smaller
cavities. Other clathrate systems are similar. Hydroquinone crystal-

lizes in a unit cell having cavities approximately spherical and 8 Å in diameter.

It might be imagined that clathrate "hosts" would be relatively nonselective agents for adductive crystallization. As Table V indicates, many different compounds having molecules of the proper size can be included in the "cage" of any host under proper conditions. Molecules small enough to slip through the "bars" of the cage cannot be contained. Those which are so big as to require undue distortion of the crystal lattice will not be included. This is normally a rather wide range. However, other factors may enter. Mandelcorn points out that essentially thiophene-free benzene was prepared by Evans and co-workers (36) using clathration with monoamminenickel cyanide. This agent forms clathrate compounds with both benzene and thiophene but evidently has a much greater affinity for benzene.

A series of Werner complexes, similar to monoamminenickel cyanide, form clathrates with many other aromatic hydrocarbons. A surprising selectivity was observed. Table VI lists a number of these complexes and contains data on the hydrocarbons for which

TABLE VI
Adductive Crystallization of Aromatic Hydrocarbons

| | | Concentration, vol. % | |
| --- | --- | --- | --- |
| Clathrate former (host) | Guest | In feed,[b] | In product (after host removal) |
| Ni(4-methylpyridine)$_4$(SCN)$_2$[a] | p-Xylene | 19.9 | 50.0[c] |
| Ni(4-ethylpyridine)$_4$(formate)$_2$ | o-Xylene | 19.3 | 53.1 |
| Ni(3-ethyl-4-methylpyridine)$_4$(SCN)$_2$ | m-Xylene | 45.5 | 56.9 |
| Ni(4-acetylpyridine)$_4$(SCN)$_2$ | Ethylbenzene | 15.3 | 54.6 |
| | | 100.0 | |

[a] This host also is selective for the para form of chlorotoluene, dichlorobenzene, toluidine, nitrotoluene, methylanisole, cymene, diethylbenzene, ethyltoluene. It also separates naphthalene from diphenyl, 1-methylnaphthalene from 2-methylnaphthalene, and anthracene from phenanthrene.

[b] Feed was a mixture of the four 8-carbon aromatics shown.

[c] In experiments where the crystal cake was washed, p-xylene concentrations as high as 70 vol. % were reached.

hey are selective. Schaeffer and co-workers (34) do not offer an
explanation for the remarkable selectivity of these complexes.
The structure is very complex. Williams (37) observed that the
complexes crystallize alone from chloroform solution as octahedra.
However, the clathrate compounds form ten-sided crystals. The
rue composition of the encaged hydrocarbon is uncertain because
of the difficulty of complete separation of solid and liquid phases.

## 2. Recovery and Recycling Clathrate Host

Clathrate compounds can be "decomposed" into their original
components by any means which destroys the crystal lattice, e.g.,
melting, dissolving, or subliming the host compound. In some
cases even mechanical grinding may serve the purpose. Even below
the melting point, there is a definite escaping tendency for the guest
component, observable as a vapor pressure in the case of volatile
materials. However, the stability of these materials is remarkable
as evidenced by the existence of hydroquinone clathrates of rare
gases (such as argon) at low pressures.

The use of clathrates in adductive crystallization would be essentially parallel to the use of solid compounds. If selectivity were
sufficiently high it would be necessary only to form the clathrate
and separate the solid phase cleanly. The clathrate could then be
decomposed, releasing the desired product. The clathrate host would
be recycled. If lower selectivity were encountered, a multistage
process would be needed, analogous to the proposed process using
solid solutions (Fig. 3). Actually little information is yet available to
permit estimation of the selectivity of clathrate formation when a
mixture of potential "guest" compounds is present. Such data are
difficult to obtain for liquid systems because of the problem of
making sure that "mother-liquor" occlusion in the solid phase is
eliminated.

## 3. Physical and Thermodynamic Properties of Clathrates

Recently J. H. van der Waals and J. C. Platteeuw (37a) summarized the physical and thermodynamic information available
on clathrates. Table VII lists some of the properties they report on
the gas hydrates. They point out that, in the great majority of
clathrates discovered so far, the so-called "compound" is formed in

TABLE VII

Physical and Thermodynamic Properties of Clathrates[a]

| Guest | Heat of formation, kcal/mole guest | Dissociation pressure, atm. at 0°C Observed | Dissociation pressure, atm. at 0°C Calculated | Fraction of cells occupied at 0°C $y_1$ | Fraction of cells occupied at 0°C $y_2$ |
|---|---|---|---|---|---|
| Structure I | | | | | |
| A | — | 95.5 | 95.5 | 0.825 | 0.841 |
| Kr | 13.9 | 14.5 | 15.4 | 0.832 | 0.830 |
| Xe | 16.7 | 1.15 | 1.0 | 0.813 | 0.835 |
| $CH_4$ | 14.5 | 26.0 | 19.0 | 0.818 | 0.836 |
| $C_2H_4$ | 15.0 | 5.44 | 1.1 | 0.837 | 0.827 |
| $C_2H_6$ | 16.3 | 5.2 | 0.5 | 0.523 | 0.879 |
| $CH_3 Cl$ | 18.1 | 311[b] | — | — | — |
| $CH_3 Br$ | 19.5 | 187[b] | — | — | — |
| $CH_3 Br$ | 16.6 | 239[b] | — | — | — |
| Structure II | | | | | |
| $C_3H_6$ | 32 | 1.74 | — | — | — |
| $C_2H_5 Cl$ | 31.9 | 201[b] | — | — | — |
| $CH_2 Cl_2$ | 29 | 116[b] | — | — | — |
| $CH Cl_3$ | 31 | 50[b] | — | — | — |

[a] Structure I is hydrate with 46 molecules of $H_2O$ per unit cell and 2 small, 8 large cavities.   Structure II is hydrate with 136 molecules of $H_2O$ per unit cell and 16 small, 8 large cavities.

[b] In mm. Hg.

a crystal lattice of the host component which is thermodynamically unstable by itself. This crystal form is stabilized by the presence of the guest molecules. The forces involved in forming the clathrate must be similar to the intermolecular forces in liquids. Thus they propose that a clathrate should be considered to be a solution rather than a "compound"; i.e., a solid solution of the guest component in the host lattice.

Based on assumptions that the trapped molecules are localized in the cages, that each cavity holds only one molecule, that there is no mutual interaction between the encaged molecules, and that the host lattice is not distorted by the guest, these authors applied classical statistical mechanics to derive generalized relations for clathrate "solutions" having $M$ entrapped components and $n$ different types of cavities. Their equation for vapor pressure of guest K in the clathrate is:

$$p_K = (1/C_{K_1})[y_{K_1}/(1 - \sum_J y_{J_1})] = (1/C_{K_2})[y_{K_2}/(1 - \sum_J y_{J_2})] = \ldots$$

where $y_{K_1}$ is the probability of finding a molecule of K in a cavity of type 1. For a clathrate host which forms only one type of cavity and for a single guest, this equation reduces to:

$$p_K = (1/C_K)[y_K/(1 - y_K)]$$

These equations are forms of Langmuir's isotherm for localized adsorption without interaction of the solute molecules. The significance of the constant $C_K$ may be explained by an analogy with a reversible chemical equation as follows:

Empty cell + K ⇋ Occupied cell

or

X + K ⇋ Y

The equilibrium constant for such a reaction would be

$$C_K = (\text{Conc. Y})/[(\text{Conc. X})(\text{Conc. K})]$$

Now the concentration of Y must be proportional to $y_K$ and of X to $(1 - y_K)$. The concentration of the guest K is proportional to $p_K$. Thus:

$$C_K = y_K/(1 - y_K)p_K \qquad p_K = (1/C_K)[y_K/(1 - y_K)]$$

Making further assumptions regarding the free rotation and the potential energy relations of the guest molecule in the cell, a relation may be derived to permit computation of $C_K$. Vapor pressure calculated from these equations are included in Table VII for certain of the gas hydrates. The agreement with observed vapor pressure is remarkably good for nearly spherical molecules. However, the hydrates of ethylene and ethane have much higher equilibrium pressures than those calculated, probably because some of the simplifying assumptions (such as that the molecules are rotating freely in their cells) do not apply.

The data in Table VII also show the difference between hydrates of structure I and those of structure II. All those listed under structure I can enter both smaller and larger cavities except the last two, $CH_3Br$ and $CH_3SH$ which cannot occupy the smaller cells. Hydrates of Structure II are formed only by those molecules too large to fit into the cells of structure I. However, in the presence of larger molecules capable of stabilizing a structure **II** hydrate smaller molecules can then be included in some of the cells.

### 4. Equilibrium Relations of Clathrates

There are several difficulties in determining phase equilibrium data for systems involving clathrates. The occlusion of mother liquor has been mentioned. In addition there is an apparent hys

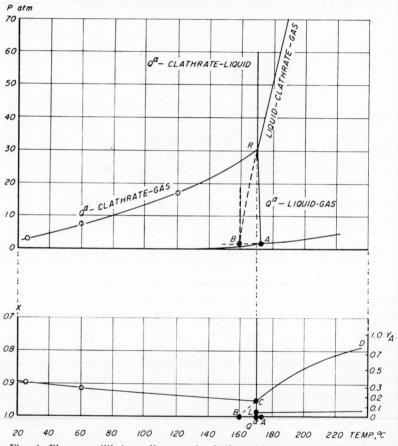

Fig. 6. Phase equilibrium diagram for hydroquinone–argon system showing three-phase lines where equilibrium is reached between α-crystal form of hydroquinone ($Q^\alpha$), clathrate (β-crystal form containing argon), liquid hydroquinone (containing dissolved argon) and argon gas in various combinations.

eresis caused by the difficulty of breaking down the wall of the
cells to permit the trapped molecules to escape. Thus even though
clathrate may have a vapor pressure of several atmospheres, it
may be stable at atmospheric pressure for long periods. Special
tricks, such as adding a nonclathratable solvent, are needed to
stablish equilibrium.

However, in spite of the experimental difficulties, some equilib-
ium data are available. Figure 6 is a P-T-$x$ diagram for the system
hydroquinone–argon as depicted by van der Waals and Platteeuw
37a). Hydroquinone by itself crystallizes in a form known as $\alpha$-
hydroquinone. In the presence of a guest it forms a different structure which has been called $\beta$-hydroquinone containing cells some of
which are occupied by the guest molecules.

As shown in the P-T portion of Figure 6 there is a three-phase
line along which solid $\alpha$-hydroquinone, clathrate, and gas (almost
pure argon) can be in equilibrium. As the temperature is increased
he vapor pressure increases. Point $R$ is a quadruple point at which
olid $\alpha$-hydroquinone, clathrate, hydroquinone-rich liquid, and
gas are in equilibrium. Since there are four phases and two components, the system is invariant. Line $AR$ is the three-phase equilibrium of solid $\alpha$-hydroquinone with liquid and argon gas. It is very
nearly vertical since pressure has only a small effect on the freezing
point and argon is only sparingly soluble in liquid hydroquinone.

The three-phase equilibrium line for liquid, clathrate, and gas is
extrapolated to lower pressures as the dashed line $RB$ to show the
triple point of the unstable $\beta$-modification hydroquinone at $B$.
The triple point of the stable $\alpha$-hydroquinone is shown at $A$.
The $\beta$-hydroquinone, of course, requires a minimum portion of
argon to exist. The pressures of both triple points have been
exaggerated in order to illustrate the principle involved.

The T-$x$ portion of the diagram is drawn in terms of both $x$
and of $y_a$. The term $y_a$ is the fraction of the cavities which are filled
with argon. It is related to $x$ (which is the mole fraction of hydroquinone) by the relation:

$$y_a = 3(1 - x)/x$$

since it requires three molecules of hydroquinone to form one
cavity.

Several other phase-equilibrium diagrams for clathrate systems are reviewed by van der Waals and Platteeuw, some of them ternary systems including the complexity of hydrates of the two different structures. Equilibrium data are available on the following hydrates: $H_2S-H_2O$; $H_2S-CH_4-H_2O$; $C_3H_6-C_3H_8-H_2O$; $CH_4-C_3H_8-H_2O$; $CHCl_3-H_2S-H_2O$; $CCl_4-H_2S-H_2O$; $C_3H_8-H_2S-H_2O$; and $H_2S-CH_3CHF_2-H_2O$. The system $C_3H_8-H_2S-H_2O$ is of interest in that it has a minimum-pressure point equivalent to an azeotrope at a ratio of approximately $27H_2S:73C_3H_8$.

## D. ADDUCTS

The clathrate structure is characterized by a closed cell or cage in which molecules are trapped. Related structures are formed in which the host compound crystallizes in such a manner as to form channels of molecular dimensions, open at one or both ends. Molecules of a suitable size and, more importantly, shape, may be held in these channels by molecular attractive forces. The earliest examples of such a structure were the choleic acids (38) discovered in 1916 in which long chain fatty acids were crystallized in the channels of deoxycholic acid unit cells.

### 1. Structure of Adducts

The most widely studied phenomenon of this nature is that of urea and thiourea "adducts." An excellent review of all aspects of these crystalline materials was published in a series of articles by Kobe and Domask (39). Urea alone normally crystallizes in a tetragonal structure. However, in the presence of long chain compounds, e.g., the normal alkanes, urea crystallizes in a hexagonal structure enclosing the foreign molecules. The urea molecules may be visualized as being wrapped loosely around the straight chain of the guest molecule in a helical fashion, much as a tape or ribbon can be wrapped around a pipe. The guest molecules are held within the hollow tunnels or channels of the unit cells of the urea, probably by van der Waals attraction forces, in a manner analogous to the way the piece of pipe in the above analogy would stick within the coccon of tape by friction. Figure 7 pictures a cross section of the unit cell of a urea adduct as represented by Kobe and Domask (39). The normal paraffin molecule is depicted in the center and the urea molecules are shown forming the wall of an enclosure around

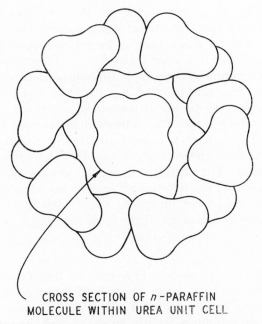

CROSS SECTION OF *n*-PARAFFIN
MOLECULE WITHIN UREA UNIT CELL

Fig. 7. Representation of a cross section of a urea–*n*-paraffin adduct showing the urea molecules forming the walls of a tunnel in which the *n*-paraffin is held by attractive forces.

the guest. Gilson and McDowell (40) have recently shown by nuclear magnetic resonance measurements that the imprisoned hydrocarbon molecule is rotating with some freedom in the channel or is at least executing torsional oscillations about an axis parallel to the length of the channel. Thus the phenomenon of adduction is basically more closely related to a physical one, such as adsorption, than to a chemical reaction.

The channel in the urea unit cell, when it forms an adduct, varies in diameter from point to point between 5 and 6 A. Normal paraffin molecules are about 4.1 A in diameter, and hence these compounds readily form adducts. Highly branched molecules such as those of 2,2,4-trimethylpentane are of the order of 6 A diameter and do not form adducts with urea under any known conditions. Molecules between these sizes may form adducts in certain cases and not form them in others. For example, benzene molecules are

about 5.9 A in the largest dimension. Benzene does not form an
adduct with urea but 1-phenyloctadecane does. The long, straight
chain of this compound is readily adducted and apparently the unit
cell can stand the distortion caused by an occasional benzene
group. Similar considerations apply to slightly branched isoparaffin
molecules, for example, those with a single methyl branch, which
may form adducts if the linear portion of the chain is sufficiently
long. When thiourea forms an adduct it produces a channel 8 A
in diameter. Thus it tends to adduct with highly branched molecules
and with cyclic compounds, for example, 2,2,4-trimethylpentane
and cyclohexane. The narrower molecules like the normal alkanes
are not held within the thiourea channels; no adducts are formed
except under special circumstances where high molecular weight
*n*-paraffins may be adducted in the form of a coiled molecule.

## 2. Adductive Hosts

Table VIII lists several "adductors" or host compounds with
typical "adductee" or guest compounds. Urea forms adducts
under ordinary conditions with all straight chain compounds
above a certain minimum length. In the case of the normal paraffins and normal olefins this minimum length is a six-carbon chain.

### TABLE VIII
#### Typical Adducts

| Host | Guests | Remarks |
|---|---|---|
| Deoxycholic acid | Fatty acid | Host/guest ratio is an integer |
| | Naphthalene | |
| | Phenol | |
| Urea | Normal alkanes | Hexane or longer |
| | Straight chain acids | Butyric or longer |
| | Straight chain ketones | Acetone or longer |
| | Straight chain esters | |
| | Normal alkenes | Hexene or longer |
| Thiourea | Cyclopentane | |
| | Cyclohexane | |
| | Isoparaffins | Highly branched, e.g., trip- tane, 2,2,4-trimethylbu- tane, etc. |
| | Highly chlorinated hydrocarbons | $CCl_4$ |

However, under elevated pressures and lower temperatures, where the escaping tendency of the guest molecules is reduced, it has been found possible to form adducts with normal paraffins having less than a six-carbon chain. Urea does not normally form adducts with branched chain hydrocarbons of short chain length, even such slightly branched molecules as 3-methylheptane. However, in the presence of a large quantity of a readily adducted hydrocarbon, such as a normal paraffin, a minor proportion of 3-methylheptane may be included in the adduct.

## 3. Composition and Equilibrium

Although adducts are not true chemical compounds they may be treated as if they were for computational purposes. Otto Redlich and his co-workers (41) considered adduction as if it were a chemical equilibrium following the equation:

$$\text{Complex(S)} \rightleftharpoons \text{Reactant} + m(\text{Urea})$$

The composition of the adduct cannot be expressed in terms of small integers. Values of $m$ for the above equation when applied to $n$-paraffins are given in Table IX and it will be observed that $m$ is a whole number only occasionally and by accident. These values of $m$ are plotted in Figure 8 showing that the composition of $n$-paraffin adducts bears a linear relation to the number of carbon

TABLE IX
Composition Equilibria and Heats of Reaction Urea–$n$-Alkane Adducts

|  | Moles urea per mole reactant | Heat of adduction, kcal/g-mole | Equilibrium constant at 25°C., log $K$ |
|---|---|---|---|
| $n$-Heptane | 6.1 | 7.3, 7.6 | −0.22 |
| $n$-Octane | 6.7 | 9.7 | −0.49 |
| $n$-Nonane | 7.4 | 11.8 | −0.77 |
| $n$-Decane | 8.1 | 13.1 | −1.05 |
| $n$-Undecane | — | 14.6 | — |
| $n$-Dodecane | 9.3 | 16.1 | −1.54 |
| $n$-Hexadecane (cetane) | 12.0 | 21.0, 22.8 | −2.64 |
| $n$-Octadecane | 14.0 | — | — |
| $n$-Tetracosane ($C_{24}H_{50}$) | 18.0 | — | — |
| $n$-Dotriacontane ($C_{32}H_{66}$) | 23.3 | — | — |

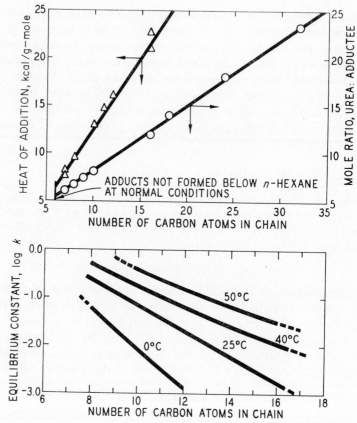

Fig. 8. Relationships between composition, heat of formation, equilibrium constants, and length of carbon chain for n-paraffin–urea adducts, showing linear change of properties with number of carbon atoms in the n-paraffin molecule.

atoms in the reactant chain. These data may be expressed in the form of an equation:

$$m = 0.68n + 1.5$$

where $n$ = number of carbon atoms in n-paraffin chain. Consideration of the composition of the adducts in terms of molecular structure indicates that the n-paraffin molecules lie end to end in the urea channel at a constant distance (about 2 A) apart, independent of the size of the molecules.

The heat of reaction for the formation of the $n$-paraffin adducts is also given in Table IX and plotted in Figure 8. The heat of adduction is probably not exactly linear with respect to the length of the paraffin chain $(n)$ or the mole ratio of urea to reactant $(m)$ but for practical purposes it can be expressed by the relation:

$$\Delta H = -6.5 + 2.37m$$

where $\Delta H$ is in kcal/mole. The heat of adduction may be expressed roughly as 1.6 kcal per carbon atom which is greater than either the heat of fusion or of vaporization but less than typical heats of adsorption, expressing the values in all cases as kilocalories per carbon atom in the molecule.

Redlich (41) defined an equilibrium constant for adduction as follows:

$$K = a_r a_u{}^m$$

where $a_r$ = activity of reactant and $a_u$ = activity of urea. Activity coefficients are available for many hydrocarbons and Redlich calculated the activity of urea in aqueous solutions, thus making it possible to compute equilibrium constants for adduction. The logarithm of the equilibrium constants proved to be approximately a linear function of the molal ratio $m$ or of the number of carbon atoms in the chain in the case of certain homologous series. For the $n$-paraffins at 25 °C this relation may be expressed as:

$$\log K = 2.20 - 0.403m$$

This equation is also approximately correct for olefins, alcohols, and halides.

Figure 8 contains a plot of the equilibrium constants for $n$-paraffins at several temperatures. Because of the manner in which Redlich defined the equilibrium constant, a low value of $K$ corresponds to a stable complex. Figure 8 shows that the adducts of hydrocarbons having higher molecular weights are more stable than those of shorter chain length. Likewise low temperatures are favorable for increasing the stability of the adducts. Redlich also supplies plots of equilibrium constants for $n$-olefins, $n$-alcohols, $n$-acids, $n$-esters, and $n$-halides. The relation between the equilibrium constant $(K)$, the temperature $(T)$, and the heat of adduction $(\Delta H)$ is given by the van't Hoff equation:

$$R[d \ln K/d(1/T)]_p = -\Delta H°$$

It should be pointed out that these various relations are limited by the assumptions which Redlich made as regards activities of the reactants and the presence of only one adductable material.

### 4. Mixtures of Reacting Substances

When several reactants are present along with nonadductable components, the situation is more complex. The adduct precipitates as homogeneous crystals; that is, it behaves in a manner analogous to a solid solution rather than a physical mixture of different crystals. It is possible to calculate what happens in such a situation by making the assumption that the activity of each component in solution is equal to its concentration. This corresponds to assuming that the activity coefficient is unity. Likewise it is necessary to assume that the activity of each component in the adduct is equal to its mole fraction calculated on a urea-free basis. Making these assumptions, a trial-and-error calculation method (similar to vapor–liquid equilibrium-flash computation methods) may be used to determine the composition of the adduct and the mother liquor. Of course, these calculations are limited by the validity of the assumptions made. They should be applied only to hydrocarbon mixtures reacting with aqueous urea. If polar organic solvents such as methanol or methyl isobutyl ketone are used, the assumption that the activity constants are one no longer applies. It will normally be necessary to determine equilibria for these special cases in the laboratory.

It should be further pointed out that, from a practical point of view, activators are necessary to achieve a reasonable rate of adduction. Suitable activators are polar organic compounds which are mutual solvents for urea and for the reactants. Such solvents as methanol, methylene chloride, and methyl isobutyl ketone are suitable. Likewise certain impurities act as inhibitors for the reaction. Naturally occurring sulfur compounds in petroleum are suspected.

## 5. Thiourea Adducts

Table X gives data on thiourea complexes comparable to those in Table IX for urea adducts. Mole ratios of thiourea to reactant are lower than those encountered with urea adducts. Likewise the heats of adduction are relatively low.

TABLE X
Composition, Equilibria, and Heats of Reaction of Thiourea Adducts

|  | Moles thiourea per mole reactant | Heat of adduction, kcal/mole | Equilibrium constant at 25°C, log K |
|---|---|---|---|
| Isoparaffins |  |  |  |
| 2,2-Dimethylbutane | 2.6 | 4.4 | −0.5[b] |
| 2,3-Dimethylbutane | 2.4 | — | −1.0[b] |
| 2,2-Dimethylpentane | —[a] | —[a] | —[a] |
| 2,3-Dimethylpentane | —[a] | —[a] | —[a] |
| 2,2,3-Trimethylbutane | 2.9 | 3.7 | −1.1[b] |
| 2,2,4-Trimethylpentane | 3.3 | 3.4 | −0.4 |
| 2,2,4,4-Tetramethylpentane | 4.0 | — | −0.85 |
| Cycloparaffins |  |  |  |
| Cyclopentane | 2.4 | 2.2 | −0.5 |
| Methylcyclopentane | 2.9 | — | −0.7 |
| Cyclohexane | 3.0 | — | −1.2[b] |
| Methylcyclohexane | 2.9 | — | −0.4 |
| Isopropylcyclohexane | 4.1 | 1.5 | −0.3 |

[a] No adduct formed down to 0°C.
[b] Extrapolated figures.

Comparison of the equilibrium constants in Table X with those of urea adducts in Table IX indicates that the thiourea complexes are much less stable. Their equilibrium constants are roughly comparable to the urea–n-nonane adduct. No thiourea adducts are known which are as stable as the urea adducts of long chain n-paraffins such as cetane. It is obvious from the data in Table X that there are no simple relations between structure or molecular weight of the reactant and stability of the adduct. In a series of isoparaffins, for example, an increase in chain length with a constant degree of branching results in a less stable complex (cf. dimethylbutanes with dimethylpentanes or the trimethylbutane with a trimethylpentane). Compact molecules like cyclohexane and 2,2,4,4-trimethylpentane form the most stable adducts. The difference in stability between a 2,2- and a 2,3-structure is remarkable as is the effect of introducing a methyl group into a cyclopentane and a cyclohexane molecule.

No simple equations have been devised to describe the relation between equilibrium constants, heat of formation, and molal ratio for thiourea adducts. In general, the lower stability of thiourea adducts combined with the fact that the temperature coefficient of the equilibrium constant is also low (requiring a greater difference in temperature between the formation and the decomposition steps) makes thiourea a much less favorable agent for adductive crystallization than urea.

## III. Analysis of Possible Processing Schemes

Crystallization processes (including adductive crystallization) have much in common with other separation techniques although they do have distinct differences, for example,

1. In many (although not all) crystallizations it is theoretically possible to achieve 100% purity in a single stage.

2. However, crystallization processes are characterized by exceedingly low stage efficiencies resulting from the difficulty of clean-cut separation of solid and liquid phases.

TABLE XI
Techniques for Applying Separation Processes

| Technique | Relative flow of phases | Examples |
|---|---|---|
| Differential | Separated as soon as formed | Batch distillation, wax "sweating" |
| Equilibrium | Concurrently until separated | Flash distillation |
| Chromatographic | One phase stationary; other flows past it | Gas–liquid chromatography |
| Zone refining | Neither phase moves—heat source is moved | Zone melting Zone freezing |
| Countercurrent | Phases flow in opposite direction | Simple extraction |
| Countercurrent with reflux | Portion of purified product returned to process and flows countercurrently to one phase | Fractionation |

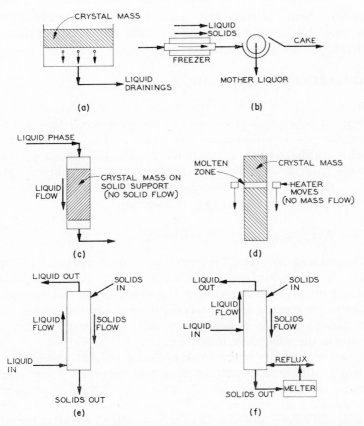

Fig. 9. Usual techniques which can be applied to carrying out most separation processes (whether vapor–liquid, liquid–liquid, or solid–liquid). Distinction by relative flow of phases is shown: (a) differential (b) equilibrium (c) chromatographic (d) zone refining (e) countercurrent (f) countercurrent with reflux.

3. Mechanical handling techniques are all-important.

4. Mass transfer rates involving solid phases are frequently much lower than in separation processes in which only liquid and gas phases are handled.

In spite of these differences it is desirable to consider the applicability to adductive crystallization of the usual techniques of conducting separation processes. Table XI lists the usual approaches to carrying out separations. Figure 9 shows the schematic differences between them, particularly with reference to crystallization processes. All could be applied to adductive crystallization and each might have merit in certain cases.

## A. DIFFERENTIAL APPROACH

In the simplest method the newly formed phase is removed, increment by increment, as soon as it is produced. This technique is usually called "differential" (see Fig. 9a). Just as differential (or batch) distillation can be used where it is desired to separate a volatile from a virtually nonvolatile material, a differential approach to crystallization processes is particularly applicable where the solid phase is practically a pure material.

### 1. Examples from Ordinary Crystallization

The old wax "sweating" process is an example. A batch of impure wax in flat pans is gradually heated and the liquid phase allowed to drain off as soon as formed. The drainings are of successively higher melting point as the process proceeds and can be segregated into various cuts as desired. Eventually a virtually oil-free wax remains as the solid phase in the sweater.

A better example is the work of Aston (42,43) and co-workers in which differential melting of a bed of crystals was used to separate cis- and trans-butene-2. A yield of 99.99% pure butene-2 was obtained amounting to 70% of that which is theoretically possible. Of course, differential processes suffer from all of the added costs associated with batch operations.

### 2. Applicability to Adductive Crystallization

The author knows of no attempts to apply differential melting to adductive crystallization. In cases where urea adducts or solid compounds were being used for small-scale preparative work, a technique similar to Aston's might prove very valuable. Particularly in cases where high purities were required, differential melting of a bed of crystals might be a preferred approach to the problem.

There is another possible differential process, i.e., differential freezing. Mechanical difficulty of separating the crystals, increment by increment, makes this process unattractive, just as differential condensation is of little interest in comparison with differential distillation.

## B. EQUILIBRIUM PROCESS

Instead of removing the new phase as fast as it is formed, the two phases can be kept in intimate contact (usually flowing concurrently) until formation of the second phase is complete (see Fig. 9b). This approach is used in flash distillation and is the most common method of conducting ordinary crystallization processes. The feed stock is chilled until the crystallization is complete. Then the mixture is fed to a settler, filter, or centrifuge for phase separation.

### 1. Usefulness for Adductive Crystallization

This technique should suffice for many adductive crystallizations where the solid phase theoretically contains nothing but the extraneous agent and the desired pure product. However, occlusion of mother liquor makes the phase separation barely 35% efficient. Washing techniques are thus necessary and result in added cost for solvent circulation. Those few adductive crystallization plants which have been built to date use an equilibrium process.

Of course the equilibrium approach is inapplicable if solid solutions are encountered. Both phases would contain some of every component capable of entering the solid solution.

## C. CHROMATOGRAPHIC SCHEME

A newer scheme for carrying out separation processes is the more unusual one in which the heavier phase is kept stationary while the lighter phase is moved past it (see Fig. 9c). Such processes have been labelled "chromatographic" and are covered in detail in Chapter 2 of this book.

### 1. Examples from the Crystallization Art

Crystallization has been used (44) in the difficult art of separating plastics into fractions of different molecular weight. This is a case where the components form solid solutions with one another. The chromatographic technique gives sharp separations. It is apparent that, as is the case with the gas–liquid chromatographic technique, a multistage separation is achieved in chromatographic crystallization. Hence it should prove a powerful approach to separation by crystallization, adductive or otherwise, where solid solutions are encountered.

## 2. Application to Adductive Crystallization

Although chromatographic crystallization is a useful tool in research, and may be of use in small-scale preparative work, it would prove an expensive expedient in commercial operations. Circulation of large volumes of solvent is required. Moreover, it is necessary gradually to change the composition of a mixture of two solvents (one a good and the other a poor solvent) or to increase the temperature of the circulating solvent slowly. Either method is expensive in terms of energy. Hence it is unlikely that chromatographic crystallization will prove to be a suitable means of preparing large quantities of pure products at a low price.

## D. ZONE REFINING TECHNIQUE

Pfann (45) recently introduced the pioneering idea of operating in such a manner that neither the heavier nor the lighter phase is deliberately moved. Instead, the source of heat is moved. Thus molten zones are caused to move along a bar of solid. The liquid phase itself does not move as a mass, since the only motion results from complete freezing of the back end of the molten zone and complete melting of the solid ahead of the zone (see Fig. 9d).

## 1. Efficiency in Applications on Molecular Crystals

Zone refining is discussed in detail in Chapter 3 of this book. Its main application has been to metals and high-melting inorganic materials. Small-scale experiments have been made also on organic substances. Sorensen (46) recently reported studies of the efficiency of zone melting for purifying phenolic compounds. Computations of zone refining are usually made in terms of a partition coefficient $K$ where:

$$K = C_s/C_m$$

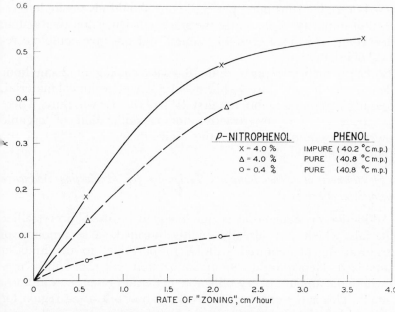

Fig. 10. Partition coefficients ($K$) for zone refining of molecular crystals ($p$-nitrophenol) showing that $K$ approaches zero when rate of zone movement is decreased. Thus the stage efficiency of each zone at finite rates of zone movement is very low. (Zero $K$ corresponds to complete removal of impurity in one stage whereas $K$ of one corresponds to no separation of components.)

where $C_s$ is concentration of impurity in solid; $C_m$ is concentration of impurity in melt; and $K$ is usually less than one. The coefficient $K$ is not a constant. Sorensen found that it varied with (a) the speed of "zoning," (b) the amount of impurity present, and (c) the presence of other impurities. Figure 10 shows a part of Sorensen's results. The lower the value of $K$ the fewer zone passes are required to accomplish the desired purification. If $K$ is 1.0 no purification is possible, even with an infinite number of zones. If $K$ is zero, one stage would be sufficient. Let us define an ideal $K$ as the partition coefficient under ideal conditions where perfect crystals are formed with no occlusion of mother liquor. The ideal $K$ should be approached as the rate of "zoning" approaches zero. The data of Figure 10, although not conclusive, suggest that the ideal $K$ for this system is zero; i.e., $p$-nitrophenol is completely insoluble in phenol crystals. Thus one "perfect" zone should give complete removal of impurity. Apparently the stage efficiency for this system is less than 10% since even 14 "zones" did not give complete removal of impurities.

Sorensen further reports that 18 zones passing at 2 cm/hour failed to produce any pure 4-chloro-*o*-cresol from technical material. It required 50 passes before the first 25% of the bar was pure. These low efficiencies are unattractive for crystallization of organic materials in comparison with the high efficiencies (70%) of the differential method (43).

*2. Effectiveness of Zone Refining Technique for Conducting Adductive Crystallization Processes*

Adductive crystallization is not likely to be used to crystallize materials which are already highly purified. The amount of extraneous agent required will be proportional to the amount crystallized. Hence adductive crystallization will prove most useful where the amount of crystallizable material present in a mixture is small. This is the exact opposite of the best operating region for zone melting. It appears likely that other techniques will prove more useful in most cases of adductive crystallization than will zone melting.

### E. COUNTERCURRENT SCHEME

In simple countercurrent extraction, for example, two immiscible liquid phases are passed countercurrently to each other, in a multistage tower (see Fig. 9e). A countercurrent adductive crystallization process might be imagined in which an adduct "host," for example, would flow down a tower in which a liquid containing the "guest" component was flowing upward. This is essentially similar to the process using solid solutions shown in Figure 3. The mechanical problems attendant upon introducing a solid material to and removing it from a column filled with liquid, make such a process less attractive. Also rates of mass transfer would probably be low and the size of the tower would have to be large.

### F. COUNTERCURRENT PROCESS WITH REFLUX

Arnold (47) invented a crystallization process using a countercurrent column. Crystals can be formed within the column, passed countercurrently with respect to a liquid phase to the end of the column, and melted within the column. A portion of the melt can be returned as reflux countercurrent to the crystals. The remainder can be removed in the liquid phase as product. One embodiment of this process is the Phillips $p$-xylene process (48). Such a process has several attractive features as a means for carrying out adductive crystallization. Findlay and Weedman (49) described a continuous countercurrent process recovering normal paraffins with urea adducts.

### 1. Description of the Phillips Countercurrent Column Process

Figure 11 is a simplified sketch of the Phillips countercurrent crystallization process using a method of operation invented by R. W. Thomas (50). Feed enters a scraped-surface chiller in which crystals are formed. The liquid and solid phase flow concurrently

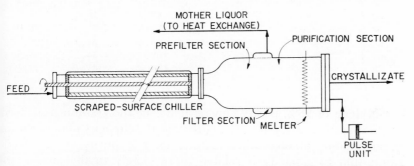

Fig. 11. Phillips countercurrent column process for purification by crystallization showing one method of operation using a pulse of frequency between 100 and 250 cycles per minute.

until they reach the filter section of a column which is connected to the end of the chiller. At this point mother liquor is removed and the crystal mass proceeds onward through the column, in which it is subjected to a pulse of suitable frequency (between 100 and 250 cycles per minute). At the end of the column the crystal mass is melted and a portion is removed as product. The remainder is forced back into the interstices of the crystal mass. High purity, warm liquid refreezes in the crystal mass as it encounters on-coming, cold crystals. This interchange results in a product of

very high purity. The small size of the equipment is noteworthy
In a pilot-plant unit, two 4-inch diameter by 8-foot chillers in series
fed a 6-inch diameter column approximately 5 feet long. The
column had a 24-inch-long prefilter section, an $11^5/_8$-inch filter
section, and an 11-inch purification section. Since the operation of
this type of equipment is less familar to the average reader than the
more usual methods of conducting ordinary crystallizations, typical
operating data from this pilot plant are given in Table XII.

### TABLE XII
Operation of Phillips Countercurrent Column Process

| Feed composition, wt. % p-xylene | Temperature, °F | | Maximum feed rate, gal/hr | Product | |
|---|---|---|---|---|---|
| | Chiller outlet | Column bottom | | Rate, gal/hr | Purity, wt. % p-xylene |
| 36.9 | −66 | +77 | 12.3 | 4.2 | 98.4 |
| 50.8 | −34 | 78 | 48.0 | 16.6 | 98.0 |
| 58.5 | −6 | 78 | 83.3 | 27.3 | 98.0 |
| 64.3 | +7 | 76 | 95.2 | 31.3 | 97.9 |
| 69.4 | 17 | 74 | 109.9 | 34.2 | 98.5 |
| 78.4 | 28 | 76 | 128.4 | 41.7 | 98.0 |

p-Xylene of 98% purity can be made in the column from feed
stocks ranging from 37 to 78%. However, the capacity of the column
is dependent, among other factors, on the purity of the feed
Limitation to capacity is related more closely to the amount of
internal freezing within the bed (which depends on the heat balance
over the operation) than to any other factor. The maximum product
rates are high, however, ranging from 4 to 40 gallons per hour
In comparison, a 6-inch packed fractionator operating at 10:1
reflux ratio would be expected to produce 3 to 4 gallons per hour
of overhead product.

### 2. Applicability to Adductive Crystallization.

A similar operation would be possible for many types of adductive
crystallizations. At the present stage of development it is not possible to predict the performance of this new equipment on untried
mixtures. Much depends on the type of crystal formed. Large

 card, chunky crystals give good operation. Small, soft, "buttery" crystals may be more difficult to handle. However, the Phillips continuous, countercurrent, crystallization process, if applicable, would make possible high purities in adductive crystallization processes without washing, repulping or other expedients. Bench-scale methods for testing this process on new systems were described recently in an article by McKay, Dale, and Weedman (51).

In cases where solid solutions are encountered, the rates of mass transfer are slow. However, it has been found possible to obtain the effect of several stages of crystallization by special techniques. K. H. Hachmuth (52) invented a process and apparatus whereby a cycle of alternating high pressure and low pressure is imposed on the column. Using a 30-second application of 1700 psi pressure, followed by 30 seconds of low pressure, more than three perfect stages of crystallization were obtained in a 7-foot-long column.

## IV. Engineering Economics of Adductive Crystallization

The cost of carrying out a separation step is composed of a number of elements, the most important of which are:

1. The cost of the solvents or other extraneous agents lost in processing.
2. The energy (steam, electricity, etc.) required.
3. Labor costs.
4. Depreciation and amortization of the equipment used.

It is normally found that ordinary distillation is by far the most economical for any separation to which it is applicable at all. The reason for this is that distillation entails no costs at all under the first and only nominal charges under the third headings above. No extraneous materials are needed, and fractionators can be instrumented to such an extent that they require practically no attention. Extractive or azeotropic distillation and liquid–liquid extraction require solvents and, hence, are more expensive although labor costs are equally low. They are normally used only in cases where ordinary distillation is impossible because of close volatility of the components.

Crystallization processes are variable in their costs. In many cases crystallization proves to be a high-cost process under all the headings above. Solvents are often used. Refrigeration, if required, is a most expensive form of energy. Labor costs are high because of problems of solids handling. Centrifuges, filters, and other necessary equipment are costly and, as a result, amortization charges will be steep. Only in special cases can crystallization be a cheap process, e.g., where the solvent is water (and hence expendable) and solar energy can be used free of charge. However, in most cases classified as adductive crystallization, such special circumstances will not pertain. In fact, in some cases (e.g., urea adduction) two extraneous materials must be used, i.e., the host agent and a solvent.

To the extent that any choice is possible, there are a number of characteristics which must be considered in choosing an extraneous agent. Many of these are identical with the classical requirements for a solvent suitable for extraction.

## A.  CHOICE OF EXTRANEOUS AGENTS

**Recoverability.**  An adductive crystallization process cannot be successful unless the extraneous agent can be readily separated both from the crystallizate and the mother liquor. Preferably it should be possible to separate the materials by distillation, since this is usually the most economical means. Thus, where possible, the relative volatility between the components of the feed stock and the extraneous agent must be high so that recovery will be inexpensive. In most cases it will be found that the ratio of agent circulated to feed volume will have to be high in order to effect separation. Hence it will normally be preferable to use a relatively low-volatility agent to avoid the cost of distilling the large volumes of extraneous agent overhead in a fractionator.

Other possible means of separating the extraneous agent from the products are extraction (preferably with water) and possibly adsorption.

**Chemical Reactivity and Stability.**  The extraneous agent must not enter into undesirable chemical reactions with the mixture to be separated. Also it should not decompose or polymerize at an appreciable rate at the highest temperatures encountered in the process. Otherwise losses will be high.

**Corrosiveness.**  A corrosive material will increase the cost of the plant. It will be necessary to use expensive alloys to resist attack.

**Viscosity.**   A low viscosity is desirable if the adductive agent is to be handled as a liquid at certain stages of the process. Pumping, heat exchange, etc., are all made easier if low-viscosity liquids are used.

**Volatility.**   Although not a determining factor, it is desirable to use materials of low volatility. This results in decreasing losses in handling and storage and may lower the cost of equipment by making it possible to design for lower operating pressure. Also, as pointed out above, recovery fractionators will be smaller if the relatively smaller amounts of products are taken overhead.

**Flammability.**   The investment required for the plant may be appreciably affected by flammability of the extraneous agent. Special precautions and equipment (such as inert gas generators) may have to be provided if it is necessary to handle material of very low flash point.

**Toxicity.**   Poisonous materials can be used safely if adequate allowance is made in the design and if proper safety precautions are taken in operation. However, the use of toxic agents will tend toward a more expensive plant and more costly operations.

**Cost.**   It is inevitable that there will be operating losses of any material circulated in the plant.   Hence, it is desirable to use an extraneous agent which is not too expensive.

**Characteristics of Crystals.**   The size, shape, and hardness of the crystals formed when the complex or solid solution of the agent and the product precipitates are of utmost importance. If it is decided to use the conventional equilibrium or concurrent approach, it is essential to have crystals which filter and wash freely and which occlude a minimum amount of mother liquor. Even if one of the newer techniques such as the Phillips countercurrent column is used, the type of crystals formed, although not quite as decisive, is still important. Soft, "buttery" crystals are relatively difficult to handle.

**Favorable Phase Relationships.**   The chosen agent should form a solid solution, solid addition compound, clathrate, or adduct with one of the desired products in a selective manner. Otherwise an inordinate number of processing stages will be required. Likewise, the composition of the compounds, clathrates, or adducts is important. For example, in the gas hydrates of propane and larger molecules, 136 molecules of water combine with 8 molecules of the guest. Although water is cheap, the cost of refrigerating, melting, and circulating such large quantities of material would be high.

**Summary of Characteristics.** Despite the wide range of possible extraneous agents, it is not easy to locate one which is suitable on all counts. In particular, many of the clathrate formers are expensive materials. Frequently the clathrates or adducts are formed as fluffy, bulky crystal masses which occlude large volumes of mother liquor. Much of the advantage of adductive crystallization may be lost in incomplete separation of the phases.

B. ENERGY CONSIDERATIONS

Meaningful generalizations about energy loads are difficult. It requires a complete and detailed study of each individual case to evaluate this factor. However, it is well to realize that adductive crystallization requires transfer of relatively large amounts of energy.

*1. Example of n-Paraffin Crystallization*

Table **XIII** contains a comparison of the heat quantities involved in considering processes for recovery of cetane (normal hexadecane) from a kerosene fraction. It will be observed that the latent heat of freezing of cetane is 101 BTU per pound. This would be of importance if cetane were made by ordinary crystallization. If the same material were to be recovered by adductive crystallization using urea, it would be necessary to supply the latent heat of formation of the adduct, i.e., 181 BTU per pound of cetane.

TABLE XIII

Energy Comparison for Ordinary and Adductive Crystallization Recovery of Cetane

|  | Ordinary | Adductive |
|---|---|---|
| Latent heat of fusion, Btu./lb. cetane | 101 |  |
| Heat of formation, Btu./lb. cetane |  | 181 |
| Solvent circulation, lb./lb. cetane |  |  |
|     Hydrocarbon solvent (ketone, methylene chloride) | 0 | 10 |
|     Urea solvent (water) | 0 | 10 |
| Estimated heat to vaporize hydrocarbon solvent Btu./lb. cetane |  | 4000–8000 |

Additionally, as Table XIII indicates, the adductive crystalliza-tion process uses two solvents. The recovery of the hydrocarbon solvent for recirculation requires additional heat as well as elec-tricity to operate the circulating pumps and cooling water for con-densers.

On the other hand, the recovery of cetane (f.p. 64.7°F) by ordi-nary crystallization would require refrigeration. The temperature level at which refrigeration would be required will depend on the concentration of cetane in the feed stream. If the feed stream is relatively dilute in the crystallizable component, low-level refrigera-tion, which is correspondingly more expensive, would be needed.

## 2. Favorable Case for Adductive Crystallization

Obviously a detailed study would be needed to balance out these factors. Adductive crystallization is favored for dilute feeds since the quantity of circulating extraneous agent is proportional to the crystallizable material, not to the total amount of the feed. In fact, adductive crystallization proves most economical where it is desired to purify a material by removing from it a small portion of "adductable" impurity. Thus the only commercial uses of this process to date have been in dewaxing lubricating oils. In fact, Standard Oil of Indiana (53) found it more economical to remove the bulk of the wax by conventional dewaxing methods (actually an extractive crystallization) down to a pour point of 0°F, then use adductive crystallization with urea to remove the last traces of wax. The advantage of urea dewaxing lies in avoiding deep refrigeration to −50°F.

## C. REACTION RATE AND MASS TRANSFER

Since adductive crystallization processes involve the solid phase, mass transfer rates are frequently lower than is common experience with systems including only liquids and gases. Additionally, there may be a rate of reaction involved as well as a diffusion rate. Little information is available, partly because the field is so new.

## 1. Solid Solutions

Fink, Cines, Frey, and Aston (16) recorded times to reach equilibrium ranging from 10 to 40 minutes for equilibrating solid-solution systems of 2,2-dimethylbutane and 2,3-dimethylbutane. They observed that the time required was roughly proportional to the difference in composition between the phases. These operations were in a temperature range from $-100$ to $-130\,°F$. Under different conditions such changes can be much faster. Observations were made during pilot-plant operation of the Hachmuth crystallization column (52) at Phillips Petroleum Company Laboratories when processing a methylcyclopentane–cyclohexane mixture. When the hydrostatic pressure on the column was dropped from 1700 psi to a low value, it remained low for 10–20 seconds and then rise spontaneously as melting of a portion of the crystals took place.

## 2. Clathrate Compounds

Formation of clathrates requires relatively long times under certain conditions. For example, in making the hydroquinone clathrates of the rare gases, the percentage of voids which are actually filled is proportional to the pressure of the gas and inversely related to the rate of cooling. At low pressures and high rates of crystallization, the solid phase is pure $\alpha$-hydroquinone. No clathration occurs. Evans and Richards (54) report the following conditions required for the argon–hydroquinone clathrate:

Voids 14% filled: 15 atm argon, 12 hours cooling

Voids 63% filled: 40 atm argon, several days cooling

It requires a matter of months to approach complete filling of the voids.

Not all clathrate systems require such low rates of crystallization. Those formed from liquid systems where components are completely miscible are more rapid. Schaeffer et al. (34) report that reaction times of 5 minutes sufficed to complete the reaction between tetra-(4-methylpyridine)nickel dithiocyanate and p-xylene.

## 3. Adducts

The rate of formation of urea adducts is also reasonably fast. Contact times from a few minutes to 1 hour are required to carry out the reaction, the time increasing with the molecular weight of the guest compound. Rates are also affected by various other factors.

A mutual solvent such as methanol can be used to increase the concentration of urea in the liquid phase and speed up the reaction. It would be necessary to determine rate data for any proposed new process.

It is apparent from the above considerations that rate phenomena will have a large effect on the size and cost of equipment for adductive crystallization.

## D. PROBLEMS OF SOLIDS HANDLING

Another factor having a pronounced effect on plant investment is the size and cost of solids-handling equipment. As a single example, processes utilizing gas-hydrate formation to recover fresh water from the ocean have been devised. This type of process has many attractive features. It is desirable to use an appropriate "guest" component which forms a clathrate compound with water at or near normal ocean temperatures, thus avoiding heating or cooling the bulk of the sea water handled. Separation and decomposition of the clathrate compound gives pure water with minimum energy consumption. Unfortunately, clathrate crystals are highly porous and act much like a sponge. In an ordinary filtration step the crystal bed occludes so much mother liquor that the decrease in salt content is nominal. Therefore, improved techniques are desirable.

### 1. Simple Equilibrium Process

If it is intended to develop an adductive crystallization process using a simple equilibrium approach (crystallization followed by phase separation) careful study of the various types of filters and centrifuges is desirable. Preliminary test work on a bench scale using a filter leaf and a laboratory centrifuge will supply data permitting rough sizing of equipment. Such techniques have been described in the literature (4,55). It will usually be found useful to consult one or more of the manufacturers of suitable equipment during the development phase. Their wide experience in scale-up of such equipment can be useful when planning a laboratory or pilot plant program.

### 2. Countercurrent Column with Reflux

In many cases it may be advantageous to consider a countercurrent process with reflux. Such an approach may be fruitful even though theoretically only a single equilibrium stage is needed. The refluxing action produces the effect of virtually complete removal of mother liquor. As a result, the Phillips continuous column approaches 100% stage efficiency under favorable circumstances. In contrast, centrifuges and filters are notably inefficient. As is the case in any process in which solids handling takes place, predictions are difficult. However, simple laboratory tests (51) will give valuable data to predict applicability.

## E. ECONOMICS OF UREA ADDUCTION

In general, adductive crystallization is not a cheap separation process. Table XIV summarizes the economics of one adductive crystallization process as depicted by Rogers *et al.* of Standard of Indiana (56). A plant handling 1000 barrels per day of oil (309,000 pounds per day) was estimated to cost $850,000. However, the oil contained only 7% adductable material, i.e., 21,600 pounds

TABLE XIV
Economics of Urea Adductive Dewaxing

| Plant investment | $850,000 (1957 figures) | | |
|---|---|---|---|
| Plant capacity | | | |
| Feedstock viscosity, SSU at 100°F | 50 | 80 | 220 |
| Feed capacity, barrels/stream day | 900 | 1000 | 1200 |
| Dewaxed oil yield, vol. % | 85 | 86 | 94 |
| Minimum pour point, °F | −63 | −48 | −17 |

| | Operating costs, cents/gal. dewaxed oil | |
|---|---|---|
| | Urea adductive dewaxing (to low pour) | Solvent (extractive) dewaxing (to medium pour) |
| Labor | 0.6 | 0.6 |
| Maintenance | 0.7 | 0.3 |
| Utilities | 0.8 | 1.1 |
| Chemicals and solvents | 0.1 | 0.1 |
| Total direct costs | 2.2 | 2.1 |

per day or approximately 7.5 million pounds per year. Thus, if this process were considered for recovery of the adductable portion as a chemical intermediate (rather than for removing 7% undesired wax from a lubricating oil), the capital investment would appear rather high. However, it would not be prohibitive if the chemical intermediate to be produced commanded a good price. For example, if it sold for 11.5 cents per pound, the annual gross income would be approximately equal to plant investment.

Operating costs were estimated at 2.2 cents per gallon of product. According to Rogers and his co-workers, these costs are of the same order of magnitude as the cost of operating a regular solvent dewaxing plant to make a medium-pour oil, a typical extractive crystallization process. Thus, the cost of adductive crystallization is, in this case, about the same as the cost of extractive crystallization. For orientation purposes it should be noted that the cost of operating a typical, moderately difficult fractional distillation step in a large plant where many other operations could be handled by the same crew would be of the order of one-third of these figures.

Furthermore, if the adductable material (7% of feed) were the valuable product the cost of operating this adductive crystallization process would be of the order of 30–35 cents per gallon or about 5–6 cents per pound. These figures, of course, do not include feed stock costs, amortization of equipment, overhead costs, etc.

It should not be concluded that the above costs apply widely to extractive crystallization. The size of the plant is an important factor. Plants producing larger amounts of product than $7^1/_2$ million pounds per year would be more economical. If 50 million pounds per year of a chemical intermediate could be sold, it might be possible to decrease costs appreciably. Of course, adductive crystallization processes using extraneous agents other than urea would be governed by a different set of economics and might be more or less expensive.

## V. Adductive Crystallization Processes

Although many adductive crystallization processes have been proposed, apparently the only ones in large-scale commercial operation are urea-adductive dewaxing processes for manufacture of oils having exceptionally low pour points.

## A. LUBRICATING OIL DEWAXING PLANTS

Three commercial plants have been described in the literature:

### 1. Deutsche-Erdol Plant, Heide, West Germany

Hoppe and Franz (57,58) described the process used by Deutsche-Erdol AG A flow diagram of the process is given in Figure 12.

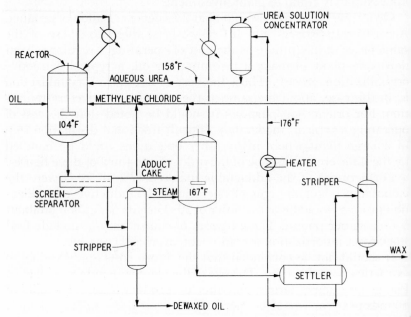

Fig. 12. Flow diagram of Deutsche-Erdol process for dewaxing mineral oil using adductive crystallization with urea. Methylene chloride serves as both internal refrigerant and activator.

Methylene chloride is used as a combined solvent and internal coolant since it boils at 104 °F which is about the desired reaction temperature. The urea is handled as an aqueous solution.

The process operates on a batch basis. A stirred reactor is charged with 100 parts of the oil to be dewaxed, 100 parts methylene chloride, and 100 parts aqueous urea. The latter is a solution saturated at 158 °F in order to carry sufficient urea into the system. Reaction heat is removed by allowing the methylene chloride to boil. The methylene chloride is condensed and returned to the reactor. Under these conditions the adduct is agglomerated into coarse globules about $^3/_8$ inch in diameter, with little or no oil remaining inside the particles.

When the reaction is complete the contents are fed to a screen separator to remove the globules of adduct from the solution of oil. Filters or centrifuges are unnecessary because of the physical form of the adduct. The adduct is not washed or deoiled in any way since it is not desired to produce purified wax. The solution of dewaxed oil is fed to a stripper to recover methylene chloride for recycle to the reactor.

Adduct is pumped to a second stirred reactor along with water and is heated rapidly to 167°F with open steam. It is essential to keep the temperature and contact time both as low as possible since urea tends to decompose. This is the main reason urea is used in aqueous solution. A small amount of methylene chloride is vaporized in this reactor.

When decomposition is complete the material is pumped to a settler where the mixture separates into an aqueous urea phase and a molten wax phase. The wax is stripped of the remaining methylene chloride. Urea solution is heated to about 176°F and pumped into a stripper where excess water is removed, bringing the solution back to a condition of saturation at 158°F.

Typical inspection tests on feed and products are given in Table XV. The wax contains 50% oil since no washing step is used to purify the adduct cake. This process is operated under patents of the Badische Anilin- und Soda-Fabrik AG.

TABLE XV
Deutsche-Erdol Urea Adductive Dewaxing

| | Feed | Oil | Wax |
|---|---|---|---|
| Yield, wt. % | 100 | 75 | 25 |
| *Inspection tests on feed and products* | | | |
| Density at 15°C, g/ml | 0.870 | 0.885 | — |
| Cloud point, °F | +59.0 | − 5.8 | — |
| Pour point, °F | +57.2 | −11.2 | — |
| Melting point, °F | — | — | +86 |
| Oil content, wt. % | — | — | 50[a] |

[a] Adduct cake was not washed or deoiled.

### 2. L. Sonneborn Plant, Petrolia, Pennsylvania

Sonneborn is reported (59) to be using urea adductive crystallization for the manufacture of white oils having exceptionally low
pour points. Urea is used in methanol solution in this plant. Further
details are not available.

### 3. Standard Oil Co. of Indiana Plant, Whiting, Indiana

Rogers and co-workers (56) described the process used by
Standard of Indiana. They concluded that urea adductive crystallization was not competitive with ordinary solvent dewaxing for
removing the easily removed, higher melting wax. Thus, they went
to a two-step process in which they dewaxed by conventional means
to a pour point of 0 °F, then applied urea. The adductive crystallization portion of the Standard of Indiana plant was disclosed as
shown in Figure 13.

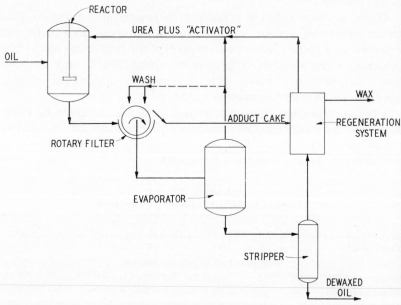

Fig. 13. Flow diagram of Standard Oil Co. of Indiana process for making
exceptionally low-pour oils by adductive crystallization with urea.  Bulk of the
wax is removed first by ordinary dewaxing (an extractive crystallization) which
was found more economical in this case.

Urea is used with an undisclosed activator or solvent and is contacted with the oil in a stirred reactor. Reactor effluent flows to a conventional rotary filter on which the adduct cake is washed to remove occluded oil. Dewaxed oil is freed of solvent in an evaporator followed by a stripper. The adduct cake is decomposed in an unspecified regeneration system.

Inspection tests on feed streams and products are given in Table XVI. The pour point which can be achieved depends on the type of feed. For higher viscosity feeds, it is not possible to reach very low pour points because the heavier oils contain material which has a high freezing point but is not adductable. Waxes produced by this process have low melting points and high viscosity indices.

TABLE XVI
Standard of Indiana Urea Adductive Dewaxing

| | Feedstock | | | | | | | | |
| | 50 SSU at 100°F 10% adductable | | | 80 SSU at 100°F 7% adductable | | | 220 SSU at 100°F 4% adductable | | |
| | Feed | Oil | Wax | Feed | Oil | Wax | Feed | Oil | Wax |
| --- | --- | --- | --- | --- | --- | --- | --- | --- | --- |
| | *Inspection Tests on Feed and Products* | | | | | | | | |
| Gravity, °API | 30.5 | 29.0 | 46.4 | 28.6 | 26.9 | 43.0 | 26.0 | 25.6 | 40.8 |
| Pour point, °F | 15 | −55 | +75 | 35 | −40 | +60 | 0 | −25 | +80 |
| Viscosity, SSU | | | | | | | | | |
| At 100°F | 59 | 64 | 44 | 82 | 92 | 55 | 229 | 246 | 68 |
| At 210°F | 35 | 35 | 32 | 37 | 38 | 35 | 51 | 47 | 38 |
| Viscosity index | 78 | 69 | 139 | 75 | 61 | 158 | 66 | 64 | 167 |

## B. $p$-XYLENE MANUFACTURE

Egan and Luthy (23) of California Research Corporation propose an extractive crystallization process using carbon tetrachloride to make possible higher recoveries of this material than would normally be permitted by the eutectic. Their adductive crystallization process is shown in Figure 14. The general similarity with processes using urea is obvious although they propose two centrifuge steps in order to attain efficient washing of the crystal cake ($p$-$C_6H_4$-

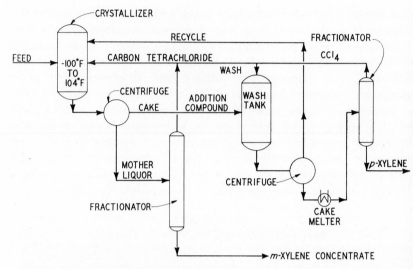

Fig. 14. Flow diagram of California Research Corporation process for producing p-xylene by adductive crystallization making use of the molecular compound p-xylene–carbon tetrachloride.

$(CH_3)_2 \cdot CCl_4$ compound). This process has an economic advantage not enjoyed by urea adductive crystallization in that only one extraneous agent is needed. Offsetting this advantage is the fact that the process operates in the range of $-100\,°F$, requiring expensive deep refrigeration.

Egan and Luthy give no economic estimates. The author knows of no published information which indicates that such a plant has been built.

C. MISCELLANEOUS PROCESS

Several other adductive crystallization processes have been proposed or tried on a small scale. These include the following:

*1. Separation of Natural Gas Mixtures by Clathration with Water (Gas Hydrates)*

Hammerschmidt (60) demonstrated in 1936 that the constituents of natural gas could be separated by clathration with water. This process has apparently never been developed to a commercial scale.

Some of the problems would be (a) large quantities of water would have to be cooled and heated, (b) rate of formation is probably limited by low solubility of gases in water, and (c) mechanical handling problems. The separation factors would be expected to be related to the dissociation pressures of the clathrates. Apparently no appreciable selectivity is involved because the dissociation pressure for ethane, ethylene, and acetylene hydrates are 5.2, 5.5, and 5.7 atm, i.e., in the same order as their volatilities. There seems little likelihood, thus, of using gas hydrates to make those separations which are more difficult to make by ordinary vapor–liquid methods.

## 2. Separation of Optical Isomers

An unusual application of adductive crystallization was made by Newman and Powell (61) in the laboratory. Tri-o-thymotide, a condensation product of thymotic acid (2-hydroxy-6-methyl-3-isopropylbenzoic acid), has two enantiomorphs. These may be considered as related to one another in a manner similar to right-handed and left-handed three-bladed propellors. No means had been found to separate these isomers. It was found that trithymotide formed clathrate compounds with certain hydrocarbons such as benzene. X-ray studies showed that any one crystal could accomodate only one form of the trithymotide, i.e., all dextro or all levo. No distinguishing crystal faces were observed which would permit sorting of the crystals by hand into their two enantiomorphs. However, large crystals were grown (up to 1 g). Single crystals were dissolved in chloroform, and it was demonstrated that some rotated polarized light to the right, others to the left.

Although this procedure is not susceptible to commercialization, it does illustrate two interesting points: (1) it is equally as feasible to use adductive crystallization to separate the "host" as it is to separate the "guest" from other materials and (2) separation of components according to very minor differences in chemical structure is possible under certain circumstances.

## 3. Separation of m- and p-Cresols

Savitt and Othmer (62) carried out laboratory adductive crystallization of p-cresol using benzidine as an extraneous agent. Their

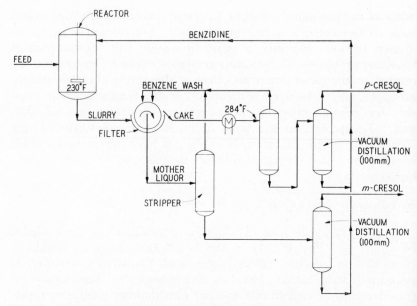

Fig. 15. Flow diagram of adductive crystallization process to separate *m*- and *p*-cresols using the molecular compound *p*-cresol–benzidine.

process is similar to others already described except that, although they used no solvent in the reaction step, they used benzene to wash the crystal cake on the filter. Distillation was used to separate mother liquor and filter cake into the end products and recover benzene wash solvent and benzidene. On the laboratory scale 98% *p*-cresol and 99% *m*-cresol were made. Figure 15 is a flow diagram for this process which is the solution, by adductive crystallization means, of the separation problem posed in the Introduction to this chapter.

### 4. Separating Hard Waxes from Flexible Waxes

Collier (63) describes the separation of different types of waxes by urea adductive crystallization. A wax made from a bright-stock cut from Middle East crude is dissolved in methyl isobutyl ketone saturated with water (2% water by volume). The resulting solution is stirred with solid urea (2 parts for each part wax). Contact time is 20 minutes at 160–170°F. The mixture is filtered and washed at reaction temperature with methylisobutyl ketone. The adduct cake is decomposed in boiling water.

Results are shown in Table XVII. The adductable wax is a high melting, hard, brittle wax suitable for an ingredient for polishes. The nonadducted wax is a flexible wax which is ideal for laminating and coating purposes. Specifications for the latter product are a nontacky wax, firm to the touch, with melting point above 140°F and a penetration less than 50.

TABLE XVII
Separating Hard Wax from Flexible Wax

| | Contact time, min. | | | | | |
|---|---|---|---|---|---|---|
| | 10 | | 20 | | 50 | |
| | Adductate | Mother liquor | Adductate | Mother liquor | Adductate | Mother liquor |
| Yields, wt. % | 10.5 | 89.5 | 24.3 | 75.7 | 25.6 | 74.4 |
| *Inspection tests on products* | | | | | | |
| Melting point, °F | 194 | 159 | 187 | 147 | 186 | 147 |
| Penetration at 77°F, 0.1mm | 4 | 36 | 5 | 46 | 9 | 49 |
| Flexibility, cycles at °C | 1 | 270 | 1 | 1000 | 1 | 1000 |

These data emphasize the possibilities of adductive crystallization for separating materials which might be completely adductable at lower temperatures. By proper choice of conditions, a selective adduction is achieved.

## VI. A Look into the Future

There are many features of adductive crystallization which are definitely challenging to the experimenter. A few of these are:

1. The theoretical possibility in some cases (common to all crystallizations involving a eutectic-type system) of making 100% pure product in a single stage.

2. Elimination of the costs and mechanical problems of low temperature refrigeration.

3. The separation of closely similar materials which can be purified in no other manner which is economically feasible.

4. The possibility of discovering highly selective "host" agents which will sort out molecules according to minor differences in shape.

These and other interesting avenues will continue to draw the attention of scientists and engineers to adductive crystallization. As a result of the ensuing research, many discoveries will be made. Of the hundreds of thousands of chemical compounds known, untold thousands may have such a crooked or bent shape that they will crystallize in the form of molecular-sized cages under suitable conditions. Thus, it may be expected that many new clathrate and adduct hosts will be discovered as time passes. Undoubtedly, some of these will have other properties making them useful as commercial agents for adductive crystallization.

Perhaps the most powerful processes will be a combination of adductive crystallization techniques with the countercurrent reflux principle of the Phillips crystallization process. This offers the possibility of bringing to reality the theoretical prospects of achieving exceptionally high purities in a single stage process.

One may picture the use of clathrate and adduct "hosts" in an adductive crystallization process as in some ways analogous to a modern "Maxwellian Demon." The new "demon" does not select the higher velocity molecules, however. It watches for and traps those of a certain definite shape and quickly removes them from the system. Of course, one does not get something for nothing. This selective removal requires moderately high energy consumption. However, it is safe to predict that much more will be heard about adductive crystallization in future.

## References

1. D. F. Othmer, S. A. Savitt, A. Krasner, A. M. Goldberg, and D. Markowitz, *Ind. Eng. Chem.*, **41,** 572 (1949).
2. D. R. Stevens, *Ind. Eng. Chem.*, **35,** 655 (1943).
3. M. R. Chivate and S. M. Shah, *Chem. Eng. Sci.*, **5,** 232 (1956).
4. R. A. Findlay and J. A. Weedman, Separation and Purification by Crystallization, in K. A. Kobe and J. J. McKetta, eds., *Advances in Petroleum Chemistry and Refining*, Vol. I. Interscience, New York–London, 1958, p. 119.
5. R. A. Findlay and D. L. McKay, *Chem. Eng. Symposium Ser. 55*, **No. 25,** 163 (1959).

6. K. H. Hachmuth, *Chem. Eng. Progr.*, **48**, 523, 570, 617 (1952).
7. R. A. Findlay and J. A. Weedman, ref. 4, p. 177.
8. M. R. Cines, Solid-Liquid Equilibria of Hydrocarbons, in A. Farkas, ed., *Physical Chemistry of Hydrocarbons*, Vol. I, Academic Press, New York, 1950, p. 315.
9. J. Smittenborg, H. Hoag, and R. A. Henkes, *J. Am. Chem. Soc.*, **60**, 17 (1938).
10. P. C. Carey and J. C. Smith, *J. Chem. Soc. (London)*, **1933**, 1348.
11. N. A. Nechitailo, *et al.*, *Doklady Akad. Nauk SSSR*, **116**, No. 4, 613 (1957).
12. N. A. Nechitailo, *et al.*, *Doklady Akad. Nauk SSSR*, **117**, No. 4, 629 (1957).
13. V. M. Kravchenko and I. S. Pastukhova, *Zhur. Priklad. Khim.*, **25**, 313 (1952).
14. V. M. Kravchenko and A. P. Eremenko, *Zhur. Priklad. Khim.*, **25**, 662 (1952).
15. V. M. Kravchenko, *Zhur. Priklad. Khim.*, **25**, 943 (1952).
16. H. L. Fink, M. R. Cines, F. E. Frey, and J. G. Aston, *J. Am. Chem. Soc.*, **69**, 1501 (1947).
17. S. L. Langdyk and W. C. Brezensinska Smithuysen, *Rec. trav. chim.*, **57**, 1050 (1938).
18. M. R. Cines, U. S. Patent 2,703,818 (March 8, 1955).
19. J. C. Phillips, *J. Chem. Soc. (London)*, **83**, 821, 1903.
20. M. R. Fenske, U. S. Patent 2,778,864 (Jan. 2, 1957).
21. A. C. Nixon and C. H. Deal, U. S. Patent 2,768,222 (Oct. 23, 1956).
22. A. C. Nixon and C. H. Deal, U. S. Patent 2,768,220 (Oct. 23, 1956).
23. C. J. Egan and R. V. Luthy, *Ind. Eng. Chem.*, **47**, 250 (1955).
24. T. Ehrlich, U. S. Patent 1,502,849 (July 29, 1924).
25. H. Schotte and H. Priewe, U. S. Patent 1,830,859 (Nov. 10, 1931).
26. F. E. Cislak and M. M. Otto, U. S. Patent 2,432,062 (Dec. 2, 1947).
27. F. E. Cislak and M. M. Otto, U. S. Patent 2,432,063 (Dec. 2, 1947).
28. T. S. Carswell, U. S. Patent 2,042,331 (May 26, 1936).
29. F. E. Cislak and M. M. Otto, U. S. Patent 2,432,064 (Dec. 2, 1947).
30. D. E. Bown, U. S. Patent 2,815,392 (Dec. 3, 1957).
31. D. E. Bown and W. O. Milligan, U. S. Patent 2,801,272 (July 30, 1957).
32. H. M. Powell, *J. Chem. Soc. (London)*, **1948**, 61.
33. L. Mandelcorn, *Chem. Rev.*, **59**, 827 (1959).
34. W. D. Schaeffer, W. S. Dorsey, D. H. Skinner, and C. G. Christian, *J. Am. Chem. Soc.*, **79**, 5871 (1957).
35. J. Milgrom, *J. Phys. Chem.*, **63**, 1843 (1959).
36. D. F. Evans, O. Ormrod, B. B. Goalby, and L. R. R. Stavely, *J. Chem. Soc. (London)*, **1950**, 3346.
37. F. V. Williams, *J. Am. Chem. Soc.*, **79**, 5876 (1957).
37a. J. H. van der Waals and J. C. Platteeuw, Clathrate Solutions, in I. Prigogine, ed., *Advances in Chemical Physics*, Vol. II, Interscience, New York–London, 1959.
38. H. Wieland and H. Sorge, *Z. Physik. Chem.*, **97**, 1 (1916).
39. K. A. Kobe and W. G. Domask, *Petrol. Refiner*, **31**, No. 3, 106, No. 5, 151, No. 7, 125 (1952).
40. D. F. R. Gilson and C. A. McDowell, *Nature*, **183**, 1183 (1959).
41. O. Redlich, C. M. Gable, A. K. Dunlop, and R. W. Millar, *J. Am. Chem. Soc.*, **72**, 4153 (1950).

42. J. G. Aston and S. V. R. Mastranglo, U. S. Patent 2,614,909 (Oct. 21, 1952).
43. J. G. Aston and R. E. Black, U. S. Patent 2,637,749 (May 5, 1953).
44. C. A. Baker and R. J. P. Williams, *J. Chem. Soc. (London)*, **1956,** 2352.
45. W. G. Pfann, U. S. Patents 2,739,045, 2,739,046 (March 20, 1956).
46. P. Sorensen, *Chem. & Ind.*, **1959,** 1593.
47. P. M. Arnold, U. S. Patent 2,540,977 (Feb. 6, 1951).
48. J. A. Weedman and R. A. Findlay, *Petrol. Refiner*, **37,** No. 11, 195 (1958).
49. R. A. Findlay and J. A. Weedman, U. S. Patent 2,676,167 (April 20, 1954).
50. R. W. Thomas, U. S. Patent 2,854,494 (Sept. 30, 1958).
51. D. L. McKay, G. H. Dale, and J. A. Weedman, *Ind. Eng. Chem.*, **52,** 197 (1960).
52. K. H. Hachmuth, U. S. Patent 2,764,878 (Oct. 2, 1956).
53. Anon., *Oil Gas J.*, **55,** No. 13, 74 (1957).
54. D. F. Evans and R. E. Richards, *Proc. Royal Soc. (London)*, **A223,** 238 (1954).
55. J. C. Smith, *Chem. Eng.*, **62,** No. 6, 175 (1955).
56. T. H. Rogers, J. S. Brown, R. Dickman, and G. D. Kerns, *Petrol. Refiner*, **36,** No. 5, 217 (1957).
57. A. Hoppe and H. Franz, *Erdol u. Kohle*, **8,** 411 (1955).
58. A. Hoppe and H. Franz, *Petrol. Refiner*, **36,** No. 5, 221 (1957).
59. Anon., *Chem. Eng.*, **36,** No. 11, 114 (1956).
60. E. G. Hammerschmidt, *Amer. Gas Assoc. Monthly*, **18,** 273 (1936).
61. A. C. D. Newman and H. M. Powell, *J. Chem. Soc. (London)*, **1953,** 3747.
62. S. A. Savitt and D. F. Othmer, *Ind. Eng. Chem.*, **44,** 2428 (1952).
63. A. Collier, U. S. Patent 2,921,012 (Jan. 12, 1960).

# 5

# FOAM SEPARATION

## Eliezer Rubin and Elmer L. Gaden, Jr.

### Contents

# I. Introduction

Although many methods are available for the separation of homogenous liquid mixtures, separation efficiencies drop rapidly as the concentration of the desired component falls. Ion exchange and selective adsorption techniques offered the first industrially practical answers to this problem, but these too have their limitations.

As technology develops, more and more situations arise where substances of high unit value are found in very low concentrations. Nuclear metallurgy and chemical technology are particularly notable examples for they involve special difficulties not previously encountered. Foam separation, a procedure old in principle but new in application, has great promise in these areas, yet no full discussion of its physical-chemical basis, operational procedures, and process design exists. The sections which follow are an attempt to fill this need.

The foam separation technique takes advantage of the tendency of surface active solutes to collect at the interface between solution and gas. This surface adsorption phenomenon is the basis for foam separation. Foaming simply provides the means for efficient generation and collection of gas–liquid interfaces.

When a solution containing surface active substances is foamed with an inert gas, the foam will be richer in these solutes than the residual liquid. This foam can then be collected and condensed to produce a rich liquid product. The similarity to distillation is obvious and has been exploited in establishing process design procedures.

Although there is a strong superficial similarity between foam separation and the froth flotation procedures long used in mineral processing, the two are entirely different in principle. Foam separation is used with true solutions—not with particle suspensions.

Foam separation has been recognized for a long time, and limited practical use has been made of it in the separation of naturally surface active substances. The salient feature of this technique is its particular effectiveness at low concentrations (the reasons for this will be put forward later). So long as the procedure was limited to materials which are naturally surface active, however, few situations arose where this special effectiveness could be used to advantage.

In 1957 it was found that metal ions could be separated and concentrated by foaming. This was done by adding to the solution a foaming agent capable of complexing the metal ions into surface active forms. These complexes would then collect at the gas–liquid interfaces formed during foaming and be carried off in the foam. By suitable choice of foaming agents and conditions it is possible to separate metals of the same as well as of different groups. This technique has great potential in nuclear technology and extractive metallurgy and has sparked a renewed interest in foam separation in general.

Since surface adsorption is the essential basis for separation by foaming, it will be examined in detail first. Next the nature and behavior of foams which permit the utilization of surface adsorption will be discussed. Finally, the various aspects of foam separation as a practical separation technique will be presented.

## II. Surface Adsorption

Adsorption may be defined as the concentration of a species at or near phase boundaries. While adsorption can take place at various interfacial combinations of gases, liquids, and solids, only adsorption at gas–liquid interfaces is of interest in foam separation. Although present understanding of all the factors affecting foam separation is far from sufficient, we are nevertheless able to make many qualitative statements and a few specific and quantitative ones. These last deal almost completely with surface adsorption.

Undoubtedly the most general and popular relationship used in quantitative descriptions of adsorption at gas–liquid interfaces is the Gibbs isotherm. In certain cases the Langmuir equation can also be used. In addition, several simplified versions of the Gibbs relationship have been offered. Equations, like Szyskowski's and Traub's rule, relating surface tension to concentration or composition are useful in simplifying the calculation of adsorption at the gas–liquid interface. All these are reviewed here.

## A. THE GIBBS EQUATION

### 1. General Forms

Gibbs (1) formulated, through rigorous thermodynamic reasoning, an adsorption isotherm (2–5). It relates the degree of adsorption at the boundary between two phases to the change in interfacial tension at that boundary and the composition of the two phases. For equilibrium at constant temperature and where the radii of curvature of the boundary surface is large compared to the thickness of the interfacial transition layer, the equation is:

$$d\gamma = -\Gamma_S d\mu_S - \Gamma_A d\mu_A - \Gamma_B d\mu_B \ldots -\Gamma_i d\mu_i \qquad (1)$$

where $\gamma$ = interfacial or surface tension; $\Gamma_S$ = surface excess of the solvent; $\Gamma_i$ = surface excess of the $i$th component; $\mu_S$ = chemical potential of the solvent; $\mu_i$ = chemical potential of the $i$th component.

Surface tension (in dynes/cm or ergs/cm$^2$) is defined as the reversible work required to increase the interface by a unit area at constant temperature, pressure, and composition. That is:

$$\gamma = (\partial G / \partial A)_{P,T,n_A,n_B,\ldots n_i}$$

$G$ is the total Gibbs free energy of the system containing the interface, defined by:

$$G = \bar{E} + PV - T\bar{S}$$

where $\bar{E}$ = total internal energy of the system; $P$ = pressure; $V$ = volume; $T$ = absolute temperature; $\bar{S}$ = entropy; $A$ = area of the interface; $n_i$ = number of moles of the $i$th component.

The chemical potential $\mu$ (Lewis and Randall's partial molal free energy, $\bar{F}$) is defined for solute $(A)$, for example, in a phase $\alpha$, by:

$$\mu_A{}^\alpha = (\partial G^\alpha / \partial n_A{}^\alpha)_{P,T,n_S,n_B\ldots A}$$

The relation between the chemical potential and the activity for solute $(A)$ is:

$$\mu_A{}^\alpha = \mu_A{}^{\alpha_0} + RT \log a_A{}^\alpha$$

where $\mu_A{}^{\alpha_0}$ = standard chemical potential of species $(A)$, and $R$ = gas constant.

The numerical value of the surface excess depends on its definition. In order to assign numerical values to the $\Gamma$ terms, it is necessary to define a mathematical interface at some arbitrary position at or near the physical interface. The validity of equation 1 is unaffected by the position chosen for this mathematical interface provided that it is planar.

In Gibbs' derivation of equation 1, $\Gamma_A$ refers to the total number of moles of component A per unit area of interface in the actual system, minus the total number of moles of A in a purely hypothetical system occupying the same volume, in which the two phases are uniform in composition up to the interface.

Guggenheim and Adam (6,7) showed that three different useful forms of Gibbs' equation could be written depending on the definition of $\Gamma$ chosen. Guggenheim and Adam called these three "convention 1," "convention $M$," and "convention $V$." The three "conventions" are summarized below for a binary system comprising a solvent and a solute.

"*Convention 1.*" This is Gibbs' original convention. If the mathematical plane is placed so that the "surface excess" of the solvent is zero, i.e., $\Gamma_S = 0$, then equation 1 reduces to the form most often used:

$$\Gamma_A{}^{(1)} = -(a_A/RT)(d\gamma/da_A) \qquad (2)$$

$\Gamma_A{}^{(1)}$ means that a portion of the solution containing unit area of interface contains $\Gamma_A{}^{(1)}$ more moles of a component $A$, than a portion in the interior which contains exactly the same quantity of solvent $S$. The physical picture ordinarily associated with this convention is that the solution remains constant in composition right up to the interface, and that $\Gamma_A^{(1)}$ consists of a monomolecular layer of $A$. This view is helpful, especially in considering surface tension data for relatively dilute solutions, but it is not necessarily a universally valid one.

*"Convention M."* In "convention $M$," $\Gamma_A^{(M)}$ is defined as the number of moles of $A$ in a portion of the solution which contains unit surface area, in excess of that in a portion of the interior which contains exactly the same mass. Using this definition the following equation is obtained:

$$d\gamma/da_A = -(RT/a_A)\Gamma_A^{(M)}(1 + N_A M_A/N_S M_S) \qquad (3)$$

where $M$ is the molecular weight.

*"Convention V."* In "convention $V$," $\Gamma_A^{(V)}$ is defined as the number of moles of $A$ in a portion of the solution which contains unit area, in excess of the number of moles of $A$ in a portion of the interior which has exactly the same volume. Equation 4 is then obtained.

$$d\gamma/da_A = -(RT/a_A)\Gamma_A^{(V)}(1 + N_A \bar{V}_A/N_S \bar{V}_S) \qquad (4)$$

where $\bar{V}$ represents partial molal volume.

Another approach, developed by Guggenheim (7), has also become popular. It avoids the somewhat artificial concept of the Gibbs dividing surface.

Guggenheim (for further details on approach, see references 2, 5, and 8) considered the system to consist of two bulk phases, $\alpha$ and $\beta$, and an interfacial phase $\sigma$, each of which has a definite mass, volume, composition, free energy, etc.

If we let $\alpha$ and $\beta$ represent the solution and gas phases respectively, we can place the boundary between the $\sigma$ phase and the phases $\alpha$ and $\beta$ so that the transition from $\alpha$ to $\beta$ takes place entirely within $\sigma$. In this case, $\Gamma$ (denoted $\Gamma^{(G)}$) is not the surface excess but rather represents the total number of moles of the various components which are present per unit area of interfacial phase. The $\Gamma^{(G)}$'s cannot therefore be negative.

The great advantage of Guggenheim's derivation is the fact that no restriction is placed on the chosen boundaries for the $\alpha$ phase so long as the transition from $\alpha$ to $\beta$ occurs entirely within $\sigma$.

Therefore, in most cases, the $\beta$–$\sigma$ interface can be chosen at the physical interphase and the $\alpha$–$\sigma$ at any convenient location in the liquid phase. It can be shown that in the case of plane liquid–gas interfaces, at constant temperature and pressure:

$$d\gamma = \Sigma[\Gamma_S^{(G)}(N_i^{\alpha}/N_S^{\alpha}) - \Gamma_i^{(G)}]d\mu_i \tag{5}$$

where $\Gamma_S^{(G)}$ = total number of moles of solvent which are present per unit area of interfacial phase; $\Gamma_i^{(G)}$ = total number of moles of solute $i$ which are present per unit area of interfacial phase; $N_i^{\alpha}$ = mole fraction of solute in bulk liquid; $N_S^{\alpha}$ = mole fraction of solvent in bulk liquid. Equation 5 is not the most general form of Guggenheim's derivation. However, in most practical cases, the general equation reduces to the form given by equation 5.

The quantity $[\Gamma_A^{(G)} - \Gamma_S^{(G)}(N_A^{\alpha}/N_S^{\alpha})]$ provides a measure of the amount of adsorption of component $A$ relative to solvent $S$. It also demonstrates that it is invariant with respect to the position of the $\alpha$–$\sigma$ boundary.

Guggenheim's concept of interfacial phase is also much easier to understand physically. It can be applied, for instance, to the case of a minimum in surface tension–concentration curve, and it can be shown, using equation 5, that this phenomenon might happen. Applying the original Gibbs equation to solutions which exhibit surface tension minima is quite difficult (5). (For some cases, it was proved that a minima in surface tension versus concentration curve is due to impurities. See, for example, reference 9.)

In addition to the various forms just discussed several approximations of Gibbs' equation for special cases exist.

## 2. Very Dilute Solutions

For ideal solutions, concentration can be used instead of activity. Since this condition can often be assumed for very dilute solution, equation 2 reduces to equation 6.

$$\Gamma_A^{(l)} = -(x_A/RT)(d\gamma/dx_A) \tag{6}$$

## 3. Electrolyte Solutions

Solutions of anionic or cationic surface active agents may be considered as electrolyte solutions. There is some contradiction in the literature regarding the manner in which the Gibbs equation can be applied to electrolyte solutions.

Brady (10), Cockbain and McMullen (11), and others (12) have considered the uni-univalent surfactant to be a completely dissociated electrolyte. The Gibbs equation is then given as equation 7.

$$-d\gamma = 2RT\Gamma d \log (fx) \tag{7}$$

where $f$ is the mean activity coefficient and $x$ the molar concentration. Below the critical concentration for micelle formation, $f$ can be calculated with sufficient accuracy from the Debye-Hückel relation

$$\log f = -\alpha'\sqrt{x}$$

The constant $\alpha'$ being 1.15 at 30°C. Equation 7 then becomes

$$-d\gamma/d \log x = 2RT\Gamma(1 - 0.6\sqrt{x}) \tag{8}$$

from which $\Gamma$ can be calculated if $d\gamma/dx$ is known.

Pethica (13), however, notes that the application of equation 7 to surface tension data for simple aqueous solution of ionic surfactants leads to values of $\Gamma$ which are approximately one-half of the surface concentration actually measured by radioisotope techniques (14). By using equation 5, he arrives at the conclusion that for very dilute solutions and a dilute surface, equation 7 should be used without the factor 2. For more concentrated solutions and a close-packed surface, equation 7 or its equivalent equation 8 can be used.

*4. Verification of Gibbs' Adsorption Equation*

Three types of measurements have been employed in order to measure directly the amount of solute adsorbed at a gas–liquid interface.

**Microtome Method.**    The microtome method was developed by McBain and co-workers (15,16). Using a precisely constructed apparatus, they succeeded in skimming off a thin layer from the surface of a solution. The concentration of the surface material removed was compared with the original concentration. The results were in good agreement with the Gibbs adsorption equation.

**Radiotracer Technique.**    This method is based on the fact that radiation above a solution of a surface active agent is greater than that of a solution in which no surface adsorption occurs. The method requires a tagging with a radioactive isotope with soft radiation. Both cationic and anionic portions of the agent may be separately tagged so that information can be obtained regarding the extent of adsorption of both ionic species. Using this method, it was found that surface active agents are adsorbed in a monolayer at low concentrations. Furthermore, adsorption agrees with the Gibbs equation. At high concentrations, this method revealed some cases of multilayer adsorption. (Reviews on the radiotracer method can be found in references 5, 14, 17, and 18.)

**Rising Bubble Technique.** The rising bubble technique is virtually foam separation itself. One classical experiment is worthwhile mentioning here. McBain with Davies (19) and DuBois (20) passed bubbles of nitrogen through solutions of surface active substances in an inclined tube. Thin films of the solution were collected and the excess solute per unit area calculated from the solute concentration in the condensed films and their area. The values of the surface excess so obtained were always considerably greater than those calculated for the same solution by Gibbs' equation. On the other hand, some other investigators, using a somewhat different experimental setup, found good agreement between experimental and calculated surface excess. (See Table II.)

## B. LANGMUIR ADSORPTION ISOTHERM

Langmuir (21,22) treated adsorption in a monomolecular layer form from the standpoint of the dynamic equilibrium between molecules striking the surface and those moving out of the surface after some time lapse. First, let us consider the case of a binary solution—one solvent and one solute. If the surface layer contains $\nu_A$ solute molecules each of area $A_A$, the fraction of the surface occupied by the solute is $A_A\nu_A$ and the fraction occupied by the solvent $(1 - A_S\nu_S)$.

It is then assumed that the rate at which solute molecules enter the surface layer is proportional to the unoccupied fraction of surface and to the activity of the solute in the surrounding phase. The rate at which solute molecules leave the surface is similarly proportional to the fraction occupied, and the equilibrium condition is described by:

$$A_A\nu_A/(1 - A_A\nu_A) = ka_A$$

or

$$A_A\nu_A = ka_A/(1 + ka_A) \tag{9}$$

In dilute solutions $\nu_A$ may be taken as equal to Gibbs' surface excess. Thus we get equation 10.

$$\Gamma_A = k_1 ka_A/(1 + ka_A) \tag{10}$$

where

$$k_1 = 1/A_A$$

Solutions with two solutes can be treated using the same type of argument (23,24). If a unit area of surface layer contains $\nu_A$ molecules, each of area $A_A$, of solute $A$, and $\nu_B$ molecules, each of area $A_B$, of solute $B$, the fraction of surface occupied by the solvent is $(1 - A_A\nu_A - A_B\nu_B)$ and equations 11a and 11b are obtained.

$$\nu_A = (1/A_A)[k_2 a_A/(1 + k_2 a_A + k_3 a_B)] \tag{11a}$$

$$\nu_B = (1/A_B)[k_3 a_B/(1 + k_2 a_A + k_3 a_B)] \tag{11b}$$

The Langmuir equations apply only to a certain concentration range below the critical micelle concentration. They might not apply well to electrolyte solutions (25).

## C. COMBINED GIBBS AND LANGMUIR EQUATIONS (SZYSKOWSKI'S EQUATION)

Szyskowski (26) measured the surface tensions of aqueous solutions of low molecular weight carboxylic acids and monohydric alcohols and found that these could be expressed in the form of equation 12.

$$\gamma = \gamma_0 - b \log(1 + k'x_A) \tag{12}$$

where $x_A$ is the solute concentration in gram moles per liter, $k'$ is a constant having a common value for all the acids at room temperature and $b$ is a constant which diminishes with an increase in molecular weight.

Butler and his co-workers (23,24), showed how Szyskowski's empirical relationship can be arrived at by using the Langmuir and Gibbs equations. Moreover, by using the same kind of argument, it is possible to arrive at some interesting equations for solutions containing two or more solutes.

Gibbs' equation offers no direct relationship between the surface tension and the activity of the solute. Since adsorption is known as a function of activity alone from the Langmuir equation, it is, however, possible to calculate surface tension by integrating equation 2

$$\gamma = \gamma_0 - RT \int_0^a \Gamma_A d \log a_A$$

Substituting the value of $\Gamma_A$ from equation 10, we get

$$\gamma = \gamma_0 - (RT/A_A) \int_0^a [ka_A/(1 + ka_A)] d \log a_A =$$
$$\gamma_0 - (RT/A_A) \log (1 + ka_A)$$

which is equivalent to Szyskowski's equation 12.

Now, if we have a solution of $A$ alone, with surface tension $\gamma_A$, and add $B$ until its activity is $a_B$, the surface tension of the resulting solution, assuming that the activity of $A$ is unaffected by the addition of $B$, is

$$\gamma' = \gamma - RT \int_0^{a_B} \Gamma_B d \log a_B$$

If the solution is dilute, $\Gamma_B$ may be substituted for $\nu_B$ in equation 11 and we obtain equation 13.

$$\gamma = \gamma_A - (RT/A_B) \int_0^a k_3 da_B/(1 + k_2 a_A + k_3 a_B)$$
$$= \gamma_A - (RT/A_B) \log [(1 + k_2 a_A + k_3 a_B)/(1 + k_2 a_A)] \quad (13)$$

Equations such as 12 and 13 can be useful. When their constants are known they can be differentiated and used in the Gibbs adsorption equation.

## D. OTHER ADSORPTION EQUATIONS

For extremely dilute solutions, the variation of surface tension with concentration is linear and

$$\gamma = \gamma_0 - b'x \quad (14)$$

where $\gamma_0$ is the surface tension of pure solvent, or

$$\bar{\pi} = b'x \quad (15)$$

where $\bar{\pi} = \gamma_0 - \gamma$ is called the surface pressure. From equation 15, $d\gamma/dx = b'$ and equation 6 may be written

$$\Gamma = -(x/RT)(d\gamma/dx) = b'x/RT = \bar{\pi}/RT$$

or

$$\bar{\pi} A_A = KT \qquad (16)$$

where $A_A$ is the area per molecule of solute $A$. Equation 16 being similar to the ideal gas law is called the equation of state of a two-dimensional ideal gas (3).

One of the first attempts to relate surface activity to chemical constitution is now known as "Traube's rule" (27). This states that for each additional —$CH_2$— group, the concentration required to give a certain surface tension is reduced roughly by one-third.

Recently Davies (25) derived an adsorption isotherm for electrolyte solutions, taking into account the superficial charge density and the potential in the plane of the surface.

## III. The Nature of Foams

When adsorption takes place in a solution, the essential basis exists for separation by foaming. One could merely scrape off the surface layers with a mechanical device but this is crude and inefficient. Foaming permits the collection of interfacial material with ease in either batch or continuous systems. Successful foam separation is therefore dependent on the nature of the foam produced as well as on the adsorption characteristics of the system.

Although substantial literature has accumulated, our understanding of foam behavior is far from adequate. This is especially true for foam separation, since most of the experimental work has been devoted to static foams or to the destruction of foams.

The discussion which follows is not intended to be definitive. It is included only to give the reader a general picture of this essential ingredient of the foam separation process. For more detailed information, the ample literature on foams may be consulted. The books by Bikerman (28) and Manegold (29), the recent review by Kitchener and Cooper (30), and the book on foams and emulsions by Berkman and Egloff (31) are typical sources.

### A. THE NATURE OF FOAMS

Foam consists of gas bubbles separated by thin liquid films. Although frequently considered as a dispersion of gas in liquid, foams differ from other dispersions of this type because the distances between individual bubbles are so small.

Many factors affect the development and stability of foams. Their relative contributions vary from situation to situation and interactions are complex. Nature and concentration of the system components, temperature, pressure, and pH are primary variables in the sense that they determine the critical secondary variables, viscosity, surface tension, and bubble size. These factors are often grouped into complexes specific to the study of foams—"stability" and "drainage."

Plateau (32) was the first to study the essential behavior of foams. Gibbs added thermodynamic examination of the gas–liquid interface leading to the adsorption isotherm discussed earlier. Following these basic contributions, foam formation and structure have been examined in great detail.

Foams may be produced by two methods. In the first, the future discontinuous phase—the gas—is originally present as a discrete and separate body. This gas is then dispersed through the continuous—liquid—phase by whipping, beating, or bubbling through fine orifices.

The second method is based on condensation or agglomeration. The gas is present as molecules or ions dissolved in the liquid. The dispersion is prepared by causing these molecules or ions to combine and form large aggregates. Foams produced on carbonated beverages are typical (28).

## B. FILM FORMATION

There are several concepts of film formation. One of the most widely held is the "balanced layer" theory. Foulk and Miller (33) state that liquid films are always formed by the mutual approach of two already existent liquid surfaces (e.g., two bubbles below the surface).

In the case of solutions, the mechanical force acting to bring these surfaces together encounters increasing resistance as the liquid layer between becomes thinner. This resistance arises from the difference in concentration between the surface layer and the mass of the solution. Solute is either positively or negatively adsorbed in the surface. This concentration difference is spontaneous, and therefore requires the expenditure of work on the system to restore the equality of concentration. In other words, thin surface layers of solution resist an attempt to mix them. This theory explains why pure liquids and saturated solutions do not foam. Since adsorption does not occur in these solutions, resisting forces cannot arise to prevent coalescence and the consequent disappearance of surface.

Hazlehurst and Neville (34) advance a "cybotactic" theory for film formation. They picture the liquid as composed of structural groups (cybotactic groups) analogous to crystals in equilibrium with their melt. The surfaces of these groups are constantly eroded to produce disordered liquid while new cybotactic groups are constantly being formed. The cybotactic groups have only a transitory existence in the bulk liquids. Any interface provides a permanent fixed nucleus or anchorage for cybotactic groups, these may become stronger and more persistent, approaching the orderliness and stability of crystals.

Recently a thermodynamic theory for foam formation was proposed using foam volume and foam life as criteria (35).

## C. FOAM STRUCTURE

Foam structures may vary between two extreme situations (3,29). In the first, the foam consists of nearly spherical bubbles separated by rather thick liquid films. The second type—which may develop from the first type as a result of drainage—contains mostly

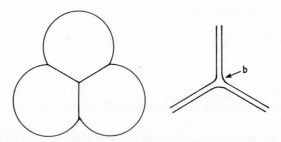

Fig. 1. Plateau's border (3).

gas and consists of gas cells separated by thin liquid films. These gas cells are polyhedral in shape. This characteristic cell shape in the second type of foam can be predicted from capillary considerations. (See, for example, page 407 of reference 3.) One can conclude that if three bubbles are joined they will appear as in Figure 1; the three septums meet to give a small triangle column known as

"Plateau's border," "Gibbs edge," or "Gibbs ring." It can be seen that the partitions between the bubbles are planes. At the points *b* the surfaces are concave and therefore the pressure in the liquid at these points is lower than in the plane surfaces. In other words, there exists a pressure gradient in the liquid. This pressure gradient causes a kind of suction and plays an important role in foam drainage.

If four bubbles meet along a single border, they may form a perfect cross; however, this is not stable. The smallest difference in pressure between the adjacent bubbles would suffice to move the laminas around until a stable configuration based on three connected patterns is obtained (Fig. 2).

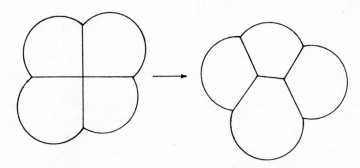

Fig. 2. Four bubbles forming a stable configuration (3).

The situation is quite complex for three-dimensional foams. Desch (36) found from observations that the most probable shape of a bubble in a foam, when the lamellae are thin, is a pentagonal dodecahedron (figure bounded by twelve equivalent pentagons). This is the only figure whose repetition can fill the space and in which all faces form angles of 120° with each other.

Evans and Epton (37) concluded from their observations that there are two packing arrangements in the foam: cubic and hexagonal. Under the pressure of the neighboring bubbles, each bubble tends to assume the shape of a rhombic dodecahedron or trapezorhombic dodecahedron. In both cases, the ratio of surface area to the unit volume is $6/a$, where *a* is the distance between opposite faces of the dodecahedron.

## D. FOAM STABILITY

### 1. General Aspects of Foam Stability

Foam persists so long as the films constituting it exist. The phenomenon now believed to be the main basis for stability of many foams was pointed out by Maragoni and by Raleigh (38). If the composition of the surface layer is different from that of the bulk solution (as the Gibbs equation predicts), its surface tension is smaller than that of the latter. When the surface layer is damaged, the underlying solution is exposed. Its greater surface tension pulls the edges of the wound together, thus causing complete healing of the surface.

Gibbs (1) believed that a stable film must possess a quality which he called "elasticity," $\bar{E}_s$, defined by:

$$\bar{E}_s = 2s(d\gamma/ds)$$

where $s$ = area of the film.

Elasticity is a measure of the change of surface tension in response to a change in area. Stated succinctly, in order to be stable, a film must have an elastic property such that if the area is changed by an external agency a force will arise in the film tending to oppose this change. This elasticity can exist for liquid films between two gas masses only if the film contains at least two components (in order that the surface tension may change). The film must be able to respond to local extensions and contractions by a rise or a fall in surface tension.

Raleigh and Gibbs' theories, similar in their conclusions, account for the inability of pure liquids and saturated solutions to foam. In these liquids there is no chemical difference between the surface and the bulk and therefore there is no "elastic surface force" to resist rupture. Foam persistance is zero at both ends of the "foaming"–concentration curve.

In addition to the adsorption of a substance at the gas–liquid interface, a foam must present an abnormal superficial viscosity (non-Newtonian) at the interface in order to be stable. For example, all the lower members of the aliphatic alcohol series considerably reduce the surface tension of water and are therefore adsorbed at the gas–liquid interface. Their superficial viscosity is, however, Newtonian, and their foams are not stable (39).

The concept that the surface layer of a detergent solution may have mechanical properties different from those of the bulk solution is old. It appears to have been proposed first by Plateau and supported by the early measurements of Wilson and Ries (40).

Brown, Thuman, and McBain (41) measured the surface viscosity of surface active solutions and found that foams of highest stability appear to be produced from solutions showing appreciable surface viscosity. Solutions yielding foams of very poor stability show very low surface viscosity. Some foams of intermediate stability which rapidly become thin and tenuous, although relatively persistent in total volume, appear as exceptions to the rule.

It appears that the high foam stability of detergent solutions is generally the result of special solute pairs. The major constituent has a relatively high solubility, but its solution yields surface films of low viscosity. The second constituent, although lower in concentration and also less soluble, is highly surface active and gives surface films of high viscosity. The solubility of the main constituent provides a reservoir of surface active material for the foam, while the stability of the foam depends on the ability of the second member of the pair to develop the necessary coherence in the adsorbed film.

## 2. Factors in Foam Stability

The important variables affecting foam formation and stability have already been noted. A brief summary of their influence follows.

**Chemical Nature and Concentration.** In general, the foaminess of aqueous solutions of inorganic compounds is small compared to aqueous solutions of many alcohols, organic acids, bases, and salts (42). Matalon (43) and Götte (44) found that maximum foam stability occurs at the critical concentration for micelle formation.

**Temperature.** Foam stability usually decreases with increasing temperature. This is due primarily to the decreased viscosity of the surface layers and increased gas pressure within the bubbles which results (27).

**Bubble Size.** From free surface energy considerations, films of large surface area are less stable than those of small area. Ross (45) states that the smaller the bubble the longer its life; at least an inverse proportion to the square of the bubble diameter should exist.

**Antifoams.** Pattle (46) concluded that antifoams act by displacing from the surface the substance responsible for foaming. They may do this either by dissolving in the foam liquid or by spreading over its surface.

*3. Measuring Foam Stability*

A variety of methods are in use for determining the foaming abilities of liquids, aqueous and nonaqueous. In general, they were developed to provide an answer to specific problems encountered in industrial practice, and they have not been completely correlated or analyzed.

There are two main methods for studying foams—dynamic and static. Dynamic methods are based on observations made during formation of the foam. Static methods employ foams formed before observations are begun. The more general methods of studying foams are given below.

**Dynamic Method.** For dynamic foams, Bickerman (47) and Brady and Ross (48) defined a unit of "foaminess" (denoted by $\Sigma$) as the average length of time that unit volume of gas remains in the foam. Foams were prepared by blowing a measured volume $(V_g)$ of air in time $t$ through a solution overlying a sintered glass disk. It was found that $(v_f t)/V_g$, where $v_f$ is the foam volume, was virtually independent of the time of streaming, air pressure, porosity, and size of disk. The value of $(v_f t)/V_g$ tended to reach a limit denoted by $\Sigma$ when the amount of superimposed liquid was increased. $(v_f t)/V_g$ has a definite physical meaning; it is the average lifetime of a bubble in the foam.

If the linear velocity of air in the foam is $u$, the foam height is $h$, and the cross-sectional area of the tube is $A_t$, then the lifetime of a bubble in the foam is $h/u$. $V_g = A_t u t$ and $h = v_f/A_t$. Hence

$$h/u = (v_f t)/V_g \tag{17}$$

**Static Methods.** Ross (49) proposed the units $L_e$ and $L_g$, denoting respectively the average lifetime in minutes of liquid and gas in the foam.

$$L_e = (1/v_{l_0}) \int_0^{v_{l_0}} t \, dv_l \tag{18}$$

$$L_g = (1/v_{v_0}) \int_0^{v_{g_0}} t \, dv_g \tag{19}$$

Here $v_g$ and $v_l$ refer to the volume of gas and liquid at time $t$, the original volume being $v_{g_0}$ and $v_{l_0}$. For static foams, both $L_e$ and $L_g$ can be measured either by graphical or analytical methods. For foams which obey the logarithmic relation for drainage, i.e., $v_l = v_{l_0} e^{-Kt}$

$$L_e = t/\log v_{l_0}/v_l = 1/K \tag{20}$$

Brady and Ross (48) proposed the average lifetime of the foam in minutes as:

$$L_f = (1/v_{f_0})\int_0^{v_{f_0}} t\,dv_f = 1/(v_{l_0} + v_{g_0})\int_0^{t_T} (v_l + v_g)dt \tag{21}$$

where $v_f$ is the total volume of foam $v_f = v_l + v_g$, and $t_T$ is the time for total collapse of the foam. By introducing the concept of relative foam density defined by

$$\rho_f = v_l/v_f = v_l/(v_l + v_g)$$

$L_f$ can be calculated from the equation

$$L_f = L_g + \rho_{f_0} (L_e - L_g)$$

or

$$(v_{g_0} + v_{l_0})L_f = v_{g_0}L_g + v_{l_0}L_e$$

where $\rho_{f_0}$ is the initial foam density. For some recent works on foam stability see, for example, references 50 and 51.

## E. FOAM DRAINAGE

### 1. General

Foam drainage and foam stability, or persistence, are entirely different phenomena. Drainage is a thinning of foam lamellae without rupture. It is true, of course, that the usual methods for determining drainage cannot differentiate between liquid originating from unbroken lamellae and that yielded by ruptured films. The mechanism of drainage was also described by Plateau (32). The liquid in the foam drains because of (a) gravity and (b) suction by Plateau's border.

Very little is known about the relation between persistence of a foam and its rate of drainage. There is no experimental information available for the rate of drainage of simple systems such as aqueous alcohols because the lifetime of their foams is too short (28). The drainage of foams is naturally affected by the viscosity of the drain ing liquid; the higher its viscosity, the lower its drainage rate. Thus an increase in temperature will cause a decrease in viscosity and an increased drainage rate.

In some cases, small amounts of polar organic compounds may markedly lower the drainage rate of detergent foams (52). This effect can be made to disappear by heating the system. This takes place over a narrow range of temperature, generally of the order of 2°C or less, termed the "drainage transition temperature." This transition is dependent only on the composition of the solution with which the foam is in equilibrium, and is independent of the distribution of bubble size or of the particular conditions in the foam These phenomena are not yet understood satisfactorily.

The effect of concentration on foam drainage is not always clear; the literature is contradictory. In some cases, foam drainage is independent of concentration over a wide range; in others, concentration has a substantial influence on foam drainage (28).

## 2. Drainage Measurements

As with foam stability, foam drainage can be measured by either dynamic or static methods.

**Dynamic Method.** In the dynamic method, the foam is continuously produced and collected. Usually the foam density is determined rather than the amount of liquid draining from the foam.

Walling *et al.* (53) found that a family of straight lines is obtained when the logarithm of foam density is plotted against drainage time (the time that a bubble stays in the foam column). A plot of this type is shown in Figure 3. It can be seen that foam density is affected by the drainage time and by the linear velocity of the foam.

A recent, basic study on foam drainage and thinning of soap films, including over 300 references, has been presented by Mysels *et al.* (54).

**Static Method.** Most of the procedures reported for measuring the rate of foam drainage are of the static type. Foam is produced by bubbling or agitation and then left alone. The liquid which collects under the foam column is measured by weight or volume at one or at different times.

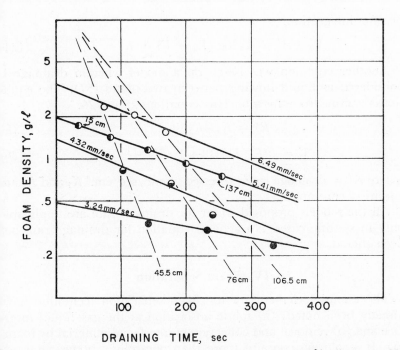

DRAINING TIME, sec

Fig. 3. Foam drainage properties of sodium "Oronite," 0.05% solution at 28°
(53).

The literature offers many equations which attempt to express the rate of drainage, or the volume of liquid produced, as a function of time. Clark and Ross (55), for example, suggested an equation of the form shown in equation 22.

$$dV/dt = K(V_0 - V) \qquad (22)$$

where $V$ = liquid volume drained; $K$ = constant; and $t$ = time. This equation states that the rate of drainage at any moment is proportional to the amount of liquid still present in the foam.

Foam has also been pictured as a bundle of cylindrical capillaries (56). It can then be assumed that the liquid column in each capillary is capped with a meniscus which exerts capillary pressure modifying the effect of gravitation. With these premises, equation 23 was arrived at.

$$dV/dt = K_1 (V_0 - V)/(K_2 - V_0 + V) \qquad (23)$$

or, after integration,

$$V_0 - V - K_2 \log (V_0 - V) + K_3 = K_1 t \qquad (24)$$

Another equation was based on a model wherein drainage is considered as liquid flowing between two plates (57). The equations resulting from this model are equations 25 and 26.

$$R' = K_1/(K_2 t + 1)^{3/2} \qquad (25)$$

$$V = (2K_1/K_2)[1 - 1/(K_2 t + 1)^{1/2}] \qquad (26)$$

where $R'$ = drainage rate expressed as $cm^3/sec/cm.^2$ $K_1$ and $K_2$ are empirical constants.

All the models proposed so far for drainage rate are applicable only in specific cases. No general equation for drainage rate has been offered.

## IV. Foam Separation

The essential elements of the foam separation technique have already been noted: (a) solute adsorption at the gas–liquid interface and (b) removal and collection of interfacial material by foaming. If a solution contains more than one solute, preferential adsorption must occur if these components are to be fractionated.

A. APPLICABILITY

In general, two types of solutes may be separated by foaming:

1. Materials which are naturally surface active. Proteins, dyes, synthetic and natural surface active agents are examples of materials which have been concentrated, fractionated, or purified by foam separation techniques.

2. Materials which are not naturally surface active but which may be rendered so by complexing or similar treatment. Separation of metal ions is an example. By associating these materials with certain surface active materials—anionic surfactants in the case of cations, cationic surfactants in the case of anions—it is possible to remove them from solutions.

It is convenient to break down the various types of solutions which can be separated by foaming into two main groups:

Binary systems (I)

I/A: One solvent + one surfactant.

I/B: One solvent + one surfactant + one surface inactive solute.

I/C: One solvent + one surfactant + two or more surface inactive solutes.

Multicomponent systems (II)

II/A: One solvent + two or more surfactants.

II/B: One solvent + two or more surfactants + one surface inactive solute.

II/C: One solvent + two or more surfactants + two or more surface inactive solutes.

In this classification "surface inactive" solutes are considered only when (a) they can be separated as a result of foaming or (b) they affect the characteristics of the foam separation process.

Foam separation can best be applied to complex, heat sensitive, and chemically unstable materials which cannot be readily separated by the common unit operations, distillation and extraction, for example. Probably the greatest advantage of the foam separation technique is its effectiveness at low concentration. Foam separation may therefore be used in the regions where other separation methods commonly encounter economical or practical limitations.

This special effectiveness at low concentration needs some further discussion. For the sake of simplicity let us look at an ideal solution of one solvent and one surface active solute. For this case we can use the simplified Gibbs equation (eq. 6) which can be written:

$$\Gamma_A = -(1/RT)(d\gamma/d \log x_A) \tag{27}$$

$$\Gamma_A/x_A = -(1/RT)(d\gamma/dx_A) \tag{28}$$

Equation 27 indicates that the surface excess, $\Gamma_A$, depends on the slope of the line obtained by plotting surface tension versus the logarithm of the concentration. A typical plot of this type is shown in Figure 4. It can be seen that the largest value of $\Gamma_A$ is between $x_1$ and $x_2$. Point $x_2$ is the critical micelle concentration (C.M.C.). Above the C.M.C. the surface excess is relatively small. There are cases where above the C.M.C. the slope of the line becomes positive. This might be due to impurities. Thus, in many cases a positive slope above the C.M.C. does not indicate a negative adsorption.

It will be shown later that in foam separation the factor $\Gamma/x$, rather than $\Gamma$, indicates the possible extent or degree of separation. $\Gamma/x$ is therefore a kind of "distribution factor." Equation 28 indicates that the distribution factor depends on the slope obtained by plotting surface tension versus concentration. A typical plot of surface tension versus concentration is given in Figure 5. As

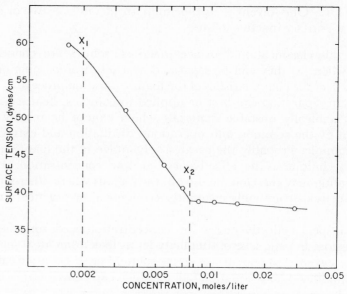

Fig. 4. Surface tension *versus* logarithm concentration for sodium lauryl sulfate (data of Brady (10)).

concentration decreases the value $|d\gamma/dx|$ increases rapidly. In other words, the distribution factor increases by decreasing the solute concentration.

Below about $x_1$ the slope becomes practically constant, and this is the range where equation 15 can be applied. Similarly, we can also conclude that foam separation will not be very effective above a certain concentration such as $x_2$ in Figure 5.

Two more advantages of foam separation should be noted here: (a) simplicity of apparatus and (b) the possibility of using this

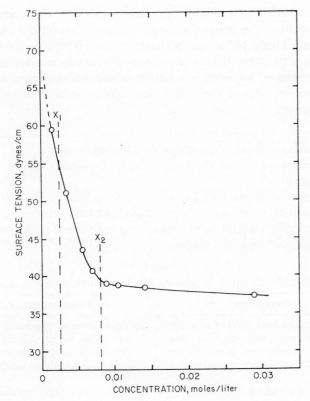

Fig. 5. Surface tension *versus* concentration for sodium lauryl sulfate (data of Brady (10)).

technique continuously. Both of these will be examined in subsequent sections.

B. FOAM SEPARATION AND DISTILLATION

Separation processes for homogeneous mixtures fall into two broad categories: (a) those in which a second phase is generated whose composition differs from that of the residue and (b) those which make use of natural or contrived composition differences within a single phase. In principle, foam separation falls in the second group. Separation is based on the composition difference which exists between the surface and bulk regions of the solution.

Despite this theoretical distinction, however, foam separation systems exhibit the general characteristics of two-phase separation processes. There is, as noted earlier, a striking resemblance to distillation in particular. Since much of the process design theory being developed for foam separation is based on this similarity, the analogous features of the two procedures are worth summarizing. For example:

1. The liquid phase in distillation is analogous to the bulk liquid from which the foam is generated in foam separation.

2. The vapor phase in distillation is analogous to the foam in foam separation.

3. The heat input in distillation (in Btu/time), is analogous to the gas–liquid interfacial area generated per unit time.

Table I offers a comparison of salient features of performance for distillation and foam separation.

TABLE I

Qualitative Comparison between Distillation and Foam Separation

| Distillation | Foam Separation |
|---|---|
| Increase in the heat applied to a distillation unit will increase the amount of entrained liquid in the vapor phase, lowering the separation factor. | Increase in area generated per unit volume of liquid will increase the amount of liquid entrained in the foam, lowering the separation factor. |
| Loss of heat in the vapor phase causes condensation and internal reflux, increasing the separation factor. | Loss of gas–liquid interfacial area (foam instability) causes "internal reflux," increasing the separation factor. |
| Multistage, countercurrent distillation columns. | Multistage countercurrent foam separation columns. |
| Reflux in multistage columns gives improved separation. | Reflux in multistage columns gives improved separation. |
| Highest separation is obtained with a total reflux. | Highest separation obtained when all the foam breaks in the foam columns and no foamate is collected (= total reflux) or by refluxing all the foamate. |

## C. APPARATUS AND TECHNIQUES

A foam separation unit consists essentially of a column atop the vessel which contains the solution to be separated and a receiving vessel. Gas (air, $CO_2$, $N_2$, etc.) is dispersed into the liquid through an orifice, a fritted glass sparger, or other bubble producer, and the resulting foam is collected in the receiver vessel. The foam is condensed (or collapsed) here and the liquid which results, called "foamate," differs in concentration from the original solution.

There are many variations in design and operation of this basic configuration. Most of the arrangements mentioned in the literature fall into one of the following categories.

1. Apparatus and techniques for the study of foam–liquid equilibrium relationships.
2. Batch-type foam separation systems.
3. Continuous foam separation systems.
4. Multistage systems.

Some systems reported belong very distinctly to one or the other of these classes. In other instances, however, the same device or procedure has been used for batch as well as for continuous experiments. In many cases, a small change in the apparatus will change its classification from one category to the other. In practically all cases the apparatus can be used to study the properties of foams as well as foam separation.

## 1. Foam–Liquid Equilibrium Relationships

Studies of foam–liquid equilibrium relationships can best be conducted with very stable foams. If the foam is not sufficiently stable, broken lamellae will produce an internal reflux. This, in turn, will cause an increased concentration of surface active solutes in the foamate. Attempts to compare results from such experiments with calculated values based on Gibbs' equation, for example, will then be in error. Experimental results for unstable foams are much higher than the calculated values.

Generally, the best apparatus for the study of foam–liquid equilibrium relationships is the closed system type, with the foamate recycled to the bulk solution chamber. If the volume of the bulk liquid is relatively very large compared to volume of foam and volume of foamate collected, a batch-type apparatus may be used.

In a study of adsorption of sodium dodecyl sulfate and dodecyl alcohol, Wilson, Epstein, and Ross used the apparatus shown in

Figure 6 (58). Foam was generated in a cylindrical column and was continuously wetted by circulation of the solution. Bubbles were formed by a platinum-rhodium spinnerette which had 40 holes, each 0.003 inch in diameter.

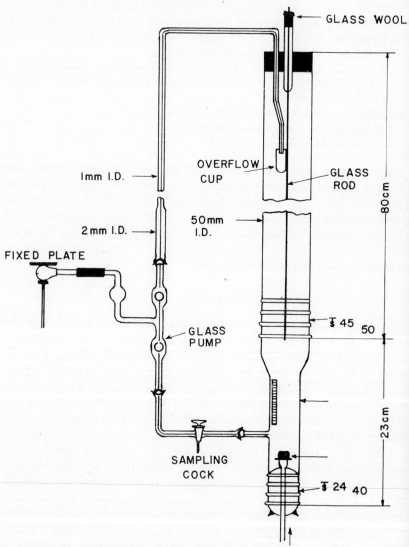

Fig. 6. Foam adsorption apparatus of Wilson *et al.* (58).

A sample of known weight was placed in the bubbler vessel at the bottom of the column and the system closed. Alternate compression and release of the rubber bulb connected to the all glass pump caused solution to be pushed up to external capillary tubing

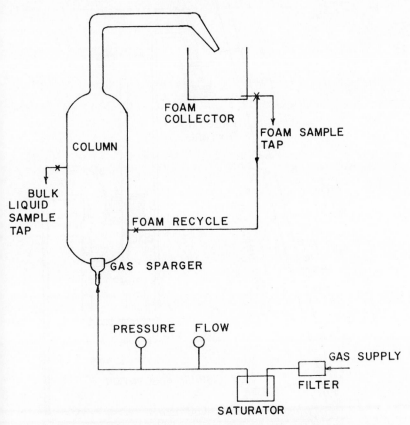

Fig. 7. Schematic apparatus of Schnepf *et al.* (59). The mechanical foam breaker, not visible in the picture, is mounted in the collector.

and through the overflow cup at the top of the column. The liquid flowed down the solid Pyrex rod which served to carry and distribute the solution over the foam. Thorough mixing for several minutes before withdrawal of a sample of bulk liquid was found adequate.

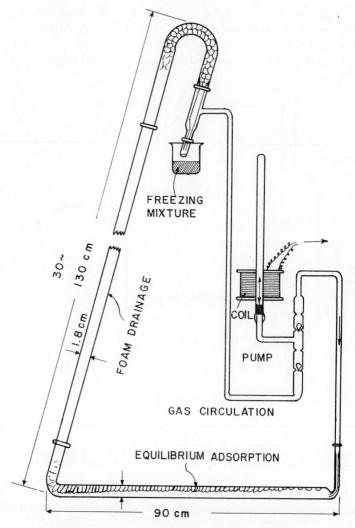

Fig. 8. Apparatus of Shinoda and Mashio (61).

A recycle-type apparatus was used by Schnepf *et al.* (59). This apparatus (Fig. 7) is similar to the one used by Kevorkian and Gaden (60). Foam chamber, column, and collector are of glass, with vinyl tubing connections, while the gas sparger is a stainless

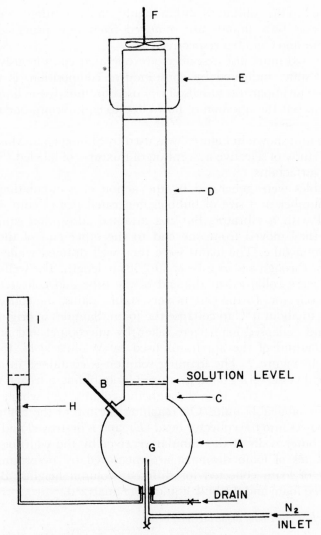

Fig. 9. Foaming apparatus of Walling *et al.* (53).

steel spinnerette containing 100 holes of 50-micron diameter. Nitrogen, filtered and saturated with solvent, streams into the column through a flow meter and the gas sparger. Foam is collected overhead, collapsed with a centrifugal foam breaker, and recycled to the column to obtain steady-state conditions. Samples of foam and bulk liquids are removed from taps provided in the collector and chamber respectively.

The two units just described are operated continuously until a steady state, indicated by constancy of composition, is reached. Batch-type apparatus has also been used to study foam–liquid equilibrium, but the question of how close to equilibrium one comes is always present.

The unit shown in Figure 8 was used by Shinoda and Mashio (61) in the study of selective adsorption of mixtures of labeled (S-35 and C-14) surfactants.

Bubbles were generated by the action of a circulating pump. The number and size of bubbles generated per minute was controlled with a vibrator. Bubbles attained adsorption equilibrium while they moved from one end to the other end of the nearly horizontal tube. The foams were then well drained while moving upward through a glass tube of 30–130 cm length. The well-drained foams were collapsed at the end of the tube and collected in the small collector. In the case of very stable foams, the collector was cooled to about 0 °C to collapse the foam. Samples of original solution and collapsed foam were taken by micropipet and analyzed.

A diagram of the apparatus used by Walling et al. (53,62) is shown in Figure 9. The foaming solution is contained in a 5 liter spherical vessel (A). Foam, produced by bubbling nitrogen through the glass nozzle (G), rises through the column (D) which consists of interchangeable units. On reaching the top of the column, the foam passes into the collector head (E), and is destroyed and thrown to the outer walls of the annular receiver by the whirling paddle (F). Rates of foam drainage are measured by determining the weight of foam collected for different column heights. Both the collapsed foam and the bulk liquid were analyzed.

### 2. Batch-Type Foam Separation Systems

In a batch foam separation system, foamate is continuously removed and the original solution is continuously depleted of the foam-producing agent. Solutions giving both stable and unstable foams may be treacted in a batch-type apparatus. Units of this type have generally been used either to purify a solution or to remove valuable material. Most of the experiments reported on

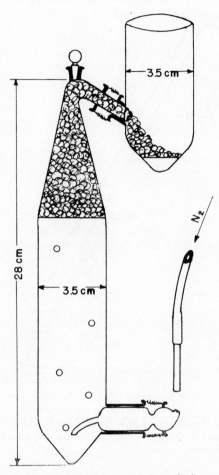

Fig. 10. Apparatus of Schutz (63).

unstable foams have been carried out in batch apparatus. Some examples are summarized in this section.

Schutz (63) used a single orifice to bubble nitrogen into a solution (Fig. 10). The gas flow rate was adjusted so that most of the bubbles broke before reaching the side vessel. The liquid falling back by drainage from the burst bubbles caused a progressive enrichment in surface active material. Schutz claimed that this method has the advantage that foam automatically ceases to be

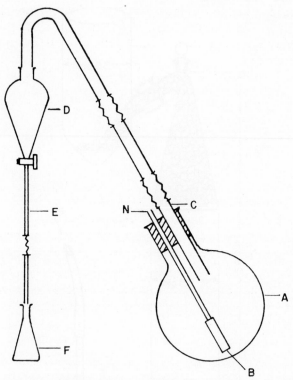

Fig. 11. "Foam Tower" apparatus (65,66): A, 5 liter flask; B, gas disperser; C, 12 foot glass column at an angle of 60° to the horizontal; D, 2 liter separatory funnel employed as a collapse chamber, ethyl ether added from time to time; E, 7 mm glass tubing; F, 500 cm³ Erlenmeyer flask; N, tube for admitting nitrogen at 20 pounds pressure.

carried over if its stability suddenly decreases, for example, when one surface active material has been completely removed from the solution. At such a point the receiver is changed, the gas pressure (and hence flow rate) is increased, and the next "fraction" collected.

Evans and Epton (37) used a somewhat similar method. The column consisted of two sections, the higher section with a larger diameter than the lower one. Solution was placed in the lower section. Gas was introduced through one or more orifices into the solution and the gas flow rate adjusted so that the foam column had a constant height. The foam collapsed spontaneously in the top section, and part of this condensed foam collected on the walls of the apparatus. Eventually liquid could be collected from a side arm in the top section.

The apparatus used by London, Cohen, and Hudson (64) consisted of a graduated cylinder fitted with a fritted glass disc through which $CO_2$ was bubbled into the solution. The foam from the top of the column was collected in graduated tubes so that series of 2–3 ml foam fractions could be taken.

Figure 11 shows the apparatus used by Gray and Stone (65) and by Perri and Hazell (66). Gas was bubbled through a porous sparger $(B)$ into the solution in $A$. The foam rose through the 12-foot glass column and was broken in the collecting chamber $(D)$ using ethyl ether. The foamate was collected in $F$.

## 3. Continuous Foam Separation Systems

In a continuous apparatus, feed solution is continuously added to the column while foamate and residue are continuously withdrawn. Both stable and unstable foam-producing solutions may be used.

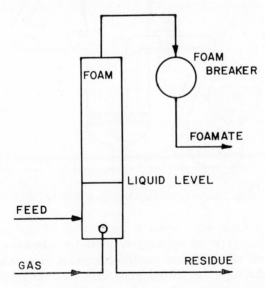

Fig. 12. Schematic diagram of a continuous type single-stage apparatus.

(With unstable foams, the system is in fact a multistage, counter-current column. These are discussed in detail later.) Practically every continuous-type apparatus can be used for batch processing by stopping feed and residue flows. All continuous foam separation systems have the same basic configuration, shown schematically in Figure 12.

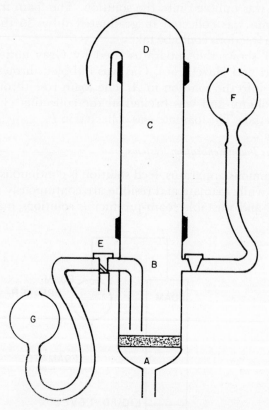

Fig. 13. Apparatus of Ostwald and Siehr (67).

Continuous foam separation is mentioned several times in the literature. One type of apparatus, used by Ostwald and Siehr (67), consisted of a column made of sections (Fig. 13). Gas was introduced through the fritted glass disk (A), feed solution from F and the residue was collected into G. The three-way valve (E)

permitted sampling the residue and collecting the residue liquid
in $G$.

### 4. Multistage and Countercurrent Foam Separation

Foam separation, like other separation schemes, can be conducted
in a series of single stages or in one multistage countercurrent column.

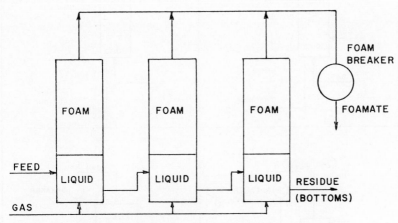

Fig. 14. A series of continuous single-stage columns.

One possible arrangement of a series of single-stage, continuous
columns is shown in Figure 14. In this example, the purpose is to
remove as much as possible of the solutes in order to recover a pure
residue. If the purpose of the operation is to recover the solute, the
arrangement of flows will be somewhat different. Figure 15 illustrates the stages in the development of a continuous, multistage
countercurrent foaming column (68). This type of column was
developed for foam separation of metal ions from nuclear process
wastes. In this procedure a "foaming agent" is added to the metal-
containing solution to complex these cations and render them surface active.

In Scheme A, continuous addition of feed containing the foaming agent, directly to the liquid pool in the column was employed.
This system can be modified for reflux (dotted line), some of the
condensed foam being returned to the top of the foam column.

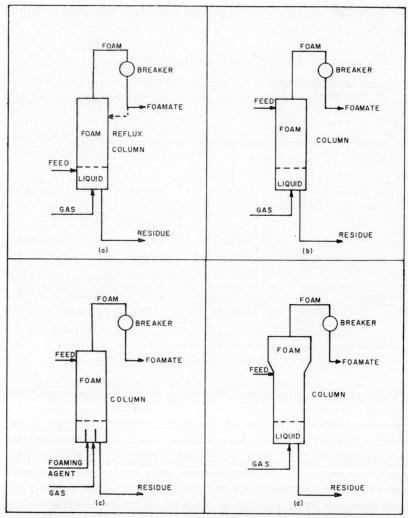

Fig. 15. Stages in the development of continuous countercurrent foam separation columns (68).

This arrangement gave high foamate concentrations but failed to decontaminate the residue satisfactorily.

In Scheme B, liquid feed is added to the top of the foam column, which is a stripping column. This system gave high decontamination

Fig. 16. Multistage countercurrent pilot-plant scale foam separation unit (68).

factors—up to 200. ("Decontamination factor" is defined here as the metal ion concentration in the feed divided by the concentration in the residue.) It was the basic scheme employed in all subsequent work.

A marked improvement was obtained with "split-feeding," shown in Scheme C. Only a portion of the foaming agent was added directly to the feed, the remainder being fed directly to the liquid in the foaming chamber. This method gave higher decontaminations and generally improved performance, but much foaming agent went out with the residue. To offset this, the foaming chamber was divided (as shown) into a central "foaming" zone, where foaming agent and gas are introduced and bubbles formed, and a surrounding "bulk" zone from which residue is drawn. This permits high decontamination without excessive loss of foaming agent in the residue.

In Scheme D, an expaned head section was added above the feed point to provide for better foam drainage and thus achieve a greater volume reduction. (Volume reduction is the feed volume divided by the foamate volume.) By combining the modified split-feed and expanded head arrangements, one has a column which will give decontamination factors of 500–600 and volume reductions up to 100-fold.

A multistage, countercurrent pilot-scale unit, basically the same as the one shown in Figure 15D, is illustrated in Figure 16.

### 5. Other Devices

Various special apparatus and improvements in techniques mentioned in the literature, often as patents, cannot be placed in any of the previous categories.

For example, Abribat (69,70) sets up two columns in series. The liquid which drains from the foam produced in the first column is sent into a second column where it is refoamed. A French patent (72) suggests building a foam column in sections. The solution is foamed until the foam height is at a maximum. The foam is allowed then to drain. The column is dismantled and the different sections of the foam are made liquid again. It was found that the components of the solution are segregated in the different sections of the column with the ones forming the most rigid interfacial films at the top.

Another French patent (73) suggests that the internal surfaces of the vessels for use in foam separation should be roughened so that they will be more easily wetted by the foam.

A British patent (74) suggests the use of changing temperatures during the separation. Each surface active material has a froth temperature above which a liquid containing this substance alone is incapable of foaming. Thus, a mixture of surface active materials may be fractionated if, during the foaming, the liquid temperature is kept above the critical frothing temperature of the other components. By successively lowering the temperature of the solution, all the components may be recovered.

## D. EXAMPLES OF FOAM SEPARATION

Published work in foam separation can be found as early as the beginning of this century. Until recently, however, virtually all experiments reported deal with the separation and or purification of naturally surface active substances, proteins, enzymes, various fatty acids, salts, and detergents, for example. The use of foam separation for the recovery and fractionation of surface inactive materials is a recent development.

Table II summarizes most of the published work on foam separation. Studies on adsorption to the gas–liquid interface, without foaming, are not included. This table should be considered only as a general reference guide; for details on any system the reader should refer to the original work.

TABLE II
Examples of Foam Separation

| Substance | System and remarks | Reference |
|---|---|---|
| | *Anions* | |
| 1-Chloromethylnaph-thalene | Concentration in foam from aqueous solutions with various surfactants such as nonylphenylpolyethylene glycol ether | 75 |
| 1-Naphthoic acid | Concentrated in foam from aqueous solutions with cationic surfactants such as polyethoxystearylmethylammonium chloride | 75 |
| 2-Naphthoic acid | Same as 1-naphthoic acid | |
| 1-Naphthylamine | Concentrated in foam from aqueous solutions with various surfactants such as sodium lauryl sulfate | 75 |
| Miscellaneous | Separation of dyes and organic (picrate, gallate, etc.) and inorganic (ferrocyanide, silicate, etc.) ions by adding a surfactant of opposite charge | 76,77 |

*(continued)*

TABLE II (*continued*)

| Substance | System and remarks | Reference |
|---|---|---|
| | *Cations* | |
| Ag | Adsorption from aqueous solutions by an-ionic surfactants | 62 |
| Be | From aqueous solutions with coco oil acid laurates | 78 |
| Ca | Same as Ag; from aqueous solutions | 62,77 |
| Co | From aqueous solutions with Aresket 300 and other surfactants; also in presence of Ni | 77–79 |
| Cs | From aqueous solutions with DBDTTA | 80 |
| Cu | From aqueous solutions | 77 |
| Fe | Same as Ag | 62 |
| | From aqueous solutions with toluenesulfon-ates | 78 |
| K | Same as Ag | 62 |
| Mg | Same as Ag | 62 |
| Mn | From aqueous solutions | 77 |
| Ni | With Aresket 300; see Co | 79 |
| | From aqueous solutions | 77 |
| Ra | From aqueous solutions with Aerosol 22 and other surfactants | 78,81 |
| Sm | From aqueous solutions with anionic surfac-tants | 80,68 |
| | With polyaminopolycarboxylic acids | 78 |
| Sr | From aqueous solutions | 77 |
| | With DBDTTA and other surfactants | 78,80 |
| | With aromatic sulfonates and other surfac-tants | 59,68 |
| | Interference of Ca and Mg | 59 |
| U | $UO_2^{2+}$ from aqueous solutions with Aresket 300 | 82 |
| | From aqueous solutions | 77 |
| V | From aqueous solutions | 77 |
| Th | From aqueous solutions | 77 |
| Zn | Same as Ag | 62 |
| | From aqueous solutions | 77 |
| | *Dyes* | |
| Azure II | Only alkali form collects in foam | 83,84 |
| Bromothymol blue | Foaming at neutral color (green) gives a yel-low foam and a bright blue residue | 85 |
| | With laurylpyridinium chloride | 76 |

TABLE II (*continued*)

| Substance | System and remarks | Reference |
|-----------|-------------------|-----------|
| | *Dyes (continued)* | |
| Congo red | Wine-red foam and a violet residue from solutions containing electrolytes | 85 |
| | With laurylpyridinium chloride | 76 |
| Crystal violet | From solutions containing surfactants such as lauryl sulfate | 75 |
| Fuchsin | Concentration in foam increases by adding substances which lower the solubility of the dye | 86 |
| Indigo | Potassium indigo sulfonate with laurylpyridinium chloride | 76 |
| Methyl orange | Concentrates in foam from solutions containing cationic surfactants such as polyethoxystearylmethylammonium chloride | 75 |
| | With laurylpyridinium chloride | 76 |
| Methyl violet | From aqueous solutions | 87 |
| | Alkali form collects in foam | 83,84 |
| New coccin | See patent blue | |
| Neutral red | Alkali form collects in foam | 83,84 |
| Night blue | Acid form collects in foam | 83,84 |
| Patent blue | In solution with new coccin; patent blue concentrates in foam | 88,67 |
| Phenolphthalein | With laurylpyridinium chloride | 76 |
| Vesuviana | Acid form collects in foam | 83,84 |
| | *Fatty acids and detergents* | |
| Alkylbenzylsulfonates | Removal from sewage solutions | 89 |
| Alkyl sulfate | Study of the factors in foam separation | 37 |
| Dodecylamine hydrochloride | From aqueous solutions | 53 |
| Dodecyl sulfate | Selective adsorption in foam in presence of impurities | 9 |
| | See *p*-dodecylbenzenesulfonate | |
| Dodecanoic acid | K salt; see *p*-dodecylbenzenesulfonate and hexadecanoic acid | |
| Fatty acid mixtures | In aqueous NaOH solutions | 90 |
| Hexadecanoic acid | K salt; studies on preferential adsorption in foams from solutions with K-dodecanoate K-tetradecanoate | 61 |
| Lauric acid | See sodium oleate | |
| | Na salt, from aqueous solutions | 91 |
| | Na and K salts concentrate in foam; hydrolyzes in foam | 92 |

(*continued*)

TABLE II (*continued*)

| Substance | System and remarks | Reference |
|---|---|---|

*Fatty acids and detergents* (*continued*)

| | | |
|---|---|---|
| Lauryl sulfate | From aqueous solutions | 10,53 |
| | Equilibrium studies | 58 |
| Laurylsulfonic acid | From aqueous solutions | 10 |
| Monobutyl biphenyl-sulfonate | (Aresket 300) from aqueous solutions | 82 |
| | Studies on reflux | 93 |
| Myristic acid | From aqueous solutions | 53 |
| Nonylic acid | From aqueous solutions; results agree with Gibbs' equation | 94 |
| Oleic acid | Alkali salts; from aqueous solutions in presence of stearic and palmitic acids | 95 |
| | Na salt; preferentially adsorbed in foam from solutions with Na-laurate | 96 |
| | From aqueous solutions | 67,91, 97 |
| | Acid soap concentrate in foam at low concentrations | 98,99 |
| | Foam contains 0.61 mole oleic acid to 1.0 mole hydrated Na-oleate | 100 |
| *p*-Dodecylbenzenesulfonate | Studies on preferential adsorption in foams from solutions with Na-dodecyl sulfate, K-dodecanoate, and K-tetradecanoate | 61 |
| Palmitic acid | From alkali solutions; also in the presence of stearic and oleic acid | 95 |
| Ricinic acid | From fatty acids | 101 |
| Saponin | From aqueous solutions; concentration of electrolytes in presence of | 102, 103 |
| | Results agree with Gibbs' equation | 94 |
| Stearic acid | Alkali salts; from aqueous solutions and in presence of oleic and palmitic acids | 95 |
| | Al salt; from aqueous solutions | 67 |
| | K salt; from aqueous solutions | 91 |
| Tetradecanoic acid | See *p*-dodecylbenzenesulfonate and hexadecanoic acid | 53 |
| Triton X-100 | From aqueous solutions | 53 |

*Miscellaneous*

| | | |
|---|---|---|
| Amyl alcohol | From aqueous solutions; some concentration in the foam | 104 |
| Bilirubin | From urine | 105 |

TABLE II (*continued*)

| Substance | System and remarks | Reference |
|---|---|---|
| | *Miscellaneous (continued)* | |
| Cellulose esters | Concentrated in foam from benzene solutions | 106 |
| Egg white | Egg white is more concentrated with a stabilizing agent | 107 |
| Gonadotropic hormones | From urine | 105, 108 |
| Lauryl alcohol | From aqueous solutions and with lauryl sulfate | 58 |
| Methyl cellulose | From aqueous solutions; foam fraction contains higher molecular weight and higher methylated fractions | 109 |
| Patents | Separation of plurality of substances by foam separation | 70,71, 72,73 74,110 |
| Sugar juice | An attempt on full scale purification of sugar juices by foaming | 111 |
| Urobiline | From urine | 105 |
| Isobutyl alcohol | A study on relation between concentration in foam and residual liquid | 60 |
| | *Proteins and enzymes* | |
| Acid prostatic phosphatase | Purified by foaming | 112 |
| Albumin | Removed from potato and sugar beet juices | 91,113 |
| | From urine | 67 |
| Albumoses | Concentrate in beer foam | 114 |
| Apple proteins | Foam fractionation of proteins extracted from apples | 115 |
| Beer proteins | Beer foam richer in proteins | 65,116, 117 |
| | Those precipitated by tanins and heat are enriched in foam | 118 |
| Bovin serum albumin | Concentrate in foam from aqueous solutions; maximum enrichment at isoelectric pH | 119 |
| Catalase | Purified by foaming | 120 |
| Cholic acid | From pure and impure aqueous solutions; free crystalline acid found in foam | 121 |
| | Separated from Na-cholate, pH of foamate different from that of original solution | 122 |

(*continued*)

TABLE II (*continued*)

| Substance | System and remarks | Reference |
|---|---|---|
| | *Proteins and enzymes (continued)* | |
| Cholinesterase | From horse serum; purified by foaming | 123 |
| Dextrins | Concentrated in beer foams | 113 |
| Diastase | Diastase concentrates in foam, lipase left in residue by pH control | 124 |
| Enzymes | From fruit juices | 125 |
| Fish scales | Partly hydrolyzed fish scales; different nitrogen concentrations in foam and bulk liquid | 126 |
| Hemoglobin | Strong salt drives hemoglobin into foam at pH 3 | 127 105 |
| | From mixtures with serum | 122 |
| Hop resins | Concentrate in beer foams | 65,114 |
| Lipase | See diatase | |
| Metaprotein | Accumulates in foam fractions from partly hydrolyzed soybean proteins | 66 |
| Pepsin | From solutions with renin; pepsin concentrates in the foam | 128 |
| Renin | See pepsin | |
| Sugar beet proteins | Crude juice of sugar beet purified; proteins accumulate in foam | 129 |
| Tyrosinase | Concentrated in the foam | 130 |
| Urease | Purified by foaming; jack bean urease purified best at isoelectric pH | 64,120 |

# V. Factors in Foam Separation

A. GENERAL

Many factors affect the performance and efficiency of a foam separation system, the relative importance of each depending on the specific case. For purposes of general examination these variables can be grouped as (*1*) "fundamental" and (*2*) "compound" factors. They are:

*1. Fundamental.* Each of these can be varied over reasonable ranges independent of the others: (a) Type of materials (solute, solvent, gas), (b) concentration, (c) pH, (d) temperature, and (e) pressure.

*2. Compound.* These are established by combination of fundamental variables listed above: (a) Solubility, (b) surface tension,

(c) viscosity, (d) equilibrium relationships, (e) kinetics of adsorption, (f) formation and structure of foams, (g) foam stability, (h) foam drainage, (i) foam density (or foam ratio), (j) bubbles: size, size distribution, and shape, (k) gas flow rate, (l) evaporation of solute or solvent, (m) flow properties of foams, and (n) equipment design.

Some factors such as adsorption to the gas–liquid interface, foam drainage, and foam stability have already been discussed in some detail. Before the theoretical approach to foam separation can be presented, however, it will be helpful to survey these factors.

## B. FUNDAMENTAL FACTORS

### 1. Type of Materials

The various systems and solutes which can be separated by foaming were grouped in Section IV-A into binary and multicomponent systems. A binary system of type I/A is the easiest to study. If a stable foam can be produced, the Gibbs adsorption equation is applicable and the surface excess or distribution factor can be calculated.

The separation of surface inactive solutes, metal ions for example, needs further discussion. The agent used to remove a particular metal ion from solution must have three characteristics:

1. It must be surface active, or form a compound with the metal ion which is surface active.

2. It must have some preferential attraction for the metal ion to be removed, an attraction exceeding or, in some cases, at least equaling that for other cations in the solution.

3. It must be capable of producing a reasonably stable foam.

There are two mechanisms whereby a metal ion in solution can be enriched by foaming. It may form a surface active complex, chelate, or other compound with the addition agent, or it may be electrostatically attracted to the surface (foam) by a negatively charged surface active agent. The first method is the more effective for separation of metal ions in presence of large amounts of sodium or other interfering ions (59).

In principle, when foam separation is to be applied, the materials must be in dissolved form. If they are not, the operation may simply be one of froth floatation. It is, in fact, often very difficult to distinguish between these two procedures. For example, various types of bacteria, although having a definite microscopic "particle size," were separated and concentrated by techniques which resemble both foam separation and froth floatation. (For example, see references 105 and 131–133.)

Many metal ions form precipitates with various surfactants above a certain concentration. If the amount of precipitate is small and the precipitate is very fine, a foam separation apparatus rather than a froth floatation apparatus will provide good separation. Bader and Schutz (121) found that, in foam separation of sodium cholate, free cholic acid in crystalline form could be found in the foam.

## 2. Concentration, pH, and Surface Tension

Concentration, pH, and surface tension are closely related since surface tension is ordinarily affected by both the concentration of the solute and the pH of the solution.

**Naturally Surface Active Solutes.** Protein enrichment in a foam depends upon both solution concentration and pH. Qualitatively, these results are in excellent agreement with theory. Gibbs' adsorption equation predicts that the enrichment ratio (concentration of the adsorbed substance in the foamate divided by its concentration in the bulk liquid) should be proportional to the rate of change of surface tension with concentration in the bulk liquid. The slope of the surface tension–concentration curve is greatest at the isoelectric point, with less negative slopes for either higher or lower pH values. Maximum enrichment is therefore obtained at the isoelectric pH.

The dependence of enrichment upon pH and surface activity indicates that protein mixtures whose components differ, either in isoelectric point or in surface activity, can be separated into their individual components (119).

According to Schutz (63) it is best to use a pH close to the isoelectric point for the solution. If a stable foam is not formed, stability can be induced by adding a liquid which reduces the solubility of the substance to be removed. London, Cohen, and Hudson (64, 120) also noticed that the optimum pH for separation is near the isoelectric point.

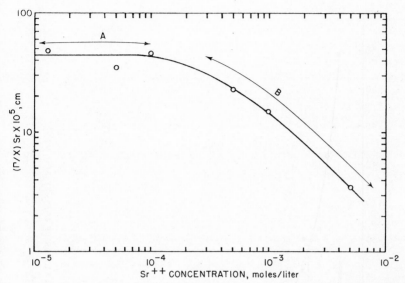

Fig. 17. Variation of strontium distribution factor with strontium concentration (68).

If a solution of several materials gives rise to a curve relating the foam stability (or, equivalently, foaming time) to the concentration which has several peaks, it is advisable to foam at the concentrations which correspond to these peaks, and this is best carried out continuously (63). If the concentration of the solution is not dictated by this phenomenon, it is best to foam at as low a concentration as possible. This is especially true when the purpose of foam separation is to separate or purify organic solutions. London, Cohen, and Hudson (64,120) found that there was an optimum concentration for their solutions both from point of view of purification and recovery.

If the efficiency of the apparatus is expressed in terms of the volume of gas required to remove 1 millimole of active material, then an increase in starting solution concentration increases the efficiency of the apparatus (37).

Dubrisay (86) points out that the addition to a dye solution of a small amount of a substance that lowers the solubility of the dye should favor the passage of the dye into the foam. This was verified by a serial addition of sodium chloride to solutions of dyes.

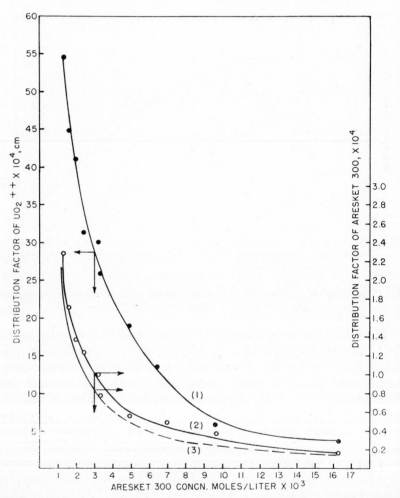

Fig. 18. Effect of foaming agent concentration on the distribution factor (83):
(1) distribution factor of $UO_2^{++}$; (2) corresponding experimental distribution
factor of Aresket 300; (3) calculated distribution factor of Aresket 300. Broken
line is extrapolation above the CMC. Calculation based on surface tension data.

**Surface Inactive Solutes.** The separation of surface inactive
solutes, such as metal ions, is closely related to both the concentration of the surface inactive solute and surface active, complexing
agent. Typical experimental results are given below.

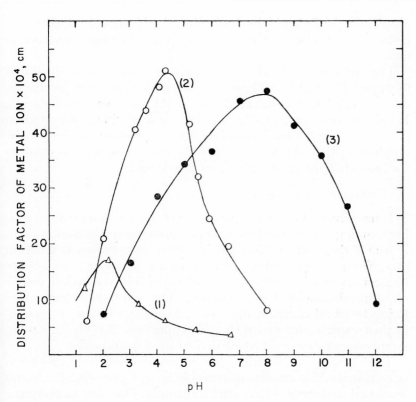

Fig. 19. Typical effect of pH on separation of metal ions (82,134): (1) La$^{+++}$ (10$^{-7}$) with RWA-100 (1.6 g/l); (2) UO$_2$$^{++}$ (10$^{-6}$) with Aresket 300 (0.5 g/l); (3) Sr$^{++}$ (10$^{-6}$) with Tergitol 7 (2.0 g/l).

Figure 17 (68) shows strontium distribution factor as a function of strontium concentration at a constant concentration of the foaming agent DBDTTA and sodium nitrate. The decrease in strontium separation at higher strontium concentrations can be explained on the basis of material balance (see Section VI-C).

The typical effect of foaming agent concentration on separation of a metal ion is shown in Figure 18 (82). Curve 1 shows the distribution factor of uranyl ion at constant uranyl bulk concentration as a function of Aresket 300 (dibutyl diphenyl sodium sulfonate) concentration. Curve 2 shows the corresponding distribution factor for Aresket 300. The close relation between the two solute concentrations is obvious, also indicating the increase in distribution factor of the metal ion with decrease in foaming agent concentration.

The importance of pH in separation of metal ions is illustrated in Figure 19 (82,134). These plots are based on experimental results obtained with columns similar to the one shown in Figure 7. It can be seen that in each case there is a maximum distribution factor at a certain pH indicating that the best separation can be obtained at that pH, and that pH control can be used to separate the individual metal ions from mixtures of ions.

### 3. Temperature and Viscosity

It has already been mentioned that changes in temperature during foaming can be used to separate surface active materials. This is true if the foam stability of the active components is different at different temperatures (74). Generally a rise in temperature hinders adsorption, but it was found impossible to correlate degree of adsorption with foam stability. The optimum temperature has to be found experimentally (63). Evans and Epton (37) found, in their experiments and with their apparatus, that an increase in temperature causes an increase in the rate of fractionation.

The viscosity of the bulk liquid affects drainage rate primarily. A high viscosity is usually unfavorable since it gives rise to a wetter foam and so decreases the enrichment ratio. One way to overcome this effect of high viscosity is to use larger foam column, thus allowing for a longer drainage time.

### C. COMPOUND FACTORS

### 1. Equilibrium Relationships

Two types of equilibrium relationships are ordinarily involved. The first is chemical equilibrium, especially important when more than one solute is present. Chemical equilibrium constants have different values in the gas–liquid interphase and in the bulk liquid (28).

Another equilibrium relates the concentration of solutes in the foam liquid (or foamate) to their concentration in the bulk liquid. Apparatuses described in Section IV-B-1 are usually used to find these equilibrium relationships. These equilibria are expressed in concentrations, concentration ratios (enrichment ratio), or distribution factors, the latter being independent of the foam ratio and bubble diameter. It is interesting to note that, for systems containing only surface active solutes, the equilibrium enrichment ratio is usually of the order of magnitude of 1–5. In the separation if metal ions, on the other hand, equilibrium enrichment ratios can be as high as 100 or more.

## 2. *Kinetics of Adsorption*

Gibbs' equation can be used only when equilibrium is reached at the interface. Experiments have shown that surface tension (and

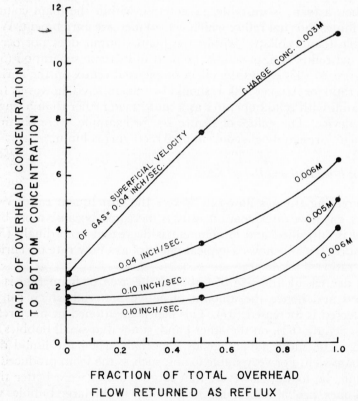

FRACTION OF TOTAL OVERHEAD
FLOW RETURNED AS REFLUX

Fig. 20. Effect of external reflux on enrichment ratio of Aresket 300 (93).

thus surface adsorption) can change with time. Roughly speaking, there are two types of phenomena—rapid surface aging and slow surface aging. In the first case, the surface tension reaches its equilibrium value within a fraction of a second; in the second, it can take hours and even days until the surface tension reaches its final concentration. There seems to be no satisfactory explanation for this phenomenon. It is generally agreed that diffusion is not the only cause of this behavior.

Reviews of the theories of surface aging are given by Molliet, Collie, and Black (5) and by Alexander (135).

### 3. Foam Stability

When a foam is unstable, its collapse within the foam column contributes internal reflux which acts to increase enrichment. With a stable foam, collapse within the foam column does not occur. External reflux can, of course, be used to increase separation (59).

Figure 20 (93) shows the effect of external reflux on the enrichment ratio for Aresket 300. It should be remembered, however, that a column with reflux operates as a multistage rather than a single-stage device. The values of Figure 20, for example, were obtained with a unit resembling a conventional rectifying column.

### 4. Gas Flow Rate and Bubble Size

Increasing the gas flow rate lowers the enrichment ratio. With higher gas flow rates, foam density is increased because more bulk liquid is entrained and enrichment is decreased accordingly (59).

Figure 21 (59) shows a typical effect of gas flow rate on enrichment ratio.

By decreasing the size of bubbles, the area of foam film is increased and hence the amount of active material which can be transferred is increased (37). This fact is mentioned in most references. Schutz (63), on the other hand, states that small bubbles are found to be more advantageous, especially when the liquid does not foam well. For very stable foams, such as the foam produced by saponin, he found, however, that large bubbles were better than small ones, probably because the drainage in the large bubbles was more effective.

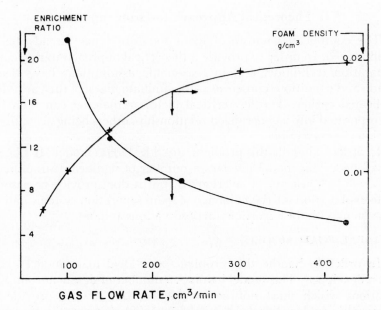

Fig. 21. Typical effect of gas flow rate on enrichment ratio. Data on separation of strontium with Areskap 100 (sodium *o*-hydroxy phenyl butyl benzene sulfonate) (59).

Although the concentration of solute in the foamate depends on both gas flow rate and bubble size, it will be shown later (Section VI) that, for stable foams, the distribution factor is independent of these two factors.

## 5. Apparatus Dimensions

Increasing the apparatus dimensions while keeping the gas flow rate constant will usually favor a better separation. By increasing the height or the diameter of the column, the residence time of the foam in the column is increased. Thus more liquid is drained from the foam and the walls of the foam bubbles become thinner. As a result, the concentration of the adsorbed liquid in the foam is higher. A longer residence time of the gas bubbles in the bulk liquid will also favor a better separation because the concentration at the gas–liquid interface can approach equilibrium.

## VI. Theoretical Approach to Foam Separation

The complicated nature of foam separation has already been emphasized. In order to provide a theoretical approach to the foam separation technique, certain reasonable assumptions have been made and conditions chosen so as to eliminate many of the variables indicated earlier. The few critical factors remaining can then be incorporated into a generalized relationship, others being accounted for later as corrections.

In order to handle this problem, an "ideal foam model" has been developed. This model involves a number of significant simplifications which must not be overlooked, but it does provide a reasonable explanation for the behavior of foam separation systems and is consistent with the experimental observations at hand.

### A. IDEAL FOAM MODEL

In order to handle this problem, an "ideal foam model" has been developed. This model involves a number of significant simplifications which must not be overlooked, but it does provide a reasonable explanation for the behavior of foam separation systems and is consistent with the experimental observations at hand.

The following idealized picture is proposed for foams:

1. The foam is composed of uniform spherical bubbles of diameter $D$.

2. The bubbles do not break ($100\%$ foam stability).

3. The liquid phase in the foam is divided into two regions: the "surface" region of thickness $\delta_\sigma$, and the "bulk" region of thickness $\delta_\beta$. $\delta_\sigma$ is constant and $\delta_\beta$ is changing due to drainage.

.4. The bulk region in the foam has the same composition as the bulk liquid phase from which the foam originated.

5. Adsorption to the surface is instantaneous.

The forthcoming discussions are based on the ideal foam model. It should be noted that point (4) restricts it to equilibrium relationships.

### B. SEPARATION OF BINARY SYSTEMS OF TYPE I/A

$x, y, z$    Concentration in bulk liquid, foamate, and surface region, respectively, moles per unit volume. Subscripts $A$ and $S$ stand for solute $A$ and solvent $S$, respectively.

$N$      Mole fraction.

$l$      Foam ratio, ml liquid/ml foam (per cent liquid in the foam).

$\bar{a}$      Area per unit volume of foam.

$E$      Enrichment ratio = concentration of $A$ in the foamate divided by the concentration of $A$ in the bulk = $y_A/x_A$.

$D$      Bubble diameter.

$n_i$      Number of bubbles of diameter $D_i$.

The number of bubbles per unit volume of foam is $6/(\pi D^3)$. This is a good approximation since the foam ratio is usually in the order of magnitude of 0.01–0.03. The available gas–liquid interface area per unit volume of foam is:

$$\bar{a} = 6\pi D^2/\pi D^3 = 6/D \tag{29}$$

When a unit volume of foam liquid (foamate) is spread out to the same thickness $(\delta_\sigma + \delta_\beta)$ that it had when it comprised the separating walls of the foam structure, it will give an area of $6/(Dl)$.

From equation 5 we see that

$$\Gamma = \Gamma_A{}^{(G)} - \Gamma_S{}^{(G)}(N_A{}^\alpha/N_S{}^\alpha)$$

Per unit volume of foam liquid

$$\Gamma_A{}^{(G)} = z_A(lD/6)[\delta_\sigma/(\delta_\sigma + \delta_\beta)]$$

$$\Gamma_S{}^{(G)} = z_S(lD/6)[\delta_\sigma/(\delta_\sigma + \delta_\beta)]$$

Therefore

$$\Gamma = (lD/6)[\delta_\sigma/(\delta_\sigma + \delta_\beta)][z_A - z_S(N_A{}^\alpha/N_S{}^\alpha)] \tag{30}$$

However

$$l = (6/D)(\delta_\sigma + \delta_\beta)$$

Therefore

$$\delta_\sigma + \delta_\beta = lD/6 \tag{31}$$

Equation 31 states that the factor $lD/6$ is equal to the average thickness of the liquid walls in the foam.

From equations 30 and 31, and since

$$N_A{}^\alpha/N_S{}^\alpha = x_A/x_S$$

we get

$$\Gamma = \delta_\sigma[z_A - z_S(x_A/z_S)]$$

Dividing both sides by $x_A$, we get

$$\Gamma/x_A = \delta_\sigma[(z_A/x_A) - (z_S/x_S)] \tag{32}$$

In equation 32 we can chose any value for $\delta_\sigma$ as long as all the transition from the bulk phase ($\alpha$ phase) to the gas phase ($\beta$ phase) occurs within the surface layer ($\sigma$ phase). If $\delta_\sigma$ is chosen so that $\delta_\beta = 0$ at the outlet of the foam column, and if we assume that the foam is not "very dry," then

$$\delta_\sigma = lD/6 \qquad z_A = y_A \qquad z_S = x_S$$

and we get the simplified form of equation 32

$$\Gamma/x_A = (lD/6)(E - 1) \tag{33}$$

The factor $\Gamma/x_A$ is called the distribution factor. Equation 33 gives the relation between the distribution factor, bubble diameter, foam ratio, and enrichment ratio. In practice we are interested in the enrichment ratio.

If $x_A$ is constant, and if we assume that Gibbs' equation can be applied, then the distribution factor is also constant and a plot of $E$ versus $1/lD$ should give a straight line. Figure 22 (82) shows a family of such straight lines, each line corresponding to a different bulk concentration.

Two corrections may easily be applied to the assumption of uniform spherical bubbles:

1. If the bubbles are of different sizes, then equation 29 indicates that the true average bubble diameter to be used in equation 33 is as shown in equation 34

$$D_{\overline{av}} = (n'_1 D_1{}^3 + n'_2 D_2{}^3 + \ldots + n'_i D_i{}^3)/$$
$$(n'_1 D_1{}^2 + n'_2 D_2{}^2 + \ldots + n'_i D_i{}^2) \tag{34}$$

2. If the bubbles change their shape due to foam drainage, the available area per unit volume of foam increases. Simple calculations indicate that if the bubbles assume the shape of pentagonal dodecahedron, then the factor 6 in equation 33 changes approximately to 6.6. In most practical cases an intermediate value between 6 and 6.6 will apply.

Since, as indicated by equation 33, the distribution factor is independent of bubble diameter and foam ratio, it is better to use

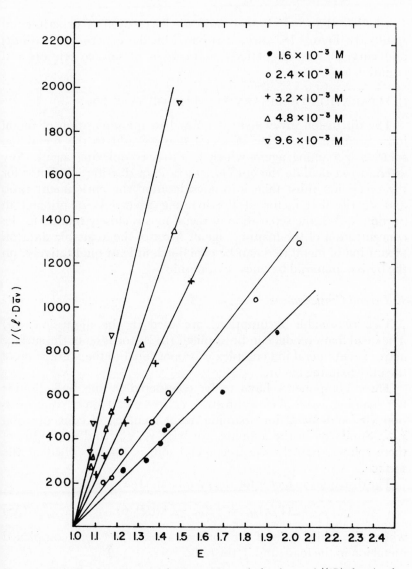

Fig. 22. Relation between enrichment ratio and the factor $1/(lD)$ for Aresket 300 (82).

$\Gamma/x$ rather than enrichment ratio for correlation of experimental results. In Figure 18, curve 2 is based on the experimental results and curve 3 was calculated on the basis of surface tension and equation 6.

### C. SEPARATION OF BINARY SYSTEMS OF TYPE I/B

The discussion given here is limited to the separation of metal ions. In foam separation of metal ions we add to the metal ion solution a foaming agent which is also a complexing agent. Any attempt to calculate the enrichment ratio or distribution factor for the metal ion must take into consideration the enrichment ratio and distribution factor of the foaming agent. As mentioned in Section V-B-2, the separation of metal ions is closely related to the concentration of the foaming agent. Most of the available data on separation of metal ions can be explained, at least qualitatively, on the basis of material balance relationships.

### 1. General Considerations

Two reasonable assumptions are used in the discussion: (a) The ideal foam model can be applied. (b) Adsorption of the surface active agent–metal ion complex is proportional to the adsorption of the pure foaming agent.

Three components have to be considered in the bulk liquid: free foaming agent of concentration $x_A$, free metal ion of concentration $x_{Me}$, and metal ion–foaming agent complex of concentration $x_{AMe}$. Similarly, in the foamate, we have $y_A$, $y_{Me}$, and $y_{AMe}$. One of these solutes, namely the free metal ion, is not adsorbed at the surface.

The distribution factor for the metal ion, $(\Gamma/x)_{Me}$ is defined as

$$(\Gamma/x)_{Me} = (E_{Me} - 1)(lD/6) \tag{35}$$

where $E_{Me}$ is the ratio of the concentration of free and complexed metal ion in the foam and in the bulk.

$$E_{Me} = (y_{AMe} + y_{Me})/(x_{AMe} + x_{Me})$$

However, since the pure metal ion is not adsorbed, then

$$E_{Me} \cong (y_{AMe} + x_{Me})/(x_{AMe} + x_{Me}) \tag{36}$$

Since separation of the metal ion depends upon both foaming agent and metal ion concentration, we will first consider the effect of metal ion concentration at constant foaming agent concentration, and then the effect of foaming agent concentration at constant metal ion concentration.

## 2. Effect of Metal Ion Concentration at Constant Foaming Agent Concentration

If the total concentration of the metal ion is small compared to the concentration of the foaming agent, then practically all the metal ion will be in a complexed form. Therefore $x_{Me} = 0$, and equation 36 reduces to

$$E_{Me} = y_{AMe}/x_{AMe} = \text{constant}$$

Similarly $(\Gamma/x)_{Me}$ is constant and independent of metal ion concentration. This fact is illustrated in part A of Figure 17.

If the total concentration of the metal ion is larger than the concentration of the foaming agent, then practically all of the foaming agent will be in a complexed form. If $y_{AMe}$ and $x_{AMe}$ are constant, then $E_{Me}$ and similarly $(\Gamma/x)_{Me}$ will drop by increasing the metal ion concentration (part B in Figure 17).

When $x_{Me}$ is very large, then

$$\lim_{x_{Me} \to \infty} E_{Me} = \lim_{x_{Me} \to \infty} (y_{AMe}/x_{Me} + 1)/(x_{AMe}/x_{Me} + 1) \to 1 \qquad (37)$$

Thus equation 37 indicates that no separation of metal ions can be obtained when the concentration of the metal ions, relative to the foaming agent, is very large.

## 3. Effect of Foaming Agent Concentration at Constant Metal Ion Concentration

Using our second assumption, the relation between $y_{AMe}$ and $y_A$ can be written as

$$y_{AMe} = Ky_A$$

when the metal ion concentration is much smaller than the total concentration of the foaming agent. Here, $K$ is a constant.

Equation 36 will then reduce to

$$E_{Me} = Ky_A/x_{AMe}$$

The enrichment ratio and, similarly, the distribution factor for the metal ion will be proportional to those of the foaming agent as indicated in Figure 18.

## Nomenclature

| | |
|---|---|
| $A$ | Area of the interface |
| $A_A$, $A_B$ | Area occupied by molecules of component $A$ and $B$, respectively |
| $A_t$ | Cross section area of a tube |
| $a_A$, $a_B$ | Activity of components $A$ and $B$, respectively |
| $\bar{a}$ | Area per unit volume of foam |
| $b$, $b'$ | Constants |
| $D$ | Bubble diameter |
| $D_{\overline{av}}$ | Average bubble diameter |
| $E$ | Enrichment ratio $= y_A/x_A$ |
| $E_{Me}$ | Enrichment ratio of metal ion $= y_{Me}/x_{Me}$ |
| $\bar{E}$ | Total internal energy of the system |
| $\bar{E}_s$ | Gibbs' elasticity |
| $f$ | Mean activity coefficient |
| $G$ | Total Gibbs' free energy |
| $h$ | Foam height |
| $K$, $K_1$, $K_2$, $K_3$, $K'$ | Constants |
| $L_e$, $L_g$ | Average lifetime of liquid and gas in the foam, respectively |
| $l$ | Foam ratio: ml liquid/ml foam |
| $M_A$, $M_S$ | Molecular weight of solute $A$ and solvent $S$, respectively |
| $N_A$, $N_S$ | Mole fraction of solute $A$ and solvent $S$, respectively |
| $N_i^{\alpha}$, $N_S^{\alpha}$ | Mole fraction of the $i$th solute and the solvent, in the bulk liquid, respectively |
| $n_A$ $n_i$, $n_S$ | Number of moles of component $A$, of the $i$th component, and of the solvents, respectively |
| $n_A^{\alpha}$ | Number of moles of component $A$ in phase $\alpha$ |
| $n'_i$ | Number of bubbles of diameter $D_i$ |
| $P$ | Pressure |
| $R$ | Gas constant |
| $R'$ | Drainage rate, $cm^3/sec/cm^2$ |

| | |
|---|---|
| $\bar{S}$ | Entropy |
| $s$ | Area of film |
| $T$ | Absolute temperature |
| $t$ | Time |
| $t_T$ | Total time for collapse of the foam |
| $u$ | Linear velocity of air in the foam |
| $V$ | Volume, volume of liquid drained out of the foam |
| $\bar{V}_A, \bar{V}_S$ | Partial molal volumes of solute $A$ and of the solvent $S$, respectively |
| $V_g$ | Total volume of gas |
| $v_f$ | Foam volume |
| $v_g, v_l$ | Volume of gas and liquid in the foam respectively |
| $v_{g_0}, v_{l_0}$ | Original $v_g$ and $v_l$, respectively |
| $x, y, z$ | Concentration of bulk liquid, foamate, and surface region, respectively, moles per unit volume. Subscripts $A$, $S$, $Me$, and $AMe$ stand for solute $A$, solvents, metal ion, and metal ion–foaming agent complex, respectively. |
| $\alpha, \beta, \sigma$ | Solution, gas, and interfacial phases, respectively |
| $\alpha'$ | Constant |
| $\Gamma$ | Surface excess |
| $\Gamma_A, \Gamma_i, \Gamma_S$ | Surface excess of component $A$, of the $i$th component and of the solvent, respectively |
| $\Gamma_A^{(I)}, \Gamma_A^{(M)}, \Gamma_A^{(V)}$ | Surface excess of component $A$: "convention $I$," "convention $M$," and "convention $V$," respectively |
| $\Gamma^{(G)}$ | Total number of moles present per unit area of interfacial phase |
| $\Gamma_A^{(G)}, \Gamma_i^{(G)}, \Gamma_S^{(G)}$ | Total number of moles of component $A$, of the $i$th component and of the solvent, respectively, present per unit area of interfacial phase |
| $(\Gamma/x)_{Me}$ | Distribution factor of metal ion |
| $\gamma$ | Surface or interfacial tension, dynes/cm |
| $\gamma_A$ | Surface tension of solution containing only solute $A$ |
| $\gamma_0$ | Surface tension of pure solvent |

$\delta_\beta, \delta_\sigma$      Thickness of bulk and surface regions in the foam respectively

$\mu$      Chemical potential

$\mu_i, \mu_S$      Chemical potential of the $i$th component and of the solvent, respectively

$\mu_A{}^\alpha$      Chemical potential of component $A$ in phase $\alpha$

$\mu_A{}^{\alpha 0}$      Standard chemical potential of component $A$ in phase $\alpha$

$\nu_A, \nu_B$      Number of molecules of components $A$ and $B$, respectively, in the surface layer

$\bar{\pi}$      Surface pressure, $\gamma_0 - \gamma$

$\rho_f$      Relative foam density: $v_1/v_f$

$\Sigma$      Unit of foaminess: average length of time that a unit volume of gas remains in the foam

## References

1. J. W. Gibbs, *Collected Works*, Vol. I, Longmans Green, New York, 1928.
2. N. K. Adam, *The Physics and Chemistry of Surfaces*, Clarendon Press, Oxford, 1938.
3. A. W. Adamson, *Physical Chemistry of Surfaces*, Interscience, New York-London, 1960.
4. S. Glasstone, *Textbook of Physical Chemistry*, Van Nostrand, New York, 1951.
5. J. L. Molliet, B. Collie, and W. Black, *Surface Activity*, 2nd ed., Van Nostrand Co., New York, 1961.
6. E. A. Guggenheim and N. K. Adam, *Proc. Roy. Soc. (London)*, **139A,** 218 (1933).
7. E. A. Guggenheim, *Trans. Faraday Soc.*, **36,** 397 (1940).
8. E. A. Guggenheim, *Thermodynamics*, North-Holland Publishing Co., 1957.
9. L. Shedlovsky, J. Ross, and C. W. Jakob, *J. Colloid Sci.*, **4,** 25 (1949).
10. A. P. Brady, *J, Phys. Colloid Chem.*, **53,** 56 (1949).
11. E. G. Cockbain, and A. I. McMullen, *Trans. Faraday Soc.*, **47,** 322 (1951).
12. E. Hutchinson, *J. Colloid Sci.*, **3,** 413 (1948).
13. B. A. Pethica, *Trans. Faraday Soc.*, **50,** 413 (1954).
14. D. J. Salley, A. J. Weith, A. A. Argyle, and J. K. Dixon, *Proc. Roy. Soc. (London)*, **A203,** 42 (1950).
15. J. W. McBain and C. W. Humphreys, *J. Phys. Chem.*, **36,** 300 (1932).
16. J. W. McBain and R. C. Swain, *Proc. Roy. Soc. (London)*, **A154,** 608 (1936).
17. G. Nilson, *J. Phys. Chem.*, **63,** 1135 (1957).
18. J. K. Dixon, C. M. Judson, and J. D. Salley, *Monomolecular Layers*, American Association for the Advancement of Science, Washington, D. C., 1954, p. 63.
19. J. W. McBain and G. P. Davies, *J. Am. Chem. Soc.*, **49,** 2230 (1927).

20. J. W. McBain and R. DuBois, *J. Am. Chem. Soc.*, **51**, 3534 (1929).
21. I. Langmuir, *J. Am. Chem. Soc.*, **38**, 2221 (1916).
22. I. Langmuir, *J. Am. Chem. Soc.*, **40**, 1361 (1919).
23. J. A. V. Butler, *Chemical Thermodynamics*, McMillan, London, 1949.
24. J. A. V. Butler and C. Ockrent, *J. Phys. Chem.*, **34**, 2841 (1930).
25. J. T. Davies, *Proc. Roy. Soc. (London)*, **A245**, 417 (1958).
26. B. Szyskowski, *Z. Physical Chem.*, **64**, 385 (1908).
27. I. Traube, *Ann.* **265**, 27 (1891); *Chem. Abstr.*, **1**, 2969.
28. J. J. Bikerman, *Foams, Theory and Industrial Applications*, Reinhold, New York, 1953.
29. E. Manegold, *Schuam*, Strassenbau, Chemie and Technik Verlagsgesellschaft, Heidelberg, 1953.
30. J. A. Kitchener and C. F. Cooper, *Quart. Revs. (London)*, **13**, 71 (1959).
31. S. Berkmann and G. Egloff, *Emulsions and Foams*, Reinhold, New York, 1941.
32. J. Platea, *Statique experimentale et theoreqieus des liquids soumis aux euless forces moleculaires*, Vol. I, Paris, 1873.
33. C. W. Foulk and J. N. Miller, *Ind. Eng. Chem.*, **23**, 1283 (1931).
34. T. H Hazlehurst and H. A. Neville, *J. Phys. Chem.*, **44**, 592 (1940).
35. M. Nakagaki, *J. Phys. Chem.*, **61**, 1266 (1957).
36. C. H. Desch, *Rec. trav. chim.*, **42**, 822 (1923).
37. H. C. Evans and S. R. Epton, *World Congr. Surface Active Agents, Paris*, **1**, 114 (1954) (in English).
38. J. W. S. Rayleigh, *Proc. Roy. Soc. (London)*, **48**, 363 (1890).
39. M. M. B. Abribat, *Chim. anal.*, **39**, 217 (1957).
40. R. E. Wilson and E. O. Ries, *Colloid Symbosium Monograph*, **1**, 145 (1923).
41. A. G. Brown, W. C. Thuman, and J. W. McBain, *J. Colloid Sci.*, **8**, 49 (1953).
42. D. L. Talmud and S. Suchowolskaya, *Z. physik. Chem. (U.S.S.R.)*, **2**, 31 (1931).
43. R. Matalon, *Compt. rend.*, **222**, 1213 (1946).
44. E. Gotte, *Melliand Textilber.*, **32**, 210 (1951).
45. S. Ross, *Ind. Eng. Chem., Anal. Ed.*, **15**, 329 (1943).
46. R. E. Pattle, *J. Soc. Chem. Ind. (London)*, **69**, 363 (1950).
47. J. J. Bikerman, *Trans. Faraday Soc.*, **34**, 634 (1938).
48. A. P. Brady and S. Ross, *J. Am. Chem. Soc.*, **66**, 1348 (1944).
49. S. Ross, *J. Phys. Chem.*, **47**, 266 (1943).
50. A. J. De-Vries, *Rec. trav. chim.*, **77**, 81 (1958) (in English); **77**, 209 (1958); **77**, 283 (1958).
51. A. J. De-Vries, "Foam Stability," *Mededel. Rubber-Sticht., Dreft, Communication No. 326*, 1957 (in English).
52. M. B. Epstein, *et al.*, *J. Phys. Chem.*, **58**, 860 (1954); *J. Colloid Sci.*, **9**, 50 (1954).
53. C. Walling, E. E. Ruff, and J. L. Thornton, *J. Phys. Chem.*, **56**, 989 (1952).
54. K. J. Mysels, K. Shinoda, and S. Frankel, *Soap Films, Studies of Their Thinning*, Pergamon Press, Glasgow, 1959.
55. G. L. Clark and S. Ross, *Ind. Eng. Chem.*, **32**, 1594 (1940).
56. G. D. Miles, J. Shedlovsky, and J. Ross, *J. Phys. Chem.*, **49**, 93 (1945).

57. W. M. Jacobi, K. E. Woodcock, and C. S. Grove, *Ind. Eng. Chem.*, **48**, 2046 (1956).
58. A. Wilson, M. B. Epstein, and J. Ross, *J. Colloid Sci.*, **12**, 345 (1957).
59. R. W. Schnepf, E. L. Gaden, Y. Mirocznik, and E. Schonfeld, *Chem. Eng. Progr.*, **55**, 42 (May 1959).
60. V. Kevorkian and E. Gaden, *Ann. Inst. Chem. Engrs. J.*, **3**, 180 (1957).
61. K. Shinoda and K. Mashio, *J. Phys. Chem.*, **64**, 54 (1960).
62. C. Walling, E. E. Ruff, and J. L. Thornton, *J. Phys. Chem.*, **61**, 486 (1957).
63. F. Schutz, *Trans. Faraday Soc.*, **41**, 437 (1946).
64. M. London, M. Cohen, and P. B. Hudson, *J. Am. Chem. Soc.*, **75**, 1746 (1953).
65. P. P. Gray and I. Stone, *Wallerstein Labs. Communs.*, **3**, 159 (1940); *Chem. Abstr.*, **35**, 3029$^5$ (1941).
66. J. M. Perri and F. Hazel, *Ind. Eng. Chem.*, **38**, 549 (1946).
67. W. Ostwald and A. Siehr, *Kolloid Z.*, **76**, 33 (1936).
68. Radiation Applications Inc., Long Island City, New York, *Eng. Mining J.*, (Aug. 1960).
69. M. Abribat, *Chim. anal.*, **39**, 217 (1957).
70. M. Abribat, U. S. Pat. 2,313,007 (March 2, 1943).
71. Kodak-Pathe, (to Kodak Ltd.) Brit. Pat. 535,099 (March 28, 1941).
72. Kodak-Pathe, Fr. Pat. 859,735 (December 27, 1940).
73. Kodak-Pathe, Fr. Pat. 942,087 (January 28, 1949).
74. F. Schutz, Brit. Pat. 498,643 (January 11, 1939).
75. B. L. Karger and L. B. Rogers, *Anal. Chem.*, **33**, 1165 (1961).
76. F. Sebba, *Nature*, **188**, 736 (1960).
77. F. Sebba, *Nature*, **184**, 1062 (1959).
78. H. M. Schoen and G. Mazzella, *Ind. Water & Wastes*, (May-June 1961).
79. D. Ghosh, M. S. Thesis, Columbia University, 1959.
80. E. Schonfeld, *et al.*, AEC, NYO-9577.
81. H. Schoen, E. Rubin, and D. Ghosh, Final Report Prepared by Northeast Research Institute, Public Health Service Research Grant No. 7409.
82. E. Rubin, Ph.D. Dissertation, Columbia University, 1962.
83. E. O. Aenlle, *Anales fís. y. quím.* (*Madrid*), **42**, 179 (1946); *Chem. Abstr.*, **41** 4649i (1947).
84. E. O. Aenlle, *Anales fís. y. quím.* (*Madrid*), **43**, 869 (1947); *Chem. Abstr.*, **42** 3624 *a* (1948).
85. H. Thiele, *Kolloid Z.*, **118**, 172 (1956).
86. R. Dubrisay, *Compt. rend.*, **233**, 781 (1951).
87. F. B. Kenrich, *J. Phys. Chem.*, **16** 513 (1912).
88. W. Ostwald and W. Mischke, *Kolloid Z.*, **90**, 17 (1940).
89. P. H. McGauhey and S. A. Klein, *Public Works*, **92**, 101 (May 1961).
90. R. Dubrisay and A. Taquet, *Ann. fals. et fraudes*, **46**, 426 (1953).
91. W. Ostwald and A' Siehr, *Kolloid Z.*, **79**, 11 (1937).
92. M. Raison, *Mém. services chim. état* (*Paris*), **37**, No. 1, 65 (1952).
93. R. Lemlich and E. Lavi, *Science*, **134**, 191 (July 1961).
94. F. G. Donnan and J. T. Barker, *Proc. Roy. Soc.* (*London*), **A85**, 557 (1911).
95. E. O. Aenlle and S. G. Fernandez, *Anales real soc. españ. fís. y. quim.* (*Madrid*), Ser. B, **44**, 191 (1948); *Chem. Abstr.*, **42**, 7549 *e* (1948).
96. R. Dubrisay, *Compt. rend.*, **194**, 1076 (1932).

97. W. Prosch, *Z. Deut. Olu Fett-Ind.*, **42**, 449 (1922); *Chem. Abstr.*, **16**, 3551 (1922).
98. M. Raison, in Surface Chemistry, special supplement to *Research (London)*, 187 (1949).
99. M. Raison, *Compt. rend.*, **232**, 1660 (1951).
100. M. E. Laing, *Proc. Roy. Soc. (London)*, **A109**, 28 (1925).
101. R. Dubrisay, *Bull. soc. chim. France*, **1953**, 280.
102. J. Zawidzki, *Z. physik, Chem.*, **35**, 77 (1900).
103. J. Zawidzki, *Z. physik. Chem.*, **42**, 612 (1903).
104. C. C. Benson, *J. Phys. Chem.*, **7**, 532 (1903).
105. A. Dognon, *Rev. Sci.*, **79**, 613 (1941); *Chem. Zentr.*, **1942**, II, 2180; *Chem. Abstr.*, **38**, 2979[9] (1944).
106. S. J. Lee, *Soc. Chem. Ind., Japan*, **40**, Suppl. binding, 459 (1937).
107. M. A. Barmore, *Colo. Agr. Expt. Sta., Tech. Bull.* **9**, 58 pp. (1934); *Chem. Abstr.*, **29**, 240[1] (1935).
108. R. Courier and A. Dognon, *Combt. rend.*, **209**, 242 (1939).
109. F. Schutz, *Trans. Faraday Soc.*, **38**, 85 (1942).
110. R. A. Dole and J. W. McBain (to Chemical Process Co.), U. S. Pat. 2,162,379 (June 13, 1939).
111. W. Meyer, *Centr. Zuckerind.*, **48**, 449 (1940); *Chem. Abstr.*, **36**, 5375 (1942).
112. M. London and P. B. Hudson, *Arch. Biochem. and Biophys.*, **46**, 141 (1953).
113. W. Ostwald and A. Siehr, *Chem. Ztg.*, **61**, 649 (1937).
114. W. Mischke, *Wochschr. Brau.*, **54**, 63 (1940).
115. S. G. Davis, C. R. Fellers, and W. B. Esseler, *Food Research*, **14**, 417 (1949).
116. H. Luers, K. Geys, and A. Baumann, *Z. ges. Brauw.*, **43**, 185, 193, 201 (1920).
117. B. H. Nissen and C. Estes, *Am. Soc. Brewing Chemists Proc.*, **1940**, 23; *Chem. Abstr.*, **35**, 3029[8] (1941).
118. G. Kraus and F. Harreis, *Wochschr. Brau.*, **57**, 33 (1940).
119. R. W. Schnepf and E. L. Gaden, *J. Biochem. and Microbiol. Tech. and Eng.*, **1**, No. 1, 1 (1959).
120. M. London, M. Cohen, and P. B. Hudson, *Biochem. et Biophys. Acta*, **13**, 111 (1954).
121. R. Bader and F. Schutz, *Trans. Faraday Soc.*, **42**, 571 (1946).
122. F. Schutz, *Nature*, **139**, 629 (1937).
123. R. Bader, *et al.*, *Nature*, **154**, 183 (1944).
124. W. Ostwald and W. Mischke, *Kolloid Z.*, **90**, 205 (1940).
125. J. M. Arrazola, *Ion (Madrid)*, **2**, 119 (1942); *Chem. Abstr.*, **37**, 1301[9] (1943).
126. H. Schoen, M. Chem. Eng. Thesis, Syracuse University, 1953.
127. A. Dognon and L. Gougerot, *Bull. soc. chim. biol.*, **29**, 702 (1947).
128. G. Andrews and F. Schutz, *Biochem. J. (London)*, **39**, li (1945).
129. O. Spengler and W. Dorfeldt, *Z. Wirtschaftsgrupbe Zuckerind.*, **92**, 279 (1942); *Chem. Abstr.*, **37**, 6923[7] (1943).
130. K. Hess and C. Hess, *Ber.*, **81**, 354 (1948).
131. A. Dognon and H. Dumontet, *Combt. rend. soc. biol.*, **135**, 884 (1941).
132. H. Ruska, *Kolloid Z.*, **110**, 175 (1948).
133. E. Weineck, *Kolloid Z.*, **100**, 403 (1942).
134. Radiation Applications Inc., Long Island City, N. Y., unpublished data.
135. A. E. Alexander, *Trans. Faraday Soc.*, **37**, 15 (1941).

# 6 ELECTROPHORESIS

## R. K. Finn

**Contents**

# I. Introduction

When an aqueous suspension of small particles is placed in an electrical field, the particles migrate either to the anode or to the cathode, depending on the sign of the charge that they carry. This behavior, called electrophoresis, applies to visible bubbles or drops, to submicroscopic colloidal particles, or to individual molecules provided they are charged or ionized. Differences in the direction

TABLE I

Basis for Fractionation in Some Unit Operations

| Method of separation | Difference in relative: |
|---|---|
| Equilibrium methods | |
| Distillation | Volatility |
| Extraction, gas absorption | Partition coefficient |
| Crystallization | Solubility |
| Dialysis | Size |
| Adsorption, foaming | Surface activity |
| Ion exchange | Exchange equilibrium |
| Rate methods | |
| Electrophoresis | Rate of electromigration |
| Special precipitations | Rate of crystallization |
| Sedimentation or elutriation | Rate of settling |

or speed of migration provide the basis for a fractionation of the various species in a mixture. Such separations by electrophoresis depend in large measure on the concentration of electrical charge near the surface of the particle or molecule. Because this electrical property may be different for two species, even though many of their other physical and chemical properties are similar, electrophoresis provides the chemical engineer with a new tool for separations.

It is an interesting distinction that electrophoresis depends upon differences in the *rate* of a molecular process, whereas most of the other unit operations depend upon differences in some *equilibrium* property to accomplish a separation. The comparison shown in Table I, although incomplete, serves to highlight this distinction.

In the methods that depend upon a difference in some thermodynamic property such as relative volatility, the statistical distribution of many molecules is involved and therefore no complete separation of individual components is possible in a finite apparatus. By contrast, electrophoresis permits such separation except as Brownian motion may blur the boundaries. In practice this feature is not so important perhaps as the inapplicability of concepts like "theoretical stage" and HTU to a rate process like electrophoresis.

The electrical charge at the surface of ionic or ionizable solids can arise from (a) the preferential removal of positive or negative ions by the water, (b) the preferential adsorption of other ions present in the water, or (c) ion exchange with other ions in the water. Even nonionic substances such as hydrocarbons will usually show a charge when finely divided and suspended in water because they tend to absorb anions, especially hydroxyl ions. The charge on the surface of an ampholyte such as a protein is influenced strongly by the pH, because the constituent amino acids can ionize either as acids or as bases. At low pH the surface has a positive charge because the exposed groups are $NH_3^+$ and COOH, whereas at high pH the surface has a net negative charge ($NH_2$ and $COO^-$). At some intermediate value of pH, called the *isoelectric point*, there is no net surface charge. Various ampholytes can be characterized by the pH at which there is no movement in an electrical field. When the pH is far removed from the isoelectric point more ionizable groups are brought into play than when the pH is close to the isoelectric point, and the velocity of the particle is correspondingly increased.

The practicality of separation depends, of course, on how fast the particles will move in potential gradients that are easily achievable. In general, proteins and other macromolecules move at speeds measured in tenths of microns per second ($10^{-5}$ cm/sec) in a gradient of 1 v/cm, whereas larger colloidal particles and emulsion droplets may move ten times as fast in such a gradient (because their surface charge density is usually higher). Potential gradients are commonly as high as 10 v/cm, and consequently separation distances are likely to range from 0.06 to 0.6 mm/min. depending on the difference in mobility of the individual fractions. By way of comparison, the gravity settling in water of 10 micron sulfur particles proceeds at about 1.2 mm/min. The simple creaming of a latex electrically (electrodecantation), with no fractionation of species, may proceed at a rate of several millimeters per minute. These rough numbers are cited to give the reader an appreciation of some of the difficulties in large-scale electrophoresis where unwanted convection currents are especially detrimental to clean separations.

It is appropriate here to distinguish electrodecantation from fractionation by electrophoresis. In the former, a suspension of colloidal particles collects near one of the electrodes and then either floats or sinks, depending on its density, to form a much-concentrated suspension that can be withdrawn separately from the clarified menstruum. In fractionation, on the other hand, the separation is between species moving at different rates. An obvious comparison is with settling or centrifuging operations; thus electrodecantation is like simple sedimentation, whereas electrophoretic fractionation is like differential sedimentation. The single word "electrophoresis" is commonly used to designate either the general phenomenon of electromigration, which includes electrodecantation or to refer specifically to fractionation by means of electrophoresis (e.g., "paper-strip electrophoresis"). This double usage is sometimes a source of confusion, but ordinarily one can tell from the context which of the meanings is intended. Much of the emphasis in this chapter will be on fractionation, although some of the apparatus and techniques of electrodecantation will also be discussed.

Up to now, fractionation by electrophoresis has been used mainly as an analytical tool and for the preparation of a few milligrams or perhaps grams of specialty chemicals, mostly biochemicals. It has proved to be a very elegant way, however, to separate chemically similar or labile substances which are not amenable to treatment by the usual engineering methods. Proteins, for example, can be fractionated at low temperature and in buffered media, conditions which help to preserve their specificity and other important biological properties. If the laboratory methods of electrophoresis could be scaled up economically from throughputs of a few hundred milliliters per day to even a gallon a day, there would be widespread applications in the manufacture of hormones, antigens and antibodies, venoms, viruses, enzymes, and various polymers.

## II. Review of Principles

A. ELECTROKINETICS

Electrophoresis is just one of the electrokinetic phenomena which include also electroosmosis, streaming potential, and the Dorn effect of spray electrification. These are interrelated inasmuch as they all depend upon the relative motion of a fluid and a charged surface, usually a solid. In *electroosmosis* the solid is fixed in place and a flow of liquid is induced by an applied electrical potential. The effect is pronounced only in fine capillaries or porous solids where the ratio of surface to volume is high. For example, the walls of a fine glass capillary are usually negatively charged in water or in a dilute salt solution, and therefore the water near the wall will have an excess of positive ions. As these positive ions move toward the negative electrode, they cause a bulk flow of the water in that direction. Such electroosmotic flow may be prevented by opposing a sufficient counterpressure which can then be used, instead of flow rate, as a quantitative measure of electroosmosis. If both ends of the capillary are sealed off, a circulation pattern is set up in which liquid near the walls flows toward the negative electrode but liquid in the center of the capillary flows in the opposite direction. For this case there is a particular distance from the wall at which the net flow of liquid is zero.

When liquid is forced through a capillary or charged particles are allowed to rise or fall through a liquid, the electrical potentials induced are commonly referred to as *streaming potential* or *Dorn effect*, respectively. These phenomena, which are essentially the converse of electroosmosis and electrophoresis, will not be discussed further here.

B. THE ELECTRICAL DOUBLE LAYER

To gain some insight into electrokinetics, we must remind ourselves that the excess ions or electrons on the solid surface are just balanced electrically by counterions (sometimes called gegenions) distributed in the nearby liquid. This system of a charged surface surrounded by a mixture of ions in which the counterions predominate is referred to as the electrical "double layer." An early model, due to Helmholtz, pictured the neutralizing counterions as concentrated in a plane at a fixed distance from the solid surface.

but the later Gouy-Chapman treatment is based on a diffuse cloud of counterions resulting from thermal agitation. For a flat charged surface, the net charge density at any distance away is calculated by combining a Boltzmanm distribution of the positive and negative ions with the Poisson equation,

$$d^2\psi/dx^2 = -4\pi \, \rho_e/D \qquad (1)$$

where $\psi$ is the electrical potential at the distance $x$ due to a volume density of point charges $\rho_e$, and $D$ is the dielectric constant of the medium. The general solution is complicated even for a plane double layer, but if the potential at the solid surface, $\psi_0$, is small compared to $kT$ (i.e., $\psi_0 \ll 25$ mv at room temperature) the potential is given by

$$\psi = \psi_0 \, e^{-\kappa x} \qquad (2)$$

Here $\kappa$ is the term appearing in Debye-Hückel theory, defined as

$$\kappa^2 = (8\pi\epsilon^2 \, \mathbf{N}/1000 \, DkT)(\Gamma/2) \qquad (3)$$

where $\epsilon$ is the electronic charge, $\mathbf{N}$ is Avagadro's number, $\mathbf{k}$ is Boltzmann's constant, $T$ is the absolute temperature, and $\Gamma/2$ is the ionic strength. At 25 °C the calculation of $\kappa^2$ reduces to

$$\kappa^2 = (8.49/D)(\Gamma/2) \quad (\text{Angstrom}^{-2}) \qquad (4)$$

The quantity $1/\kappa$ has the dimensions of length, and according to equation 2 represents the distance at which the potential has reached $1/e$ of its value at the surface. Therefore it is often used to define a "thickness of the double layer," even when the necessary assumptions of low surface potential and dilute electrolyte are no longer strictly true. For monovalent electrolytes the thickness according to equation 4 is 10 A for $0.1M$, 100 A for $.001M$, and 1000 A for $10^{-5}M$ concentration.

In electrophoresis the surface potentials are often too large for the simplified result shown in equation 2 to be valid. Under such circumstances, however, even the more exact results of the Gouy-Chapman analysis break down; absurdly high ion concentrations are predicted for the region close to the solid surface. Accordingly the theory has been modified in recent years, chiefly by Stern, to allow for the finite size of the counterions and to allow for some specific binding of the counterions by weak chemical forces or by van der Waals forces. In qualitative terms the inner Stern layer consists of a compact portion of the double layer about one molecule thick. It contains solvated counterions which are held in the Stern layer by adsorption on the solid.

The electrical potential right at the surface of the solid is not readily measured, but it is known to be altered by ions added to the solution. Such "potential-determining ions" can be considered as desolvated and forming a part of the surface. The example of hydrogen ions affecting the charge on a protein molecule, cited in the Section I may be given as an illustration. Another classical example is the specific effect of $Ag^+$ in producing a positive charge on colloidal $AgI$, presumably because of its direct addition onto sites in the ionic lattice. Sometimes it is not so clear whether ions added to the water are adsorbed in the Stern layer or whether they are more directly attached to the surface.

## C. THE ZETA POTENTIAL AND ELECTROPHORESIS

The various electrokinetic phenomena depend upon an immobile layer of liquid which adheres to the solid and is not sheared off by the relatively slow creeping motion induced by the electrical field. This layer is not to be confused with the "stagnant film" sometimes pictured in discussions of heat or mass transfer. Rather it is a structured layer extending only one or two molecular diameters and consisting of solvent molecules bound or adsorbed onto the solid surface. It coincides roughly with the Stern layer but may sometimes extend farther out into the liquid. Although various solvated ions are imbedded in the immobile layer, a most important feature is that not all of the excess charge on the surface of the solid is neutralized within the immobile layer. Therefore a net potential called the zeta potential $\xi$, is established between the slip plane and the bulk of the liquid. The magnitude of the zeta potential will depend partly on the charge density at the surface and partly on the thickness of the electrical double layer. If the double layer is thick, the potential decreases only slowly with distance from the surface and therefore at the plane of shear it is still appreciable. Figure 1 shows diagrammatically how the thickness, as measured by $1/\kappa$ for example, is related to the zeta potential. Obviously, if the double layer is so thin that all of the excess charge on the surface is neutralized within the immobile layer, then the zeta potential will be zero.

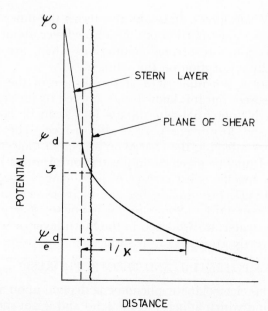

DISTANCE

Fig. 1. The fall of potential in the double layer. The potential at the beginning of the diffuse portion, $\psi\ d$, is reduced by a factor of $1/e$ in the distance $1/K$ for low potentials. (Redrawn from K. J. Mysels, *Introduction to Colloid Chemistry*, Interscience, New York, 1959.)

A force balance relates the velocity of electrophoresis to the zeta potential. If we disregard size and shape of the particle for the moment and consider a plane surface, the force exerted per unit area is $\sigma E'$ where $\sigma$ is the surface charge density at the slip plane and $E'$ is the field, in electrostatic volts per centimeter, which is applied to induce motion. This force, $\sigma E'$, is balanced by the viscous drag, $\eta\ v/\tau$ so that

$$v = \sigma\tau\ E'/\eta \qquad (5)$$

Here $v$ is the linear velocity in centimeters per second, $\tau$ is the effective thickness in cm of the double layer from the shear plane out to the point where all charges are neutralized, and $\eta$ is the viscosity of the solution in poises. For the product $\sigma\tau$ one can substitute its electrostatic equivalent $D\ \xi'/4\pi$, a relationship used in the theory of parallel-plate condensers. Equation 5 becomes

$$v = \xi'\ E'D/4\pi\eta \qquad (6)$$

where both $\xi'$ and $E'$ are in electrostatic volts (i.e., 1 e.s.v. $= 300$ ordinary volts). In practical units and for water at 25 °C, equation 6 may be abbreviated to

$$\mu = 7.78 \times 10^{-6}\,\xi \tag{7}$$

where $\mu$ is the *electrophoretic mobility* defined as the velocity in a potential gradient of 1 v/cm. In equation 7, $\mu$ is expressed in (cm/sec)/(v/cm), and $\xi$ in millivolts. Typical values for the zeta potential range from zero to a hundred millivolts or slightly more. The zeta potential is not independently measured, but is calculated from measurements made on one or another of the electrokinetic phenomena.

Several kinds of corrections to equations 6 and 7 must be made. If the particles are spherical and if the double layer is so thick that its curvature must be taken into account, then the numerical constant in equation 6 should be $1/6\,\pi$ instead of $1/4\,\pi$. For spheres of radius $a$, the correction need not be made unless the ratio of particle radius to thickness of the double layer, $\kappa a$, is less than 100. Thus for bacteria with $a = 1 \times 10^{-4}$ cm, $\kappa a$ is about 1000 in 0.1 $N$ NaCl, but for small colloidal particles or proteins the $\kappa a$ factor is commonly less than unity.

Another correction which applies especially to small particles is described as a relaxation effect. As the particle moves through the background electrolyte, there is a delay in the formation of the double layer in front of the particle and a persistence of the double layer behind the particle. The net effect is to slow down the particle, sometimes by as much as 50%, so that the calculated $\xi$ potentials are too low. Still another correction is for surface conductance of electricity. This conductance, which arises from the high concentration of ions near the charged surface, acts as a partial short-circuit in reducing the electrophoretic velocity. The correction may amount to as much as 20% of the zeta potential for large particles at low ionic strength.

No further discussion of the theory itself seems appropriate here because the interested reader can refer to the general treatments by Overbeek (1) and Abramson (2) on electrokinetic phenomena, or to the detailed discussions presented in several chapters of Bier's book on electrophoresis (3). The interpretation of electrophoretic mobilities in terms of charge densities instead of zeta potentials is not yet on firm theoretical ground, but much of the recent experimental work is directed to this end (4,5).

## D. FACTORS INFLUENCING THE MOBILITY

From the physical picture and theory one can gain some insight into factors that influence the electrophoretic mobility. Most important is the influence of ionic strength on the zeta potential and hence on mobility. To a first approximation the mobility varies inversely as the square root of the ionic strength. For ions of the $i$ species with valence $z$ and molar concentration $c$ the ionic strength is defined as

$$\Gamma/2 = 1/2 \, \Sigma \, c_i z_i^2 \tag{8}$$

Therefore it is not only the concentration but also the valence of the ions that becomes important.

Often, however, changing the ionic environment also changes the charge, and therefore the potential, at the surface or within the Stern layer. Then one cannot simply predict the effects on mobility and recourse must be made to particular examples. Especially with heavy-metal ions as counterions, small increases in the external concentration may markedly decrease the zeta potential. The penetration of thorium ions into the Stern layer on a glass surface is well known; a concentration of only $10^{-6}M$ of Th$^{+4}$ reduces the zeta potential to zero, and at higher concentrations the glass becomes positively charged. Even within a series of monovalent ions there are differences in ability to penetrate the double layer. The concentrations required to just reverse the charge on a negatively charged phosphate surface are $0.15N$ Ag$^+$, $1N$ Li$^+$, or $2.8N$ Na$^+$ (1). The relatively greater effectiveness of a particular ion in reducing the zeta potential also pertains to the anions; for monovalent anions the order of effectiveness is CNS$^-$ > I$^-$ > Br$^-$ > Cl$^-$. Such observations are related, of course, to the "Schulze-Hardy rule" and "lyotropic series," terms frequently used in connection with the flocculation of colloids.

Because the amount and nature of electrolyte has such a large effect on electrophoresis, salts of known composition are usually added to any mixture being fractionated by electrophoresis. Buffer salts are used with ampholytes whose mobility would otherwise shift with pH. Sometimes by changing the electrolyte, differences in the relative mobilities of various fractions can be enhanced, because adsorption depends not only on the ion but also on the nature of the surface. Thus Longsworth (6) reported that a barbital buffer was better able to resolve the components of human blood serum than a phosphate buffer but that the phosphate buffer gave better results for horse serum. Despite the theory therefore, much trial and error experimentation is still involved in devising the best buffer system for each particular separation.

More easily predictable are the effects of changing the viscosity, dielectric constant, or conductivity. According to equation 6, the velocity of a particle will vary directly with the dielectric constant and inversely with viscosity, a fact of importance when considering the addition of materials like sucrose or glycerol to alter the density of the suspending liquid. Furthermore, if there are local high concentrations of electrolyte so that the electrical conductivity is not uniform across the fractionating chamber, then the voltage drop $E'$ will be correspondingly lower in such regions and the velocity of electrophoresis will be reduced.

### III. Brief Review of Laboratory Methods

Laboratory apparatus of two types is available, analytical and preparative. The two types are generally quite different, although paperstrip electrophoresis, for example, can be used either to detect differences in mobility or to prepare pure fractions. Only preparative methods with low throughput, just a few milliliters per hour will be treated in this section.

#### A. ANALYTICAL METHODS

##### 1. Microelectrophoresis

If the particles are large enough to be seen easily in the microscope, direct calculation of their speed is possible by simply timing their passage across the optical field. Even proteins can be studied by this method because when coated onto small glass beads, the protein usually imparts its own mobility to the beads. Figure 2 shows a simplified diagram of the apparatus. Because the electrophoresis cell is thin, there is an appreciable flow of the liquid by electroosmosis. Observations on the particles must either be cor-

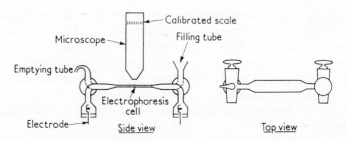

Fig. 2. Principle of a microscopic method of measuring electrophoretic mobilities. (From K. J. Mysels, *Introduction to Colloid Chemistry*, Interscience, New York, 1959.)

rected for this flow or else the observations must be made at a depth in the cell at which there is no net flow. With the stopcocks closed, flow toward the cathode near the walls is balanced by flow in the opposite direction in the center of the chamber. Chamber design permits the approximation of infinite flat plates for which the points of zero velocity are 21.2% of the distance from either wall. As in most electrophoresis work, the voltage gradient $E$ is calculated by applying Ohm's law to measured values of the current, the specific conductance, and the cross-sectional area of the chamber.

## 2. Moving Boundary

In this method, refined by Tiselius, the mixture to be analyzed is placed in the bottom of a U-tube and is layered over with dilute buffer so that there are initially two sharp interfaces. Under a voltage gradient, ascending boundaries are formed in one limb of the U-tube while descending boundaries are formed in the other limb. Each species within the mixture forms a boundary moving with characteristic speed. Slight differences in refractive index among the layers are detected by optical scanning which locates the boundaries very exactly. Only the fastest and slowest components can be separated out in pure form, however.

As might be expected careful adjustment and control of density, buffer strength, and temperature must be maintained if the moving boundaries are to remain sharp. One of the difficulties in all such free-boundary methods is that an abrupt difference in conductivity arises at each boundary. Even though slight, the difference in conductivity causes a discontinuity in the potential gradient at that point. A blurring or tailing of the boundary results ("boundary anomaly") which can only be minimized by using very dilute colloids so that their contribution to the conductivity is small. This limitation will be mentioned again later in considering large-scale methods of electrophoresis.

Alberty (7) has presented a concise review of the essential features of this method.

## 3. Zone Electrophoresis

In the moving boundary method just described, convection is avoided by density differences at each boundary; the density increases with concentration toward the bottom of the U-tube and so the system remains stable. Instead of such a "frontal analysis," each of the components may be separated into distinct zones provided some means of stabilizing against density differences can be devised. Anticonvection supports include sheets of filter paper (8,9) or various gels (10,11). Columns can be packed with cellulose, starch powder, or glass beads to give higher capacity for separation than is possible with thin sheets of material. In batchwise operation the procedure is similar to adsorption or partition chromatography, and in fact the word electrochromatography has been applied to zone electrophoresis with solid anticonvection media. Mobilities observed on such media appear to be much lower than free-boundary mobilities, but if enough corrections are made it is sometimes

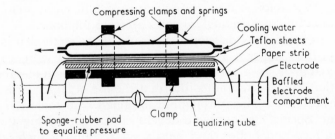

Fig. 3. Principle of a typical cell for paper electrophoresis. The Teflon sheets on either side of the paper strip help to prevent evaporation. Other types of cell are also in common use. (Courtesy Dr. S. M. Raymond of E-C Apparatus Co., Swarthmore, Pa., and K. J. Mysels, *Introduction to Colloid Chemistry*, Interscience, New York, 1959.)

possible to estimate true values. Convenience and simplicity of apparatus are the chief virtues of this useful analytical method which is described in more detail elsewhere (12). Figure 3 shows a typical paper-strip cell.

## B. PREPARATIVE METHODS

Svensson (13) has reviewed the preparative methods up to 1948 and Bier (14) has brought the subject up to date. Even though capacities are low in laboratory apparatus, the principles can be used for scale-up. Besides, it must be remembered that for expensive materials high rates may not be necessary. It has been pointed out (15) that, even though a 500-g batch of toxoid or vaccine takes 2–4 weeks to process, it may represent half a billion units of biological activity and serve to vaccinate as many as 100,000,000 people.

### 1. Continuous-Flow Curtain Electrophoresis

Several kinds of curtain devices using filter paper are available for laboratory preparative work. A mixture of proteins in buffer, for example, flows in a narrow streak down the vertical or inclined sheet of filter paper, with a buffered solution of suitable pH as background electrolyte saturating the paper. Under the action of a transverse electrical field, the various protein fractions fan out into individual streams. The purified components are collected at the bottom edge of the paper, which is serrated to form numerous drip points. Flow rates of the feed rarely exceed 5 ml/hour, although Karler (15) has found that crude mixtures can be given preliminary separation by "overfeeding" at rates up to 15 ml/hour.

Brattsten (16) has developed a similar flow method using, instead of filter paper, a rectangular column packed with starch or powdered glass. In a valuable discussion of the design features and limitations, Brattsten pointed out that the use of larger glass beads would permit a higher throughput although with some loss in resolution. Special devices were developed for controlling the flow rates of feed and buffer, and mostly on account of such complications the Brattsten device has not been widely used. The recent commercial development of a similar column (JKM Instrument Company, Durham, Pa.) may make the method more popular, however.

## 2. Column Methods

Zone electrophoresis in columns has already been mentioned as an analytical technique, and it is sufficient to state that the procedures are like those used for column chromatography. The separation is necessarily done batchwise, with the electrode chambers connected to the ends of the vertical column. After separation into stabilized zones, the contents must be removed without remixing and the separated components must be eluted from any gel or granular supporting medium. Porath (17) has carried out rather large-scale fractionation in such packed columns.

Solid packing materials have many disadvantages, as will be pointed out later, and therefore much interest has recently centered around stabilization by a strong density gradient instead of by solids. This density gradient is produced not by the colloid, as in the Tiselius cell, but by an electrically neutral solute, such as sugar or glycerol. The trick, of course, is to establish a gradient in density which will maintain stability of the individual zones all during their movement. Brakke (18) introduced density gradient stabilization to column electrophoresis, although the stabilizing principle had been used much earlier by Philpot (19) in a flow device. Its recent development both experimentally and theoretically has been promoted by Svensson et al (20). They have shown that a nonlinear density gradient in the column is favorable and have devised a clever system of two mixing chambers in series to load the column with a continuously decreasing sample concentration and continuously increasing sucrose concentration. After fractionation such columns can be emptied in a matter of a few minutes instead of the hours required for a powder column. The same apparatus can often be used either with a density gradient or with packed solids.

A novel modification of column electrophoresis has been explored by Kolin (21) in which the components of a mixture are separated by virtue of differences in their isoelectric points rather than by differences in their mobilities. Essentially the method depends upon establishing a pH gradient along with a density gradient in the column. The mixture is layered between an acidic buffer and a basic buffer so chosen that the isoelectric points of all components will lie within the extremes of pH. When a voltage gradient is applied along the column, components migrate in *both* directions until they arrive at the region corresponding to their individual isoelectric points. The so-called "isoelectric spectra" are rapidly established and moreover the zones are sharp. Such movement in both directions to form a concentrated zone of particles starting from a diffuse suspension is also described as a "focusing effect." Critical to the success of this procedure is the establishment and maintenance of a uniform pH gradient. The various charged buffer ions will themselves tend to migrate in the voltage gradient, often at different speeds, and in doing so will cause a shift in the pH gradient.

Besides pH gradients and density gradients still other simultaneous conditions have been superimposed onto column electrophoresis in attempts to improve it. These include the use of magnetic fields, conductivity gradients to sharpen the zones, and use of the adsorptive or sieving action of solid or gelatinous media (21).

## 3. Electroconvection

In all of the methods described so far, more than two fractions can be simultaneously separated in the same apparatus. In electroconvection, on the other hand, a split can be made only between mobile and nonmobile components. For a typical application to the separation of proteins, the mixture is first buffered at the isoelectric pH of one of its components, and then placed between two vertical semipermeable membranes. When an electrical field is applied, charged proteins migrate toward one of the electrodes, but since they cannot penetrate the membrane they accumulate close to it in a dense concentrated layer which tends to sink to the bottom of the apparatus. At the end of a run, mobile components are concentrated in a bottom reservoir, while the single component that has been immobilized at its isoelectric point is distributed evenly in the entire apparatus. Near the top of the apparatus, however, the immobile component will be relatively pure.

Electroconvection can also be operated under conditions where all components are mobile and move toward the same membrane. The faster-moving components are preferentially swept toward the bottom reservoir so that a partial separation results.

In recent years the theory of electroconvection, which is similar to the theory of the thermal diffusion column, has been developed in detail by Kirkwood and his associates. Improvements in design have also been made by narrowing the gap between the semipermeable membranes and by providing for cooling during the long periods of operation that are sometimes necessary. Several versions commercially available for laboratory use are described by Bier in his thorough review of the method (14).

### 4. Countercurrent Electrophoresis

There is still another preparative method, quite distinct from the ones already described in that it depends on a flow of the mixture being separated. The bulk flow of liquid is countercurrent to one or more mobile components as indicated in Figure 4, where the lengths of the arrows represent relative velocities in the voltage gradient.

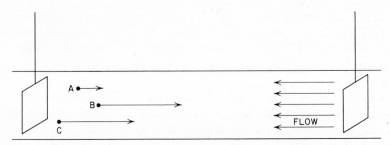

Fig. 4. Principle of countercurrent electrophoresis. Component A will be removed from the more rapidly migrating components B and C.

Components A, B, and C all tend to migrate toward the cathode in this example, but A is swept out of the apparatus by a counterflow of buffer. The stream leaving is depleted in components B and C, both of which tend to accumulate in the apparatus because they can migrate upstream faster than the flow. Careful control of flow rate is, of course, necessary if a cut must be made between components that differ only slightly in mobility. As in electroconvection, the mixture is separated into just two fractions on a single pass. The apparatus can be equipped for continuous withdrawal of both fractions, however, by feeding continuously at the bottom of an upright U-tube and withdrawing fractions from each arm of the tube. High purity is attained in only one of the streams under such conditions.

The countercurrent flow method was developed by Brewer and Madorsky at the U. S. Bureau of Standards and later applied to the separation of rare earths by Clusius and Ramirez (22). Chemla (23) has recently reviewed its utility for isotope separation. Because its main application has been to inorganic ions this technique is often referred to as "countercurrent electromigration" rather than countercurrent electrophoresis. Bickel *et al.* (50) have used the method for purifying an antibiotic.

### 5. Summary

There are perhaps three broad classes of preparative electrophoresis, each having many modifications. The following short statements serve to summarize the essential features and to point up some of the similarities and differences.

**Zone Electrophoresis.** Simultaneous separation of several individual components in a single pass is possible. Stabilization is necessary. The method can be carried out batchwise or continuously; if continuous, the voltage gradient is *transverse to the direction of fluid flow within the apparatus.*

**Electrodecantation or Electroconvection.** Separation into only two fractions is possible in a single pass. An essential feature is self-stabilization because of the higher density of more concentrated colloid. The method usually depends on natural convection to remove one stream, but forced convection can also be used.

**Countercurrent Electrophoresis.** Separation into only two fractions is possible in a single pass. The method necessarily involves flow and the voltage gradient is in the *same direction as flow of fluid within the apparatus.*

## IV. Problems in Scale-Up

To scale-up electrophoresis from a throughput of several milliliters per hour to several milliliters per minute might not seem like a very formidable task, but it offers a number of challenges to the chemical engineer. For example, his usual reliance on film theory or penetration theory to understand mass transfer is of no help in attempting such scale-up. Another point of difference for the engineer is that instead of trying to promote turbulence he must try to avoid it because even the slightest distortion in flow pattern may cause remixing of already-separated components. The usual definition of laminar flow based on pressure drop becomes inadequate, since wavy patterns are known to appear in pipes well below a Reynolds number of 2100 (24).

Joule heating is probably the single factor that causes most difficulty in scaling-up. Heating is a problem primarily because it gives rise to unwanted convection currents, but it also wastes power and damages many of the materials to be treated. As the equipment is scaled up in order to increase its capacity, the dissipation of internally-generated heat becomes more and more difficult. It is for this reason large packed columns do not appear to be as promising as some of the other devices.

## A. ZONE ELECTROPHORESIS

Some of the special problems that arise in trying to increase the throughput in zone electrophoresis will now be considered.

### 1. Disadvantages of Solid Packing

The reason for using solid packing is clear enough; it stabilizes migration of zones against convection currents and consequently permits the use of simpler equipment. On the other hand, solid packing slows down the mobility and increases the heat generation to such an extent that it often accentuates the very ills it is supposed to cure. Kunkel and Tiselius (25), for example, showed that mobilities in filter paper are often as much as five times lower than those in free electrophoresis because the path length for migration is increased by a tortuosity factor. Because the electrical resistance is correspondingly high, heat is generated at a rate considerably above the rate in free liquid.

Electroosmosis is another difficulty encountered with packing materials like cellulose, starch, and glass which are themselves charged with respect to the liquid filling the pores. Finely divided solids, which are the most effective for suppressing convection, are also the most active in causing electroosmotic flow. It is fairly easy to cope with this problem when electrophoresis is proceeding at a leisurely pace, but when attempts are made to improve migration rates by stepping up the voltage or by reducing the ionic strength of the buffer, there is so much electroosmotic flow of liquid that migration of the zones is distorted.

The presence of an electrical charge on the solid packing suggests that there may be an interaction with the migrating components of the mixture being fractionated, and indeed this is usually the case. Temporary adsorption of the particles onto the solid surfaces acts to reduce the electrophoretic mobility in a manner analogous to what happens in chromatography. This adsorption effect may be helpful in some separations, but it slows down very considerably the rate of electrophoretic movement.

Other complications include (a) the difficulty of getting rapid enough flow rates through fine packing, and (b) the tendency for transverse dispersion caused by the interweaving action of the porous structure on the fluid streamlines (26). A more quantitative discussion of anticonvection media does not seem warranted here, as most of the efforts to scale-up zone electrophoresis have sought to avoid the use of solids for stabilization. Interested readers are referred to the excellent discussion of supporting media by Kunkel and Troutman (27).

## 2. Resolving Power and Heating Effects

It is interesting to consider some of the design limits for a continuous flow system without packing. If free convection can somehow be suppressed, the mixture will be resolved into a spectrum of discrete bands or zones under the action of a potential gradient transverse to the flow. The separation of these bands under conditions of plug flow is simply

$$\Delta s = E(\Delta\mu)\theta_r = E(\Delta\mu)l/u \tag{9}$$

where $\Delta s$ is the distance between centers of any two bands in cm, $\theta_r$ is the retention time in seconds, $\Delta\mu$ is the difference in mobility in $cm^2/(v)(sec)$, $l$ is the effective length of the fractionation chamber in cm, and $u$ is the fluid velocity in cm/sec.

Power dissipated in the fractionation chamber in watts, $P$, expressed by the product of voltage and current

$$P = (Ed)(kAE) \tag{10}$$

where $d$ is the distance between walls of the chamber in the direction of the electrical field in cm, $A$ is the area transverse to the field in $cm^2$, and $k$ is the electrical conductivity of the background buffer in $ohm^{-1}cm^{-1}$. In terms of the volume of the chamber, $V$,

$$P = V E^2 k \quad \text{(watt)}$$

$$P' = 0.24\ VE^2 k \quad \text{(cal/sec)} \tag{11}$$

The total heat in calories dissipated in one holdup time, $Q$, is $P'\theta$. and since the total heat capacity of one holdup volume is $V\rho c_p$, the rise in temperature is given by

$$\Delta t = Q/V\rho c_p = 0.24\ E^2kl/u\rho c_p \quad (^\circ\text{C}) \tag{12}$$

where $\rho$ is density in g/cm³ and $c_p$ is heat capacity in cal/(g)(°C). Equation 12 states that the temperature rise depends only on the effective length of the fractionation chamber and on operating variables $E$, $k$, $u$, and $c_p$.

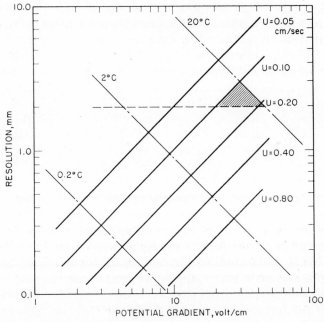

Fig. 5. Resolution and thermal effects for a particular separation problem (see text for details). ($k = 10^{-4}$ ohm⁻¹ cm⁻¹ and $\Delta\mu = 10^{-5}$ cm²/(v)(sec).)

Figure 5 illustrates the relationships of equations 9 and 12 for a fractionation chamber 100 cm long and $\Delta\mu = 0.1$ (micron/sec)/(v/cm), $k = 10^{-4}$ ohm⁻¹cm⁻¹ and unit specific gravity and

specific heat. These would be typical conditions for a protein separation in dilute buffer. The triangular cross-hatched area in
Figure 5 shows the working region for a minimum resolution of
2 mm, a minimum flow rate of 0.1 cm/sec and an upper limit of
20°C for rise in temperature. Although the conditions chosen for
this example are arbitrary, similar charts could be prepared to
examine other design limits and to explore the feasibility of zone
electrophoresis.

### 3. Strength of Buffers

There is considerable advantage in using a background electrolyte of low ionic strength. Separations are faster because of the increased mobility of all components and also because the lower electrical conductivity allows the application of a more intense electrical field at sufficiently low current to avoid overheating. The
presence of some electrolyte is probably necessary to maintain the
pH and to minimize "boundary anomalies" which arise when the
feed mixture has a higher conductivity than the background solution (see also Section II-D).

For sharp bands or zones it is desirable to pretreat the mixture
to be separated so as to lower its conductivity below that of the
background solution. Then as the various components move out
from the mixture, the trailing particles are in a stronger electric
field than the leading particles. In tending to overtake the leading
particles these laggard ones sharpen up what would otherwise be a
trailing edge. It is not always possible, of course, to deionize the
feed because some colloids are unstable in solutions of low ionic
strength. Many proteins, for example, would not be sufficiently
soluble in distilled water. For the electrophoresis of living cells which
would plasmolyze in water, the adjustment of osmotic pressure can
be made with weakly dissociated compounds rather than with ionized salt mixtures, so as to hold down the electrical conductivity.

## V. Techniques for Large-Scale Electrophoresis

Some of the newer developments which hold promise for fractionating gallons per day will be described according to the classification of preparative methods outlined in Section III-B-5.

## A. CONTINUOUS-FLOW ZONE ELECTROPHORESIS

### 1. Stabilization by Density Gradient

In a series of recent publications (28–30) Mel has described an improved flow apparatus based on horizontal layering of sucrose solutions to provide stabilization of the separating zones. This is the principle used earlier by Philpot (19) who was unable, however, to accomplish protein fractionations successfully; or in his own

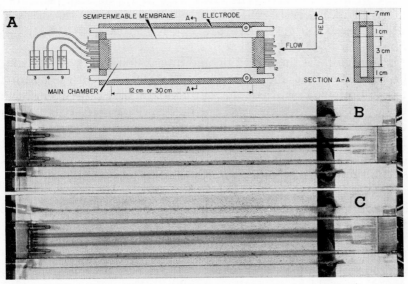

Fig. 6. Flow apparatus for zone electrophoresis stabilized by a density gradient (30). A, Diagram of apparatus. B, Dye admitted through inlets 5 and 7, without electrical field, showing stability obtainable. C, Migration of dyestuffs in opposite directions upon application of electrical field, showing "crossover" and a reaction product being separated as a middle component.

words, "Considerable progress has been made in overcoming the many small difficulties involved; but at the moment of writing, the apparatus must be classed with those aeroplanes at South Kensington which never left the ground." The improvements by Mel may make the method possible.

The Mel device, built of Plexiglas as shown in Figure 6, has 12 inlets and 12 outlets in the fractionation chamber so that single or multiple samples can be injected along with background fluid. The electrode chambers are isolated hydrodynamically as is usual in this type of apparatus. A unique feature, however, is the collection system which ensures equal withdrawal rates by syphoning each of the 12 discharge streams into separate containers set at exactly the same level. Such an arrangement is simpler than pumping in and out at identical rates, and is self-adjusting besides.

Figure 6B shows the stability obtainable as two dye streams enter at inlets 5 and 7. The flows were at 1.2 ml/min per outlet (14.4 ml/min overall) and typical sucrose concentrations of: Nos. 1–4, none; No. 5, 0.4%; No. 6, 0.5%; No. 7, 0.8%; No. 8, 1.0%; Nos. 9–12, 2%.

Figure 6 shows the migration and interaction of cresyl violet and bromophenol blue under a superimposed pH gradient from 4 to 7, top to bottom. Further details on this particular experiment have been published (30) and will not be described here. It illustrates the versatility, however, of this device in applying other gradients. Mel emphasizes that the apparatus can be used to study rapid chemical or enzymatic reactions that occur during "crossover" of streams moving in opposite directions in the electrical field.

## 2. Stabilization by Laminar Viscous Flow

Dobry and Finn (31, 32) reasoned that one way to avoid the disturbing convection currents would be to enforce a laminar flow regime so that the ratio of Grashof number to Reynolds number, $N_{Gr}/N_{Re}$, would be as small as possible. Theoretical studies (33) have shown that this modulus can be used to predict flow disturbances.

The apparatus, shown in Figure 7, is in many ways similar to the Mel device except that it is set vertically. Since no density gradient is artificially established within the chamber, upward flow is desired so that any slight decrease in density of the liquid caused by electrical heating will aid rather than oppose the flow of fluid. Electrode chambers, $E$, are separated by porous walls, $PW$, from the separation chamber, $S$. The mixture to be separated is injected at the bottom, $I$, of the 4-foot column through a centrally located inlet duct. Later models of the apparatus have multiple inlet ducts for either the feed mixture or for background buffer.

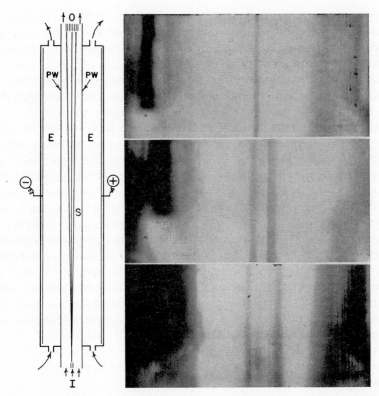

Fig. 7. Apparatus used for stabilization of zones with flow and a thickening agent (31). At the right are photographs taken near the top of the column, showing separation of a mixture of basic fuchsin, bromthymol blue, and bromphenol blue at pH 5.3. At the bottom right, no voltage; middle right, 6 v/cm and a linear flow of 0.34 cm/sec; upper right, 6 v/cm but with flow rate reduced to 0.29 cm/sec. At the reduced flow rate separation distances were 7 mm, red to yellow, and 3 mm, yellow to blue. The suspending medium of methylcellulose in acetate buffer had a viscosity of 10 centipoise.

At the outlet, $O$, knife edges permit separate withdrawal of the individual bands or zones.

Typical results for separating a dye mixture are shown at the right in Figure 7. A mixture of three dyes was split into separate bands at a flow rate of about 5 ml/min. Operating conditions for dye separation, cited in the caption of Figure 7, were close to the upper limit of the apparatus so that considerable improvement is necessary to fractionate proteins that are only about one-tenth as mobile as dyes. The direction of such improvements has been discussed by Dobry and Finn (32) and use of the apparatus has been extended to the fractionation of certain natural pigments.

Useful separations were not possible unless a thickening agent was added to increase the viscosity of the aqueous buffer and thereby to reduce still further the $N_{Gr}/N_{Re}$ modulus. Ordinarily one might suppose that any such advantage from high viscosity would be partly offset by a proportional reduction in electrophoretic mobility (see eq. 6). Structural viscosity as exhibited by dissolved polymers is quite different, however, from the viscosity contributed by solutes like sucrose or glycerol. Although the polymer solution is effective in suppressing eddies, its fibrillar structure permits the easy passage of water-soluble molecules or even larger particles. Therefore the electrophoretic mobility of many substances is almost unaffected by the presence of polymer. The thickening agents chosen for electrophoresis should be water-soluble polymers such as dextran or methylcellulose which are essentially uncharged. The necessity for later separation of such thickening agents and the possibility of their interaction with some components of the mixture being separated are certainly disadvantages of this method.

As an example of how engineering principles may lead to improved design, it is instructive to examine the implications of the Grashof number:

$$N_{Gr} = l^3 g \rho^2 \beta \Delta t_i / \eta^2 \tag{13}$$

where $l$ = length of the chamber; $g$ = acceleration of gravity; $\rho$ = density of fluid; $\beta$ = coefficient of thermal expansion; $\Delta t_i$ = characteristic temperature difference; and $\eta$ = viscosity of fluid. If $N_{Gr}$ is to be made as small as possible, it might seem that length of the chamber should be drastically reduced. This is true, but the exponent of $l$ is more properly 2 instead of 3, as regards its effect on convection. If, for example, the length is cut in half, the potential gradient must be doubled in order to get the same resolution. Even though the magnitude of the characteristic temperature difference ($\Delta t_i$) is not known, it may be expected to double under the new conditions in general accord with equation 12. The over-all result is that variation in length will affect convection as $l^2$ rather than as $l^3$.

## 3. Stabilization by Porous Barriers

Instead of depending on density gradients or viscous flow to prevent convective mixing this method reintroduces porous solids into the fractionating chamber. Only a few thin sheets are used, however, and these are arranged parallel to the flow so that each stream entering the chamber can maintain its identity throughout the length of the chamber. The horizontal fractionating chamber is essentially the same as in the apparatus of Mel, except that thin membranes of porous plastic or paper isolate the inlet streams so that each passes without mixing to the exit. These porous flow barriers reduce somewhat the mobility of the migrating particles, but do not provide nearly as much interference as if the whole chamber were packed with solids.

Work on this method was begun independently at Cornell University (34) and at the University of Zurich (35). Ernst Schumacher and his students in Zurich have perfected the apparatus to a high degree and have demonstrated its stability under extreme conditions of heat generation. Their apparatus was water cooled to permit the dissipation of as much as 180 w of power in a fractionation chamber only 30 cm long and 2.6 cm² in cross section. Considerable heating took place, of course, but the channels were so thin (3 mm) that flows were stable. All of their work has been done with inorganic ions and in such separations they have made full use of pH gradients and gradients of complexing agents to achieve a very strong "focusing effect." Schumacher (36) has treated the theory of such separations in detail, paying special attention to the chemical reactions and to diffusion which enter so prominently into the so-called "focusing ion exchange."

For electrophoresis, a rather simple two-channel apparatus was used by Mizma (34) at Cornell to study the transfer of dyes from one channel to the other. The over-all length of the apparatus was 5 feet. Each channel was 2.5 mm deep and 1 inch wide, and the separation barrier of 9-micron porous Teflon was 1/16-inch thick. A number of modifications of this crude model would have to be made if an effective production unit were built, but the efficiency of electrophoretic transport could be tested in preliminary fashion. In this type of equipment the appropriate linear dimension to insert into the Grashof number is, $b$, the depth of channel between porous barriers, rather than the total length $l$ of the fractionating chamber. Because the depth is only 2.5 mm in the Mizma apparatus, there is little opportunity for convection eddies to grow large.

The theory of barrier electrophoresis can begin at least with a simple model of laminar flow filling one of the channels. The channel is fed with a stream which has only one migrating species. The fractionation chamber must be long enough so that a particle in the uppermost part of the channel, for example, can migrate to the floor, i.e., across the entire depth of the channel. The fraction removed at any distance downstream (by "falling through the floor," so to speak) can be readily calculated. If one neglects molecular diffusion, the combined effect of a parabolic flow profile and electrophoresis results in

$$(R^2/2) - (R^3/3) = \mu El/ub \qquad (14)$$

where $R$ is the fraction of mobile component removed over a length $l$ cm with flow at an average linear velocity $\mu$ cm/sec in a channel of depth $b$ cm. Streamline flow gives more complete removal than turbulent flow as shown by comparison of equation 14 with the corresponding equation for complete mixing in the channel at all times, which is

$$R = 1 - e^{-\mu El/ub} \qquad (15)$$

The equations 14 and 15 for laminar flow and complete mixing, respectively, are plotted together in Figure 8, where the superiority of laminar flow is shown. One can also understand intuitively that mixing should be avoided during the electrophoresis. The dimensionless group $\mu El/ub$ gives a measure of performance for various other assumed conditions of operation. The condition for complete removal of a mobile component is that $\mu El/ub = 1$, regardless of the flow profile so long as there is no mixing. In other words, the minimum length of channel to remove a mobile component, $l_{\min}$, is $ub/\mu E$.

To test performance of his equipment, Mizma (34) studied the transfer of dyes from a feed stream across the Teflon barrier into a parallel-flowing stream of buffer. For basic fuchsin, removal from the feed was about 95% of that predicted from the theory, whereas for bromophenol blue removal was only 70%. During the test, flow rates were 10–30 ml/min and potential gradients were 2–6v/cm. The

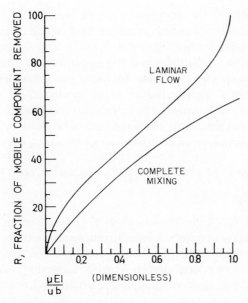

Fig. 8. Theoretical efficiency of removal for a mobile component from a single channel in "barrier electrophoresis" according to equations 14 and 15. The importance of avoiding turbulence is shown.

absence of convection currents was shown by the fact that the addition of methylcellulose as a thickening agent to the feed stream containing the dyes did not improve the efficiency. There was, however, good separation of the mobile dyes from the nonmobile methylcellulose.

The lower efficiency of removal for bromophenol blue may depend upon the fact that it was negatively charged at the pH used, whereas basic fuchsin was positively charged. Mizma showed from streaming potential measurements (34) that porous Teflon has a rather high zeta potential and therefore will develop an appreciable negative charge in dilute aqueous buffer. Because of surface conductance of electricity by positive ions in the double layer, an accumulation of buffer ions will occur on the side of the porous barrier facing the negative electrode (37), i.e., on the side which a negative dye would first encounter in migrating toward the anode.

This phenomenon, the accumulation of buffer ions, would bring about a decreased potential gradient and hence a decreased velocity of migration for the negative dye as it approached the porous barrier. The effect would be just the opposite, of course, for a positively charged species like basic fuchsin, and therefore its removal should have been slightly higher than predicted by equation 14. The above analysis is admittedly somewhat speculative, but it points to the type of development work that must be done in trying to improve the performance of electrophoresis as a unit operation.

## B. ELECTROCONVECTION AND ELECTRODECANTATION

### 1. Design of Equipment

The scaling up of electrodecantation from a simple batch operation to a high-capacity, semicontinuous operation involves no radical changes in concept. Consequently there has been steady improvement in practical design features over the years. Considerable ingenuity has been displayed in providing for multiple membranes to increase the capacity, and in arranging for the control of temperature, pH, and flow rate to improve the efficiency. As might be expected, many special designs have evolved. These have been

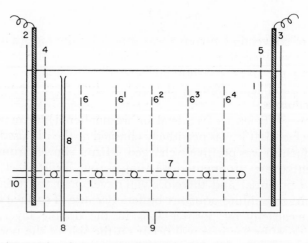

Fig. 9. Multimembrane electrodecantation device of Stamberger, used for concentrating rubber latex.

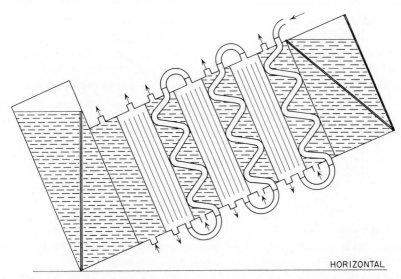

HORIZONTAL

Fig. 10. Electrodecantation apparatus of Polson (38) showing three stages in series with interstage cooling. Feed entering at the far upper right in the figure is depleted in its mobile components as it leaves from the top of the third stage, on the left. Supernatant from each stage enters at the bottom of the succeeding stage. Individual fractions containing mobile components are withdrawn from the bottom of each of the stages, which commonly contain about 20 membranes.

rather completely reviewed by Bier (14) and therefore no detailed descriptions will be given here.

The simple principle of a multimembrane apparatus suitable for continuous feed of a latex and continuous discharge of a cream is shown in Figure 9, which is fairly self-explanatory. Latex particles in the feed (which enters through port 7) migrate to the membranes and then rise to the top to form a layer which is continuously withdrawn through the outlet 8. Nonmigrating components collect in the bottom of the chamber and are discharged intermittently through 9. It may be noted here that if a continuous discharge through 9 is established at an appreciable rate, then the separation begins to depend on countercurrent migration within the fractionation chamber and control of relative flow rates becomes more critical than membrane spacing or length of membranes.

Polson has considerably improved electrodecantation by applying sound physical principles to control the convection currents.

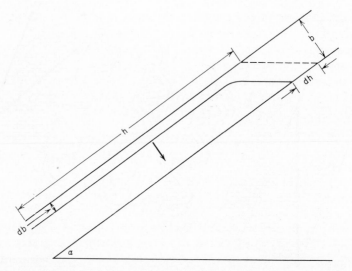

Fig. 11. An element in the electrodecantation cell, bounded by two membranes and tilted at an angle $\alpha$ with the horizontal. (Redrawn from reference 38.)

A recent review by Polson and Largier (38) gives detailed information about such improvements and shows how the method can be used to purify various proteins. Figure 10 shows a simple Polson apparatus, in which the fractionation chamber is surrounded by buffer which cools the chamber and washes away products of electrolysis. The electrodes, shown as heavy black lines in Figure 10, are not parallel but slope so that more current flows through the upper portion of the apparatus. Such an arrangement insures that temperatures near the top of the fractionation chamber are higher than near the bottom, and so avoids adverse thermal convection currents.

Another noteworthy feature is that the whole apparatus is tilted. To see the advantage of this requires a closer look at the theory of electrodecantation. Figure 11 shows one element of a Polson cell, bounded by two membranes and held at an angle $\alpha$ with the horizontal. If the mobile component tends to migrate perpendicularly toward the lower membrane, it leaves a thin stratum of lower density near the upper membrane. The gap will be partially filled, however, by the more dense layer slipping back into this space on account of the gravitational field. The fluid in this space will then be displaced upward on account of its lower density. Up near the meniscus the mobile component will migrate to the lower membrane over relatively short distances to leave a mobile-free region above the meniscus. If diffusion and other complicating factors can be disregarded, Polson and Largier (37) show that the rate at which the upper meniscus of a protein layer will fall is

$$dh/d\theta = \mu E(h/b + 1/\sin \alpha) - (m\delta h \sin \alpha/b) \qquad (16)$$

where, besides the symbols already defined, $\delta$ is the density difference between the suspension and the medium and $m$ is a proportionality constant. Equation 16 shows that as the angle $\alpha$ is made smaller, the rate of decantation as measured by $dh/d\theta$ will increase; there are, of course, practical difficulties in operating by free convection in a position close to the horizontal. The advantage of tilting has been known ever since Boycott (39) observed its effect on the settling of blood cells, and the explanation had also been well established (40). Nevertheless it is a design feature often overlooked by engineers.

## 2. Industrial Use of Electrodecantation

Electrodecantation is used successfully for the concentration of rubber latex by the Dunlop Rubber Company, Ltd, in Malaya. In several articles describing the process, (41, 42) Murphy states that losses in electrodecantation are usually less than 3%, whereas in centrifugation the skim may contain as much as 7% of the rubber latex. The cream from electrodecantation is also free from contaminating creaming agents so that it is especially suitable for uses requiring low electrical conductance.

Latex with 30% content of dry rubber was treated at rates up to 7 gallons per hour in a single decantation unit to give a cream with 60% dry rubber and serum with 1.5% dry rubber. Multiple units were fed from a central supply but Murphy gives no over-all production figures. There is a tendency for latex particles to deposit on the membranes but operating periods of about a week were possible before cleaning. Periodic reversal of the current was necessary, however. Power consumption at a feed rate of 2 gallons per hour was 20–40 w and no provision for cooling was necessary.

Rubber latex normally contains about 0.5% ammonia, added as a preservative, and at least this amount is important because it increases the mobility of the latex particles. Various ionic surface active agents are often added to raise the electrophoretic mobility. Such detergents also reduce the tendency for latex particles to deposit on the membranes.

In his review of preparative electrophoresis, Bier (14) states that electrodecantation is also used to concentrate aqueous dispersions of polytetrafluoroethylene. He cites a production unit measuring only about 2 feet by 1 foot by 1/2 foot which can produce as much as 500 pounds of 60% latex in 8 hours.

### C.  COUNTERCURRENT ELECTROPHORESIS

The Bier technique for large-scale electrophoresis was developed as an outgrowth of effort to improve the performance of electroconvection, but, especially in its later modifications, it resembles more nearly countercurrent electrophoresis. Bier has recently described the method in detail (14) and its application to the pilot-plant treatment of blood fractions has been reported (43). A schematic drawing of the operation of a Bier cell (filter paper modification) is shown in Figure 12. The mixture to be separated flows in at the top and the electrical polarity is adjusted so that the mobile component migrates toward the membrane at the left and is withdrawn from the bottom. There is a bulk flow of liquid, containing now only immobile components, through the porous paper septum and out through the compartment on the right. The filter paper offers enough pressure drop so that fluid flow is uniform across its entire surface. In describing the theoretical requirement for separation, Bier states that the rate of flow of liquid through the filter paper must be less than the rate of the electrophoretic migration of the mobile component in the opposite direction. The critical velocity which cannot be exceeded if the isoelectric component is to be free of mobile material, is simply

$$u_{\text{crit}} = \mu E \tag{17}$$

where $u$ is the linear velocity within the apparatus parallel to the electrical field. In terms of volumetric flow, $q$, of the stream stripped of mobile component, equation 11 becomes

$$q_{\text{crit}} = \mu E A = I\mu/k \tag{18}$$

where $A$ is the area of the filter paper partition. Bier has found that the predicted proportionality between critical flow rate and current holds good over a considerable range of operating conditions. He

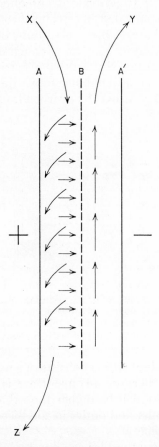

Fig. 12. Diagram of the Bier electrophoresis cell, filter paper modification. AA′ outer membranes, semipermeable; B, intermediate membrane of paper. The entering feed is X and the separated fractions are Y and Z.   Stream Y is depleted in negatively charged components in this example.

points out that the theory of his apparatus does not correspond to that for electroconvection, although some of the earlier "window" cells had certain similarities in concept. The Bier cell makes full use of natural convection in addition to the forced flow and constitutes a very clever way to separate two fractions.

By increasing the electrical current it is possible to withdraw from the top outlet at a high rate. Consequently the mobile components become concentrated in passing through the cell, and this is often a desirable feature. Bier (44) points out, for example, that flow through the top outlet may be as much as four times the flow through the bottom outlet. Since the isoelectric component coming off the top is pure, a material balance shows that 80% of the amount originally in the feed is recovered overhead. Only 20% is mixed in

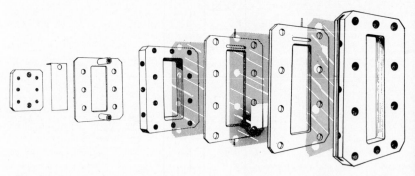

Fig. 13. Projected view of the Bier cell.   Shaded areas represent membranes; the center one consists of paper or, as shown here, of semipermeable material with a window cut out near the bottom.   Only one electrode assembly is shown, at the extreme left.   (Courtesy Perkin-Elmer Corp., Norwalk, Conn.)

with the bottom product which consists of a five-fold concentrate of the mobile material. Because a concentrate is ordinarily taken off the bottom, its density will be higher than that of the feed stream, and the location of inlet and outlet in the Bier cell takes advantage of this natural convection.

Figure 13 shows how the Bier cell can be built up of spacers and membranes (shaded areas) almost like a filter press. Furthermore, if heating is not too severe, i.e., if ionic strengths can be kept low enough, such cells can be set up in parallel between just one pair of electrodes. Rates up to 4 ml/min were obtained from a single cell in some experiments on hemoglobin recovery, and a variety of other applications are cited in Bier's book (14). It is stated there that Worthington Biochemical Laboratory has adopted this countercurrent electrophoresis device for preparing purified elastase and horseradish peroxidase.

## VI. Equipment and Costs

Preliminary development work on electrophoresis can be done in equipment of the type described in Section III-B. Such equipment can be purchased from various laboratory supply houses at a cost of $1000 to $2000 including power supply. For pilot plant studies on electrodecantation the Webcell electrodialyzer (Brosites Machine Company, New York, N.Y.) can be used, provided slight modifications are made (45). The only other readily available device capable of separating mixtures at rates of 2–10 ml/min is that developed by Bier (Perkin-Elmer Corporation, Norwalk, Conn.). Such equipment may cost $5000 or more depending on the requirements for auxiliaries like pumps, power supplies, cooling devices, etc. Under many circumstances the investigator may end up building his own unit for the pilot plant or for commercial production. Therefore some general comments on materials of construction and cell design may be in order.

### A. MATERIALS OF CONSTRUCTION

The apparatus itself and components in the immediate vicinity must be good insulators because several hundred volts are applied to the electrodes. A polyacrylic resin like Plexiglas is most commonly used because it is easy to machine and often allows direct observation of the performance of the device.

Whereas reversible electrodes like Ag–AgCl are used in analytical electrophoresis, large-scale equipment requires the use of simple metal electrodes. Corrosion of the electrodes can introduce contaminants, so platinum is often used. Stainless steel or carbon may be used as cathode materials in many applications, although as anodes they corrode or disintegrate. Noble metals, though high in initial cost, become economical on prolonged use, especially since there are now improved methods for plating and coating these onto base metals. Tirreloy B (Ionics, Inc., Cambridge, Mass.) is a very satisfactory anode material. Hastelloy C or specially prepared lead dioxide may also be suitable.

Gases are evolved and pH changes occur near the electrodes so they must be separated from the fractionation chamber by some sort of porous wall. Semipermeable membranes like cellophane may be used although more porous materials like filter paper or sintered plastic offer less electrical resistance and exhibit less electroosmosis. Porous membranes are also used in the Bier cell and in barrier electrophoresis. Bier (14) reports that hardened wet-strength filter paper, like Whatman No. 52 or 54, was satisfactory for the center membrane in his cell, whereas cotton, silk, or nylon cloth were not. From measurements of streaming potential Mizma (34) has suggested that porous polyethylene, filter paper, or Millipore filter should cause less electroosmotic flow than sintered membranes of glass, Teflon, or polyacrylic resin. Choice of the porosity represents a compromise; voltage drop across the wall is less when the porosity is high, but the pores must be fine enough to prevent bulk flow of liquid. Satisfactory pore size is 10–25 microns. The mechanical fragility and tendency to bulge of flexible membranes must be weighed against the advantage of their thinness. In "barrier electrophoresis," for example, the membranes should be thin so that there is a minimum of holdup inside.

## B. POWER CONSUMPTION

The electrodes should be located as close as possible to the fractionating zone so that power loss and heat generation in the apparatus will be minimized.

The power requirements and heat generated within the fractionating zone for a typical separation in the Bier cell are shown in Table II. For a flow of 1 ml/min, as assumed in Table II, the temperature rise in degrees Centigrade of the solution passing

TABLE II
Power and Heat Relations in Bier Cell[a,b]

| Cell area, cm$^2$ | $\mu = 1 \times 10^{-5}$ cm$^2$v$^{-1}$sec$^{-1}$ | | $\mu = 5 \times 10^{-5}$ cm$^2$v$^{-1}$sec$^{-1}$ | |
|---|---|---|---|---|
| | Power, w | Heat, cal/min | Power, w | Heat, cal/min |
| 10 | 167.0 | 2400 | 6.7 | 96.0 |
| 100 | 16.7 | 240 | 0.67 | 9.6 |

[a] Taken from reference 14.

[b] Assumed conditions: flow rate = 1 ml/min; $k = 2 \times 10^{-3}$ ohms$^{-1}$; distance between membranes = 0.3 cm.

through the cell will be equal to the heat generated in calories per minute. As Bier points out (14) the first case is clearly impossible under all conditions. The last example in the table would require no cooling since the temperature rise would be only 9.6 °C. The two intermediate cases would require rapid circulation of cold buffer around both sides of the cell for adequate heat removal.

Table II also shows the probable magnitude of power costs for commercial applications. Usually the disrupting effects of heating on performance intervene before the cost of power becomes excessive. It is especially interesting to note the 25-fold decrease in power and heat generation to be gained from a five-fold increase in electrophoretic mobility. This fact explains in large measure the commercial success of electrophoresis in separating latex as contrasted to its limited use at present in fractionating proteins or other slow-moving species on a large scale.

## VII. Summary and Prospects for Future Development

The development of equipment for electrophoresis is still so much of an art that standards for performance of the equipment cannot be rigidly specified. The capacities of various methods have been compared here on the basis of relative flow rates simply because flow patterns within the fractionation chamber are critical and an upper limit to flow can often be set. Grams of output per hour or per day might have afforded a better comparison if sufficient data were available on a particular feed mixture with components of known mobility. Other bases for comparison such as capacity per square foot of surface or per dollar of capital investment can also be made when, to continue the analogy used earlier by Philpot, more of the aircraft are actually flying in commercial service.

A striking advantage of both the electrodecantation and countercurrent flow methods is their capability to process more concentrated proteins or colloids than zone electrophoresis. Slight convection currents that would upset zone electrophoresis can still be tolerated in the other two methods.

The attractive, and unique, feature of zone electrophoresis is its ability to yield several pure fractions by a single pass through the apparatus. It must be pointed out, however, that multiple passes and various other refining techniques can be incorporated into electrodecantation or countercurrent electrophoresis. Polson and

Largier (38) cite a particular example of multiple staging which allows at least preliminary fractionation of 2–3 liters/day of undiluted blood serum. The apparatus is similar to that shown in Figure 10 but the three separation chambers differ in width (they are 2, 3.5, and 5.5 cm in this example). Because the rate of movement of the feed up through the different chambers will vary inversely as the cross-section, only components with the highest electrophoretic mobility will separate out in the first, narrowest chamber. Successive fractionations will hold back intermediate and slow-moving components until only the isoelectric material passes out, in a purified state, from the widest chamber. The separation of serum proceeds as follows:

"After the whole apparatus has been filled with $0.03M$ phosphate buffer, with $0.015M$ $MgSO_4$, at the isoelectric point of $\gamma$-globulin (pH 6.8) and cooled to 5 °C, the narrowest cell is drained. This cell is then filled with the dialyzed serum, diluted to 3 mg/ml protein, after the removal of precipitated euglobulin by filtration or centrifugation. A potential gradient of the order of 5 v/cm is applied and after approximately 30 minutes the flow of serum into the first cell is started. A high flow rate of approximately 200 ml/hour is maintained. After about 2 hours the concentrated layer of albumin is slowly tapped off from the bottom of the cell. This tapping is essential to prevent a high protein concentration developing in the first cell. After approximately 5 hours the concentrated layer of $\alpha$-globulin at the bottom of the second cell is slowly drained off in a similar fashion. After about 8 hours, the $\beta$-globulin layer at the bottom of the third cell is similarly removed, while $\gamma$-globulin is collected at the top of this cell."

It is thus possible to get a pure $\gamma$-globulin, and purified fractions of $\alpha$- and $\beta$-globulins and albumin in three stages. Each of the fractions may be made homogeneous by further refining. The authors go on to relate that a most crucial factor in the success of such a separation is the correct choice of cell widths. Slight turbulence develops in some of the cells which makes it necessary to rely on trial and error for finding the proper width ratios. Nevertheless, the performance just cited is very good and it must be emphasized that similar feats are possible by multiple-staging of the Bier cells.

Zone electrophoresis retains many unique features, as shown especially by Mel (29), so that continued development work is probably worth the effort. The "focusing effects" of gradients in pH or conductivity provide a powerful advantage for rapid processing. Separations are clean with a minimum requirement for reworking or for holdup in the apparatus. The "barrier electrophoresis" technique probably gives the most positive stabilization of the zones and may be best for treating concentrated solutions where heating is especially troublesome. More work needs to be done in developing barrier materials which will not disrupt the electrophoresis; some preliminary work with Millipore membranes looks hopeful, for example. On the other hand, stationary zone electrophoresis in columns does not seem to have much future for large-scale commercial work, however convenient it is for preparative work in the laboratory. The reason is that laminar flow helps to stabilize the zones, even in the Mel apparatus, and every advantage should be taken of this fact. It makes no engineering sense to let a mixture stand quietly generating heat during electrophoresis.

One attractive area of future development is in nonaqueous electrophoresis, i.e., separation of charged particles or molecules in media with low conductivity and a low dielectric constant. Bier (14) has reviewed some possibilities of "dielectrophoresis," and several workers have had success in separating ions on paper (15,46,48). While joule heating is less of a problem than with aqueous media, other types of convection currents do arise in liquid dielectrics in strong electrical fields (49).

## Notation

$A$     Area, cm²
$a$     Radius of particle, cm
$b$     Distance between membranes, cm
$c_i$     Concentration of $i$ species, moles/liter
$c_p$     Heat capacity, cal/(g)(°C)
$D$     Dielectric constant
$d$     Depth of electrophoresis chamber, cm
$E$     Voltage gradient, v/cm ($E'$ is in electrostatic v/cm)
$g$     Acceleration of gravity, cm/sec²
$h$     Height of suspension in decantation cell, cm
$I$     Current, amp

**k**    Boltzman constant, $1.38 \times 10^{-16}$ erg/°K
$k$    Electrical conductivity, $\text{ohm}^{-1}\text{cm}^{-1}$
$l$    Length of electrophoresis chamber, cm
$m$    Proportionality constant, dimensionless
**N**    Avagadro's number, $6.02 \times 10^{23}$ molecules/mole
$P$    Power, w ($P'$ is in cal/sec)
$Q$    Heat dissipated, cal
$q$    Volumetric flow rate, $\text{cm}^3/\text{sec}$
$R$    Ratio mass of mobile component removed to mass of mobile component entering, dimensionless
$\Delta s$    Separation distance between adjacent zones, cm
$T$    Absolute temperature, °K
$\Delta_t$    Temperature rise, °C
$\Delta t_i$    Characteristic temperature difference in Grashof number, °C
$u$    Linear velocity, cm/sec
$V$    Volume, $\text{cm}^3$
$v$    Electrophoretic velocity, cm/sec
$x$    Distance, cm
$z$    Valence of $i$ species
$\alpha$    Angle with horizontal deg.
$\beta$    Coefficient of thermal expansion, $\text{cm}^3/°C$
$\delta$    Difference in density between suspension and medium, $\text{g/cm}^3$
$\Gamma/2$    Ionic strength, $1/2\Sigma c_i z_i^2$, g moles/liter
$\epsilon$    Electronic charge, $1.60 \times 10^{-19}$ coulombs or $4.80 \times 10^{-10}$ e.s.u.
$\xi$    Zeta potential, mv ($\xi'$ is in e.s.v.)
$\eta$    Viscosity, poise
$\theta$    Time, sec
$\theta_r$    Retention time in apparatus, sec
$\kappa$    Parameter in Debye-Hückel theory, $\text{A}^{-1}$
$\mu$    Electrophoretic mobility, $\text{cm}^2/(\text{v})(\text{sec})$
$\rho$    Density of buffer solution, $\text{g/cm}^3$
$\rho_e$    Volumetric charge density, $\text{e.s.u./cm}^3$
$\sigma$    Surface charge density, $\text{e.s.u./cm}^2$
$\tau$    Thickness of double layer from shear plane, cm
$\psi$    Electrical potential near a particle, e.s.v.
$\psi_0$    Electrical potential at the surface, e.s.v.

# References

1. J. Th. G. Overbeek in H. R. Kruyt, ed., *Colloid Science*, Vol. I, Elsevier, Amsterdam, 1952, pp. 115–244.
2. H. A. Abramson, *Electrokinetic Phenomena*, Reinhold, New York, 1934.
3. M. Bier, ed., *Electrophoresis*, Academic Press, New York, 1959.
4. R. A. Brown and S. N. Timasheff, in M. Bier, ed., *Electrophoresis*, Academic Press, New York, 1959, Chap. 8.
5. D. A. Haydon, *Proc. Roy. Soc. (London)*, **258A**, 319 (1960).
6. L. G. Longsworth, *Chem. Revs.*, **30**, 323 (1942).
7. R. A. Alberty, *J. Chem. Educ.*, **25**, 462 (1948).
8. E. L. Durrum in R. J. Block, E. L. Durrum, and G. Zweig, *Manual of Paper Chromatography and Paper Electrophoresis*, 2nd ed., Academic Press, New York, 1958, p. 537.
9. Ch. Wunderly in M. Bier, ed., *Electrophoresis*, Academic Press, New York, 1959, Chap. 5.
10. P. Bernfeld and J. S. Nisselbaum, *J. Biol. Chem.*, **220**, 851 (1956).
11. S. Raymond, *Science*, **130**, 711 (1959).
12. H. G. Kunkel and R. Trautman in M. Bier, ed., *Electrophoresis*, Academic Press, New York, 1959, Chap. 6.
13. H. Svensson, *Advances in Protein Chem.*, **4**, 251 (1948).
14. M. Bier in M. Bier, ed., *Electrophoresis*, Academic Press, New York, 1959, Chap. 7.
15. A. Karler, *Anal. Chem.*, **31**, 848 (1959).
16. I. Brattsten, *Arkiv. Kemi*, **8**, 347 (1955).
17. J. Porath, *Arkiv. Kemi*, **11**, 259 (1957).
18. M. K. Brakke, *Arch. Biochem. Biophys.*, **55**, 175 (1955).
19. J. S. L. Philpot, *Trans. Faraday Soc.*, **36**, 38 (1940).
20. H. Svensson in P. Alexander and R. J. Block, eds., *Analytical Methods of Protein Chemistry (Separation and Isolation of Proteins)*, Vol. I, Pergamon Press, New York, 1960, Chap. 7.
21. A. Kolin in D. Glick, ed., *Methods of Biochemical Analysis*, Vol. VI, Interscience, New York, 1958.
22. K. Clusius and E. R. Ramirez, *Helv. Chim. Acta*, **36**, 1160 (1953).
23. M. Chemla in M. Lederer, ed., *Chromatographic Reviews*, Vol. I, Elsevier, Amsterdam, 1959.
24. R. S. Prengle and R. R. Rothfus, *Ind. Eng. Chem.*, **47**, 379 (1955).
25. H. G. Kunkel and A. Tiselius, *J. Gen. Physiol.*, **35**, 89 (1951).
26. F. E. Crane and G. H. F. Gardner, *Chem. Eng. Data*, **6**, 283 (1961).
27. H. G. Kunkel and R. Trautman in M. Bier, ed., *Electrophoresis*, Academic Press, New York, 1959, Chap. 6.
28. H. C. Mel, *J. Chem. Phys.*, **31**, 559 (1959).
29. H. C. Mel, Univ. of Calif. Lawrence Radiation Laboratory Report *UCRL 9108*, 1960.
30. H. C. Mel, *Science*, **132**, 1255 (1960).
31. R. Dobry and R. K. Finn, *Science*, **127**, 697 (1958).
32. R. Dobry and R. K. Finn, *Chem. Eng. Progr.*, **54**, 59 (1958).

430     R. K. FINN

33. T. J. Hanratty, E. M. Rosen, and R. L. Kabel, *Ind. Eng. Chem.*, **50**, 815 (1958).
34. E. J. Mizma, Ph.D. Thesis, Cornell University, Ithaca, New York, 1959.
35. E. Schumacher and R. Flühler, *Helv. Chim. Acta*, **41**, 1572 (1958).
36. E. Schumacher, *Helv. Chim. Acta*, **40**, 2322 (1957).
37. R. D. Miller, *Science*, **122**, 373 (1955).
38. A. Polson and J. F. Largier in P. Alexander and R. J. Block, eds., *Analytical Methods of Protein Chemistry (Separation and Isolation of Proteins)*, Vol. I, Pergamon Press, New York, 1960, Chap. 6.
39. A. E. Boycott, *Nature*, **104**, 532 (1920).
40. K. Kinosita, *J. Colloid Sci.*, **4**, 525 (1949).
41. E. A. Murphy, *Trans. Inst. Rubber Ind.*, **18**, 173 (1942).
42. E. A. Murphy, *Ind. Eng. Chem.*, **44**, 756 (1952).
43. *Chem. Eng. News*, **38**, 60 (Oct. 17, 1960).
44. M. Bier, *Science*, **125**, 1084 (1957)
45. P. Stamberger, *J. Colloid Sci.*, **1**, 93 (1946).
46. G. Haugaard and T. D. Kroner, *J. Am. Chem. Soc.*, **70**, 2135 (1948).
47. M. H. Paul and E. L. Durrum, *J. Am. Chem. Soc.*, **74**, 4721 (1952).
48. H. J. McDonald and M. B. Williamson, *Naturwissenschaften*, **42**, 461 (1955).
49. A. Gemant, *Liquid Dielectrics*, Wiley, New York, 1933.
50. H. Bickel *et al.*, *Helv. Chim. Acta*, **43**, 2105 (1960).

# INDEX

431

**Date Due**